Introduction 1
  How to Use This Book ii
  Anatomy Tips iv
  Palpation v

Head & Face 25

Neck 45

Torso & Back 65

Shoulder & Arm 91

Forearm & Hand 113

Hip, Thigh & Knee 135

Leg, Ankle & Foot 159

Neurovascular 183

Muscle Tables 207

Exercise Rehab. 224

Final Exams 232

Congratulations in the purchase of this text and the best investment you can make - your education. This text is designed to be used in conjunction with the best selling **Muscle Manual text, Flashcards**, on-line video at **proCentral** and directed classroom instruction involving anatomical models & palpation for **the best integrated learning results**. However this text can also be used as a standalone anatomy review text or coloring book - that will challenge you as your knowledge base grows - perfect for basic learning and exam review.

Human beings are tactile learners; physically writing out answers & coloring images results in more neural stimulation than the repetitive, generic circling of multiple choice answers or the typing/tapping action of a keyboard or smart phone (Scientific American - Why the brain prefers paper).

Neural pathways are better established to recognize the shapes & contours of letters written and muscles colored. When writing multiple choice tests, students who have been trained by writing out the answers perform better because they **look for the correct answer**, rather than eliminating wrong answers. Beyond test writing, in real world application and professional communication, fill-in-the-blank learners often find it easier to be more articulate, avoid spelling errors & develop a more professional demeanor.

Illustrations in this text have been drawn and adapted from the **greatest anatomy illustrators of all time** (Dr. Paul Richer "Artistic Anatomy", and Dr. HV Carter "Gray's Anatomy" - the same source used by Frank Netter). A numbered labeling system allows students to self-quiz directly from the text (which is further by numerous student, clinician & instructor **quizzes, video & patient handouts on our website**). The chapters are marked with soft tabs.

To help ensure gender equity, 'his' & 'her' are used interchangeably throughout the text. The ☺ symbol signifies a section containing humor, **while it is recommended - laughter is optional** ☺.

For instructors:
- PowerPoints, syllabi & learning objectives
- **5000⁺ question** test generator & **video tutorials**
- Regional quizzes & final exams
- 1500⁺ image bank for quizzes and exams
- Best selling, Evidence Based **Muscle Manual** text and **anatomy flash cards** & ortho pathology texts

For students:
- **Printable blank quizzes** to improve retention
- On-line
- Answers
- Gray's A
- **Video** o
- **The bes**

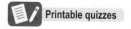 Printable quizzes   Handouts   Stretch & Strengthen   Video on prohealthsys.com

Introduction | Forearm. Wrist & Hand | Head & Face | Hip, Thigh & Knee | Neck | Leg, Foot & Ankle | Torso & Back | Neurovascular | Shoulder & Arm | Muscle Tables

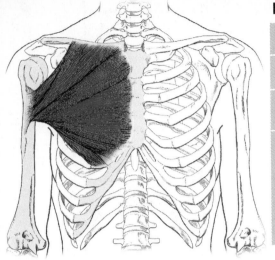

Name: _____

O **ORIGIN:** *more proximal or fixed point of attachment*

I **INSERTION:** *more distal or movable attachment*

A **ACTION:** *movement performed (insertion closer to origin)*

C **CLINICAL (or Crazy ☺):** *section to write notes on palpation, muscle testing, stretching, strengthening, anatomical variation, synergist, antagonists, trigger point referral patterns, nerve supply, blood supply, injuries, treatment or any other topic that is required to know for the specific class*

- If you **require the Muscle Manual text** in class you are free to copy pages from this book - use pages or blank anatomy drawing on the last pages to create a quiz on any topic you want (origins, insertions, ligaments, muscles, nerve pathways, ROM, orthopedic tests for each body region) - **A bonus question** on every quiz is a good way to get students excited!

- **Start each week with a quiz** – this allows students to accurately self-evaluate their progress through the material. To avoid changing their answers, encourage students to write their quizzes in pen. Always test on any of the material you cover even on lessons from the first day of class. It is important to hold students responsible for the information – this encourages students to review the material more frequently and improves retention of the information. Students will thank you in the end – **remember, life is cumulative!**

- **Always include practical testing** and give direct feedback to your students whenever possible – one of my favorite questions to ask a student is "give me a list of the structures below my hand _____" (bone, muscle, ligament, nerve, blood vessel, fascia, viscera) or to ask students to palpate structures directly on you!

- **Start each class by asking if there are any questions** from last day's material or the homework assignments - if there are none or few, ask students to give their interpretation of what they learned last class (verbalize points or come to the front and demonstrate palpation or muscle test - this will help them grow in ability).

- Make your classroom a safe place to make mistakes and ask questions – **it is OK to say "I don't know."** While keeping a positive and respectful interaction in mind – challenge students by **gently putting them on the spot to answer questions or demonstrate a skill.**

- **Give a 5 minute review at the end of class** to reinforce your important points and overall message. Ask students to help you recall the key points from the class.

- Learning new terms in class can incorporate kinesthetic learning – **"Say it with me, with a smile ☺"** helps students correlate positive associations with the new term and this activity also ensures correct pronunciation which is very important in professional communication.

- **Less is more.** Less desk time (~30-45 minutes max) and more physical hands-on time will result in increased student performance and real world application. One of my favorite methods is to **use washable markers** and draw on a classmate; the class gets covered in 'anatomy paint' having fun and applying the topic 3 dimensionally on a person (real world application). "Get up, stand up."

- **Before each break**, have students in groups of 2-4, share information that they just went over to further improve synaptic binding. This will help introverted students verbalize what they just learned but to a group they are familiar and comfortable around. This peer learning often generates great questions and conversation.

- **Random quizzes** at the beginning of each class (not for marks). It can be ligaments of a previous chapter, blank muscle sheets, or even multiple choice questions. The fact that students won't know what it could be on, will either encourage them to quickly skim through previous chapters or it will be a test to see how much content the individual retained from that chapter; giving students direct feedback on areas they need to review more.

- **Think outside the box!** Make this workbook meet the specific needs of your class or lab; the "C" section on the individual muscle pictures stands for "Clinical." This section should be filled out based on the specific focus or needs of your class;

  - **Palpation:** the student's pre-class assignment could be "record the steps required to palpate this structure;"

  - **Muscle testing:** "record the steps required to muscle test x, y & z muscles;" or read pages 2-10 for tomorrow

  - **Any parameter you need the students to know** may be recorded in the clinical section (palpation, innervation, stretching, strengthen, synergists, antagonist, trigger point referral, injuries, ADLs or anything you need)

 **Printable quizzes**   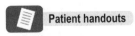 **Patient handouts**

 **Stretch & Strength**   **Video on prohealthsys**

> "Is this going to be on the test?" – **Yes, is always the correct answer** – LIFE IS CUMULATIVE

- **Turn off your 'smart' phone - it is making you dumb.** Research shows having your **cell phones can impair learning, by reducing attention and memory.** The Journal of Educational Psychology found students who had smartphones or laptops present while a lesson was being taught **scored ~10% lower on exams** than students not using electronics. Smart phone usage has also been associated with many positive & negative effects:

  ### Positives (+)

  - **Convenience** to information - you can check facts and access data in real time (not all facts are accurate)
  - **Increased security and emergency communication**
  - **Entertainment & Socialization** (can be a distraction)
  - Self organization & spacial navigation (mapping apps)

  ### Negatives (-)

  - **Distraction & Health Hazards** (sedentary lifestyle, eyestrain, fatigue, potential cancer correlation)
  - **Increased stress, anxiety and sleep loss**
  - **Increased accident rates** (walking and driving)
  - **Smart phone addiction** and withdrawal (#truth)

- When self-testing, write answers in pencil so they can be erased, and re-entered later for further quizzing; or **use the plastic transparency sheet and write over top with a non-permanent marker** - repetition works and helps save paper - this is a better environmental choice.

- **Do not flip to the answer** section every time you are stuck; attempt to answer as many questions as possible. Sometimes different questions & answers trigger memories for others.

- Complete the homework assignments & pre-reading before class; **write down any questions** you have as they come up so they are remembered for the next class session. At the start of class ask your questions to the instructor or TA - chances are if you have a question ~50% of the class has the same one!

- **Ask for a 5 minute review** of the high points from last day's material to ensure you have recorded it correctly.

- Start an anatomy club for group study **"See it, do it, teach it"** … Study in a dedicated group to review bony land-marks, muscle origins & insertions, nerve pathways, **give a list of structures below your palpating hand** - social creatures learn best through interaction - 'monkey see, monkey do.'

- **Think outside the box** (literally & figuratively): if you have large hand writing or more information to write, move outside the area provided.

- **Use the Muscle Manual text, Flash cards, eBooks, proCenral video resources** - depending on the source there may be some subtle difference - **this is OK**. It is important that students realize different sources vary in **anatomical variation** - just as people vary in height, weight and shape, so does anatomy ☺

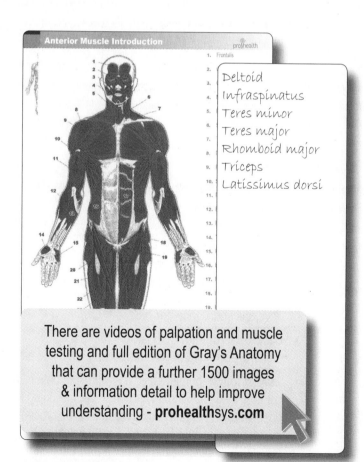

There are videos of palpation and muscle testing and full edition of Gray's Anatomy that can provide a further 1500 images & information detail to help improve understanding - **prohealth**sys.com

Use this book as a coloring book and retest yourself often (it was designed to improve your knowledge, exam scores & save you time & money)

Text layout allows for covering of drawing labels with a piece of paper to repetitively self-quiz on any diagram

As your level of knowledge increases don't just quiz on names - consider listing all origins or insertions, etc. for better learning!

prohealthsys

Pain Scale for Use with Palpation or Manual Therapy

Grade	Description
1	'Very light pressure' - patient feels no pain
2	'A little pressure' - but patient feels comfortable
3	'Firm pressure, but is good' - might be painful over tender spots
4	'Considerable pressure' - painful but you can breathe through it
5	**'STOP'** - the pressure is too much & no longer tolerable

Printable version for clinic at **proCentral**

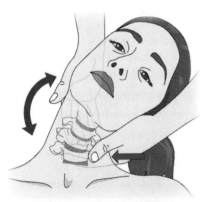

- **Mental concentration & understanding** of the regional anatomy are required for competent palpation (this book helps give you that - you should be able to give a list of all structures below your hand (bone, ligament, muscle, fascia nerve, vessel)

- **Rapport must be developed** that allows the patient to feel safe in expressing how they are experiencing the situation - **always attend to patient comfort** - "if at any time anything is uncomfortable please let me know," and repeatedly verbalize to monitor how they are doing and use the palpation pain scale below for both assessment and treatment

- **Professionalism** must be maintained at all times - with clothing, hygiene and all interaction communication (wash your hands & table between visits)

- **Good biomechanics are required** to help prevent the development of postural injuries, practice injuries & to set a good example to patients (practice what you preach and try to work in your 'strike zone' - torso region ASIS to mid chest)

- Have fun in classroom and in practice but be mindful that the casualness of classroom learning can spill over into the public clinical arena. **Be professional and know your anatomy** - the classroom is a safe place to make mistakes - you will learn more if you have the courage to make them...

- **Learn anatomy terminology** - say the name out loud "with a smile" - (class, lab & prohealthsys.com)

- **Visualize** structure, **verbalize** the name, then **palpate on yourself** (confirm with TAs or instructor)

- **Visualize, verbalize, then palpate on classmate** (classmate should give feedback - painful? good?)

- **Palpate on other people and different body types & ages** (other classmates, friends, family)

  - **Set up rotation stations** in class or during study time to move from body to body ("clinicians up, patients down on table... please locate the_____, now the _____, now the _____ ... and rotate")

- **Take a deep grounding breath before you start.** Excellent palpation & physical exam skills demand relaxed hands, good anatomical understanding & hours of practice with direct mental concentration

- **Confident Hands.** Students and patients can quickly tell if their clinician is nervous or not comfortable, be patient with yourself, realize repeated practice is what develops confidence and skill

- **Develop a routine.** Standardize your palpation method, apply it to all patients & compare bilaterally

- **Stay in touch** (pun intended ☺) with your patient's comfort level - continually ask how they are doing & observe their mental & emotional affect (be present in the moment, ask for feedback & self-analyze)

1. **Have fun.** Any task, including learning, is easier with a positive attitude - the importance of a positive mind-set can never be overstated.

2. **Good sleep, nutrition & exercise habits.** Regular sleep patterns, whole foods and exercise schedules are statistically proven to increase learning capability, reduce stress and result in a longer, healthier life.

3. **Make time use efficient & productive.** Consider **coloring images or writing** information down (the tactile sensation of writing improves retention); draw on a white board, use flash cards, make your own quizzes. Use the prohealthsys on-line resources!

4. **Re-read lecture/lab notes EVERY DAY.** Research shows if you read your notes for 10-15 minutes a day, you will perform better on your exams. Repetition works!

5. **Ask questions.** If you don't understand something, do not be ashamed to ask; it is your right to understand. Good students & practitioners always ask questions.

6. **Attend all classes.** Statistics show that 'A' students almost never miss class or lab and sit closer to the front of the classroom.

7. **Actively learn.** Don't just stare at notes or powerpoints, cover the list and label it yourself (**write it down** - 'Why the Brain prefers paper' Scientific American, 2013). Test your comprehension and retention by discussing or teaching the material using a white board. *"Say it out loud with a smile."*

8. **Fill in the blank NOT multiple choice.** Your learning is vastly improved if you quiz yourself with fill-in-the-blank type questions where **you write out** the correct answers. Icon below shows printable content:

   Printable quizzes prohealthsys

9. **Break the material** into manageable sections. Learning anatomy is like learning a new language, you do not just see or hear words once and become fluent, it takes time and practice. Greek & Latin root meanings are inside the back cover.

10. **Real life application.** Make the transition from "why do I need to know this?" to "how can I use this information?" - make it real!

11. **Bonus Tip.** Before you go to sleep each night, after reviewing your anatomy notes, ask yourself "what was my favorite part of the day?" – this simple practice will warm both your anatomical & spiritual heart. ☺

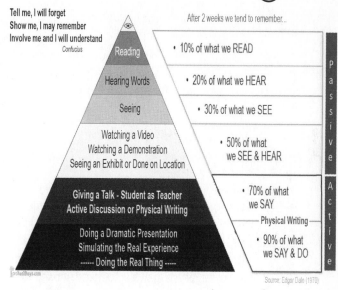

Tell me, I will forget
Show me, I may remember
Involve me and I will understand
Confucius

After 2 weeks we tend to remember...

Reading — • 10% of what we READ
Hearing Words — • 20% of what we HEAR
Seeing — • 30% of what we SEE
Watching a Video / Watching a Demonstration / Seeing an Exhibit or Done on Location — • 50% of what we SEE & HEAR
Giving a Talk - Student as Teacher / Active Discussion or Physical Writing — • 70% of what we SAY — Physical Writing
Doing a Dramatic Presentation / Simulating the Real Experience / ----- Doing the Real Thing ----- — • 90% of what we SAY & DO

Passive / Active

Source: Edgar Dale (1970)

prohealthsys.com

Full-sized download & printing for personal & classroom use on website

Video demonstrations at:

proCentral

prohealthsys

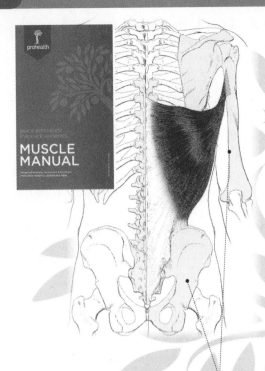

MUSCLE MANUAL

O   **ORIGIN: more proximal or fixed point of attachment**
- *bold indicates primary attachment point(s)*

I   **INSERTION: more distal or moveable point of attachment** - *bold indicates primary attachment point(s)*

A   **ACTION: main actions performed by muscle**
- *bold indicates primary or important action(s)*
- *for reverse actions simply use the opposite of the concentric action (eccentric muscle lengthening action)*

N   **NERVE: nerve that activates muscle tissue**
- *bold indicates primary innervation*

B   **BLOOD SUPPLY: blood vessel supplying muscle**

S   **SYNERGIST:** other muscles that assist the primary muscle

Aⁿ   **Antagonist:** listed by *joint action* at the start of each chapter

Bony attachments are shaded light grey
General origins (red) & insertions (dark grey) are shown in at the start of each chapter

Clinical Notes

- **Anatomical variation**: people may have subtle differences in the attachment of their muscles. Some of us are taller, thinner or wider due to the shape & length of our bones, so too do our muscles vary. Because of anatomical variation certain people can run faster, jump higher or lift more; others may also be predisposed to injury and/or slower healing times

- Interesting information & facts about the muscle are also stated in this section

- **ADL:** Activities of Daily Living (ADL) that require activity of the specified muscle
- **Common injuries:** common injuries or sports & activities that may cause muscle damage
- **DDx:** Differential Diagnosis - a common error is to have a bias toward a single cause for a given patient issue - when in it is often more commonly a combination of a variety of factors & coexisting conditions (patients do NOT read the text books to know how to present in your office ☺)

Palpation

- Suggested palpation methods for the muscle tissue
- Excellent physical palpation skills demand **relaxed hands, good understanding of anatomy, muscle fiber direction & hours of practice with direct mental concentration**
- Use the least amount of pressure possible (touch receptors respond best to light touch)
- **Compare results bilaterally - to palpate ligaments and joints muscles need to be relaxed**
- Numerous studies show excellent inter-examiner reliability for the palpation of bony & soft tissue tenderness (palpation is the best assessment & treatment tools we have)
- Stay in touch (pun intended) with your patient's comfort level - continually ask how they are doing

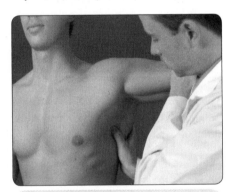

You should be able to pick up any bone and list all the muscles, ligaments, nerves, vessels and tendons that attach or pass by that bone and list the structures below your hand on any person (palpation is a functional anatomy review)

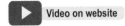
Video on website

Muscle Test - ABCs

Patient: Position prior to application of patient's resistance/force
Examiner: Direction & location of clinician's pressure
Stabilization: Used to avoid excessive or inappropriate movement

A: AROM
B: break test
C: concentric RROM
S: stretch (lengthen)

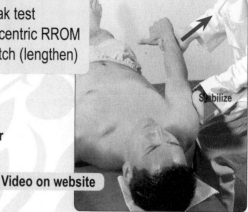

Stabilize

▶ Video on website

Muscle testing is graded on a scale of 0/5 to 5/5:

5/5 - Normal strength

4/5 - Movement possible against some resistance from examiner

3/5 - Movement possible against gravity, but not against the examiner

2/5 - Movement possible, not against gravity

1/5 - Muscle flickers, no movement

0/5 - No contraction

◆ **Trigger Point Referral**

- Diamond '◆' shows common locations of myofascial trigger point (MFTP)
- Dark red region shows *primary area of pain referral*
- Light red shows *secondary or 'spill-over' area of pain referral*
- Other somatic observations are also noted in this section

Stretch & Strengthen

Self Stretch

- **Stretch:** deliberate lengthening of muscle & fascia, in order to increase muscle flexibility and/or joint range of motion (stretches develop passive tension)
- Sample stretches are given for each muscle or muscle group & should be performed **bilaterally**. Realize there are also many variations & stretches that must be specifically designed to each patient's ability
- It is crucial to ask patients to demonstrate the stretches they are performing to ensure proper technique & injury avoidance
- Stretches should be held for 15-30 seconds & performed after a mild warm up

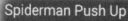
Wall Slide

Strengthen **Exercise:** repetitive resisted contraction of muscle

- Sample strengthening exercises (although there are many others)
- None of the exercises demonstrated require expensive equipment or gym memberships, they may be performed at home with weights, therapy bands, soup cans, pots or any other device that can provide muscle resistance

Tips for Better Compliance

Spiderman Push Up

- **Keep it simple.** Exercises & stretches should be easy to perform & remember (e.g., show patients how to do it, have them demonstrate it & give handouts with pictures to use at home) - Try to fit home-care suggestions into a patient's existing schedule, such as "stretch at your desk"
- **Keep it short.** Time is precious, keep home routine to under 15 min
- **Keep it pain-free (joyful discomfort).** The patient should not work in painful areas; the amount of stretch, weight & reps should be started at below what the believed patient's ability (progress slowly)

prohealthsys

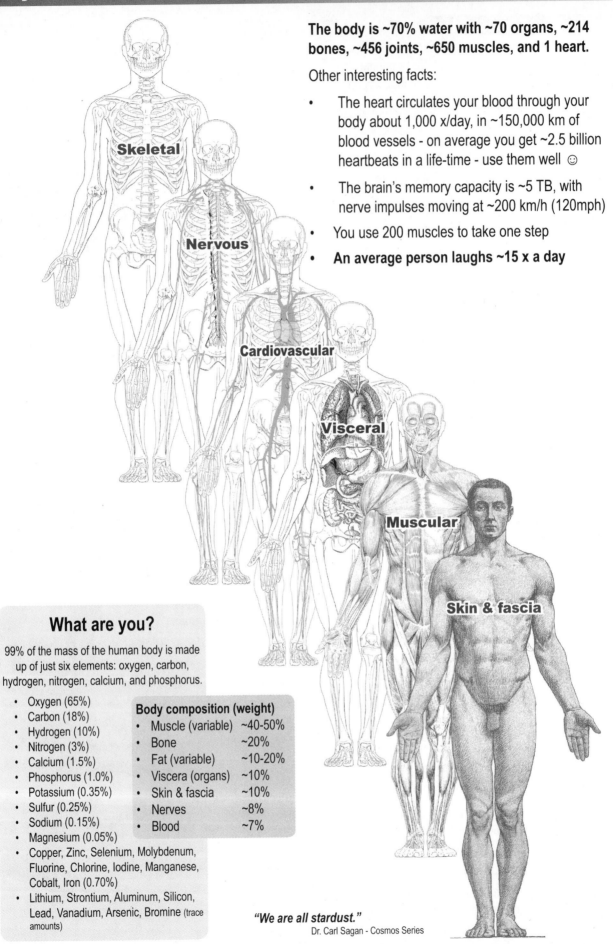

Skeletal

Nervous

Cardiovascular

Visceral

Muscular

Skin & fascia

The body is ~70% water with ~70 organs, ~214 bones, ~456 joints, ~650 muscles, and 1 heart.

Other interesting facts:

- The heart circulates your blood through your body about 1,000 x/day, in ~150,000 km of blood vessels - on average you get ~2.5 billion heartbeats in a life-time - use them well ☺

- The brain's memory capacity is ~5 TB, with nerve impulses moving at ~200 km/h (120mph)

- You use 200 muscles to take one step

- **An average person laughs ~15 x a day**

What are you?

99% of the mass of the human body is made up of just six elements: oxygen, carbon, hydrogen, nitrogen, calcium, and phosphorus.

- Oxygen (65%)
- Carbon (18%)
- Hydrogen (10%)
- Nitrogen (3%)
- Calcium (1.5%)
- Phosphorus (1.0%)
- Potassium (0.35%)
- Sulfur (0.25%)
- Sodium (0.15%)
- Magnesium (0.05%)
- Copper, Zinc, Selenium, Molybdenum, Fluorine, Chlorine, Iodine, Manganese, Cobalt, Iron (0.70%)
- Lithium, Strontium, Aluminum, Silicon, Lead, Vanadium, Arsenic, Bromine (trace amounts)

Body composition (weight)	
Muscle (variable)	~40-50%
Bone	~20%
Fat (variable)	~10-20%
Viscera (organs)	~10%
Skin & fascia	~10%
Nerves	~8%
Blood	~7%

"We are all stardust."
Dr. Carl Sagan - Cosmos Series

prohealthsys.com   Vizniak & Richer

What is Anatomical Position? _____

_____

_____

Name: _____   %

1. _____

2. _____

3. _____

4. _____

5. _____

6. _____

7. _____

8. _____

Name the Plane

9. _____

10. _____

11. _____

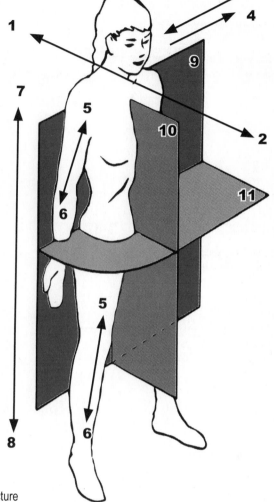

Match the Definitions

1. _____: front of the body

2. _____: back of the body

3. _____: toward head or upper part of a structure

4. _____: towards the head

5. _____: away from head or lower part of a structure

6. _____: towards the tail

7. _____: toward the midline

8. _____: away from midline

9. _____: closer to the point of origin

10. _____: further away from the point of origin

11. _____: near the surface of the body

12. _____: away from the surface of the body

13. _____: same side

14. _____: opposite sides

15. _____: both sides

16. _____: one side

17. _____: lyiging on spine or back

18. _____: lying on belly or front

Anterior	Lateral
Bilateral	Medial
Caudad	Posterior
Cephalad	Prone
Contralateral	Proximal
Deep	Superficial
Distal	Superior
Inferior	Supine
Ipsilateral	Unilateral

Muscle Manual page 3

Introduction

Head (cranial)

1. _____
2. _____

Back

3. _____
4. _____
5. _____
6. _____
7. _____

Upper Limb

8. _____
9. _____
10. _____
11. _____
12. _____
13. _____
14. _____
15. _____
16. _____

Lower Limb

17. _____
18. _____
19. _____
20. _____
21. _____ □ _____
22. _____

Name: _____ %

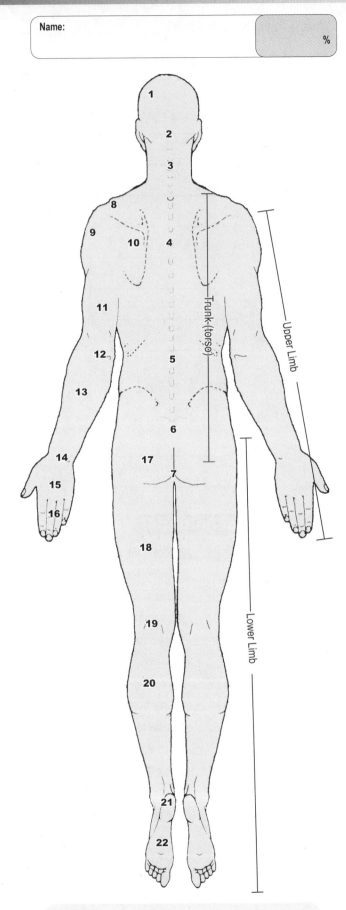

Trunk (torso)

Upper Limb

Lower Limb

Muscle Manual page 4

*Slang term - the loose skin over the posterior elbow is known as the 'wenis' (funny but true ☺)

Head (cranial)

1. _____
2. _____
3. _____
4. _____
5. _____
6. _____
7. _____

Chest (thoracic)

8. _____
9. _____
10. _____
11. _____
12. _____

Upper Limb

13. _____
14. _____
15. _____
16. _____
17. _____
18. _____
19. _____
20. _____

Abdominal

21. _____
22. _____
23. _____
24. _____
25. _____

Lower Limb

26. _____
27. _____
28. _____
29. _____
30. _____

Name: _____   %

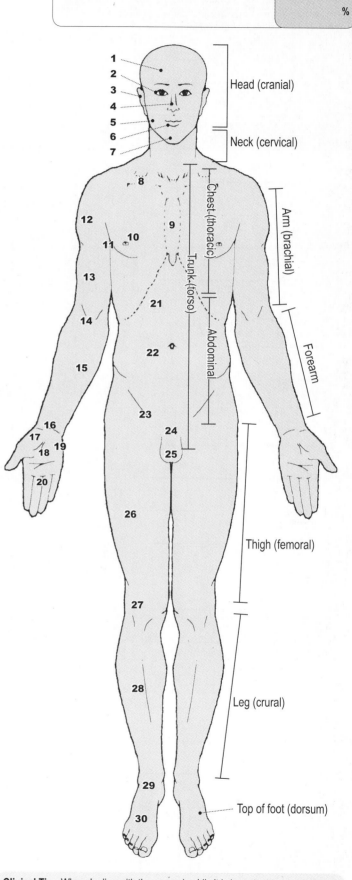

Clinical Tip - When dealing with the general public it is important to use common anatomical terms to ensure understanding

Introduction

prohealthsys

Start with labeling the bones then progress to naming
□ ligaments, □ muscle attachments, □ joints, □ ROM

Name:

%

broken bones are
called fractures

1. _____

2. _____

3. _____

4. _____

5. _____

6. _____

7. _____

8. _____

9. _____

10. _____

11. _____

12. _____

13. _____

14. _____

15. _____

16. _____

17. _____

18. _____

19. _____

20. _____

21. _____

22. _____

23. _____

24. _____

25. _____

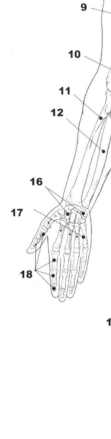
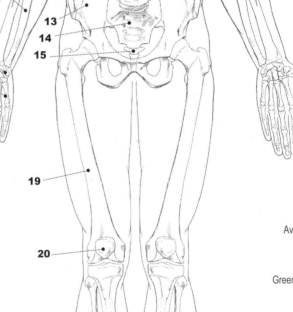
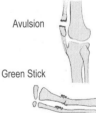
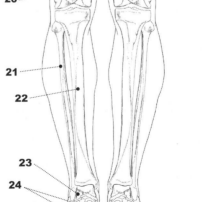

Avulsion

Green Stick

Comminuted

Compression

prohealthsys

Start with labeling the bones then progress to naming
□ ligaments, □ muscle attachments, □ joints, □ ROM

Name: _____ %

1. _____

2. _____

3. _____

4. _____

5. _____

6. _____

7. _____

8. _____

9. _____

10. _____

11. _____

12. _____

13. _____

14. _____

15. _____

16. _____

17. _____

18. _____

19. _____

20. _____

21. _____

22. _____

23. _____

24. _____

25. _____

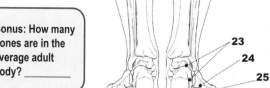

Bonus: How many bones are in the average adult body? _____

prohealthsys

Introduction

Bones of the Hand

Name: _____ %

1. _____

2. _____

3. _____

4. _____

5. _____

6. _____

7. _____

8. _____

9. _____

10. _____

11. _____

12. _____

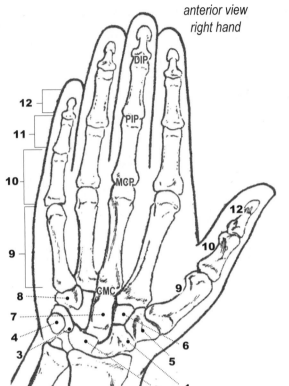

anterior view right hand

Carpals mnemonic

Proximal Row	L	**S**ome
		Lovers
		Try
	M	**P**ositions
Distal Row	L	**T**hat
		They
		Can't
	M	**H**andle

M = medial, L = lateral

Bones of the Foot

1. _____

2. _____

3. _____

4. _____

5. _____

6. _____

7. _____

8. _____

9. _____

10. _____

11. _____

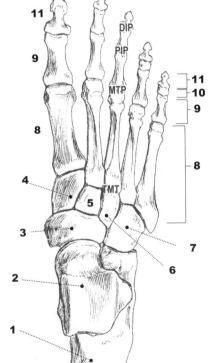

superior view right foot

Tarsals mnemonic

posterior	**C**razy
	Tall
	Nerds
	Make
	Internet
	Lovers
anterior	**C**ry

MUSCLE MANUAL

Muscle Manual page 8

Dark red indicates regions where bony landmarks are usually easily palpable - say the name out loud & find them on yourself

Name:

%

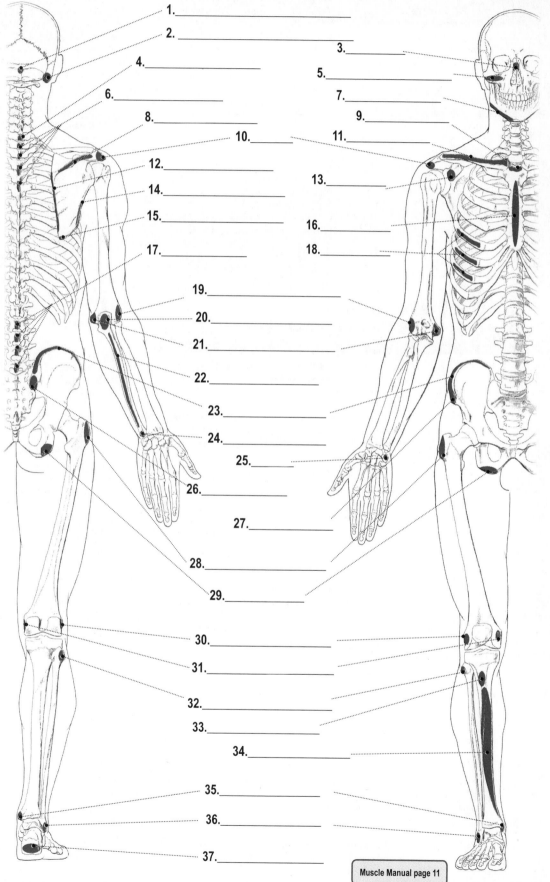

1._____

2._____

3._____

4._____

5._____

6._____

7._____

8._____

9._____

10._____

11._____

12._____

13._____

14._____

15._____

16._____

17._____

18._____

19._____

20._____

21._____

22._____

23._____

24._____

25._____

26._____

27._____

28._____

29._____

30._____

31._____

32._____

33._____

34._____

35._____

36._____

37._____

Muscle Manual page 11

prohealthsys

Introduction

Name: _____ %

Without a joint cavity - Fibrous joints*

	Type	Definition (example)
Synarthrosis (immovable)	1.	Two bone grow together, with only a thin layer of fibrous periosteum between (_____ of the skull)
	2.	Temporary joint with cartilage that is later converted to bone (between diaphysis & epiphysis of long bones)
	3.	Cone shaped peg fits firmly into a socket (root of the teeth into the mandible & maxilla)
	4.	Slight motion permitted by meager elasticity of ligaments between two bones (inferior tibiofubular joint)
	5.	Bones are separated by a fibrocartilaginous disc, whose fibers join the bones. Motion is only allowed by deformation of the disc (vertebrae discs, symphysis pubis)

With a Joint Cavity - Synovial joints

	Type (technical name)	Definition (examples)
Diarthrosis (moveable)	6.	**Uni-axial.** Allows gliding or twisting (intercarpal/intertarsal joints, vertebrae zygapophyseal joint)
	7.	**Uni-axial.** a concave surface glides around a convex surface allowing flexion and extension (elbow joint - humeroulnar joint)
	8.	**Uni-axial.** Rotation around a vertical or long axis is allowed (atlantoaxial joint, proximal radioulnar joint)
	9.	**Bi-axial.** Condyle or ovoid articular surface with an elliptical cavity to permit flexion, extension, adduction, abduction and circumduction, but no axial rotation (wrist, 2nd to 5th metacarpophalangeal joints)
	10.	**Bi-axial.** Both joints have saddle-shaped surfaces (reciprocally concave-convex) fitted into each other. Allows flexion, extension, abduction, adduction, circumduction (carpometacarpal joint of thumb)
	11.	**Poly-axial.** Spheroid ball and sockets allows flexion, extension, abduction, adduction, true circumduction, and rotation on long axis (shoulder and hip joints)

Depending numerous factors, functional AROM can vary greatly (anatomical variation, bone/joint shape, flexibility, muscle mass, training adaptation, scar tissue, injury, pain, contracture, posture, ADLs, genetics)

C-spine
Flexion .... **80-90°**
Extension .... **60-70°**
Lateral flexion ..... **20-45°**
Rotation .... **70-90°**

T-spine
Flexion .... **20-45°**
Extension .... **25-45°**
Lateral flexion ..... **20-40°**
Rotation .... **35-50°**

L-spine
Flexion .... **40-60°**
Extension .... **20-35°**
Lateral flexion . **15-20°**
Rotation .... **5-20°**

Shoulder
Flexion .... **160-180°**
Extension .... **50-60°**
Abd/add .... **180/35°**
Med/lat rotation. **90/80°**
Horizontal ab/ad. **45/130°**

Elbow
Flexion .... **~150°**
Extension .... **0 to -5°**
Supination* .... **~90°**
Pronation* .... **~90°**
*From neutral - 'thumbs up'

Wrist
Flexion .... **80-90°**
Extension .... **70-90°**
Ulnar flexion .. **30-45°**
Radial flexion . **~15°**
Sup/pro .... **85-90°**

Hip
Flexion (SLR) .... **~90°**
Flexion (knee bent) **~120°**
Extension .... **10-15°**
Abd/add .... **~40/30°**
Med/lat rotation. **~40/50°**

Knee
Flexion .... **130-150°**
Extension .... **0-15°**
Medial rot* .... **20-30°**
Lateral rot* .... **30-40°**
*knee must be flexed 90°

Ankle
Plantar flex ... **50°**
Dorsiflexion .. **20°**
Supination .... **45-60°**
Pronation ...... **15-30°**
Big Toe
Flex MTP/IP **45/90°**
Ext MTP/IP . **70/0°**

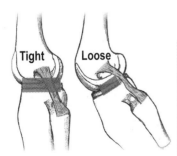
Tight   Loose

Tight (close) packed position - articular surfaces become maximally congruent (joint capsule/ligament becomes twisted causing the joint surfaces to become maximally compressed; usually occurs near end range of motion (eg. full extension of knee or elbow)

Loose (open) packed position: surfaces are not compressed, joint capsule/ligaments are lax (usually mid range of joint)

Muscle Manual
page 14

prohealthsys

Introduction

A joint is the location at which two bones make contact. There are ~456 joints and they are usually named for the two bones that make them up (e.g. sternoclavicular joint)

Name: _____ %

Generic Synovial Joint

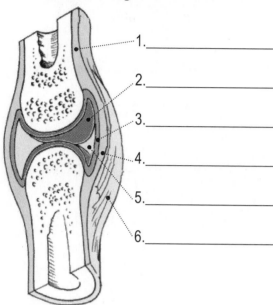

1. _____
2. _____
3. _____
4. _____
5. _____
6. _____

What are the 3 functions of synovial fluid?

15. _____
16. _____
17. _____

Three main types of cartilage:

1. **Hyaline** (articular cartilage) - most common cartilage, found lining the articular surfaces of bones in synovial joints

2. **Elastic** (yellow cartilage) - found in the ear, larynx, nose, trachea

3. **Fibrocartilage** (white cartilage) found in areas of high stress like the vertebral discs, meniscus of the knee & TMJ disc

• Because cartilage is mostly avascular, it has very limited repair capabilities; damaged cartilage is usually replaced by fibrocartilage scar tissue. Osteoarthritis (OA) develops as the cartilage eventually is worn away & bone rubs on bone

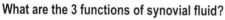
hyaline cartilage
elastic cartilage
fibrocartilage

Progression of Osteoarthritis (OA) Joint Degeneration

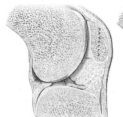

Vizniak & Richer prohealthsys.com

7 _____
coronal suture

8 _____
acromioclavicular joint

9. _____
elbow joint

10. _____
proximal radioulnar joint

11. _____
trapeziometacarpal joint

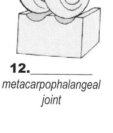

12. _____
metacarpophalangeal joint

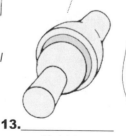

13. _____
hip joint

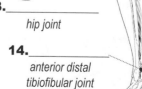

14. _____
anterior distal tibiofibular joint

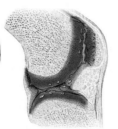
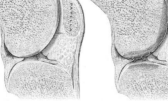

Muscle Manual page 15

prohealthsys

Define the term & give an example

Name:

%

Type	Movement & definition (all movements are defined from anatomical position)
Gliding	Gliding:
Angular	Flexion:
	Extension:
	Lateral flexion:
	Abduction:
	Adduction:
	Circumduction:
Rotation	Rotation: .
	Medial (internal) rotation:
	Lateral (external) rotation:
Special	Inversion:
	Eversion:
	Dorsiflexion:
	Plantar Flexion:
	Supination:
	Pronation:
	Radial Flexion (deviation):
	Ulnar Flexion (deviation):
	Elevation:
	Depression:
	Protraction:
	Retraction:
	Opposition:

Open kinetic chain =

Closed kinetic chain =

Muscle Manual page 20

Start with labeling the action, then progress to naming

- ☐ Muscles that cause action
- ☐ Nerves that cause action
- ☐ ROM in degrees
- ☐ Tissues stretched or compressed

Name: _____ %

Neck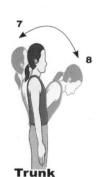

Shoulder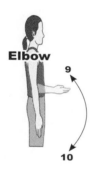

Hip

Trunk

Elbow

Knee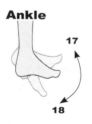

Wrist

Ankle

Fingers

1. _____
2. _____
3. _____
4. _____
5. _____
6. _____
7. _____
8. _____
9. _____
10. _____
11. _____
12. _____
13. _____
14. _____
15. _____
16. _____
17. _____
18. _____
19. If you flex all the joints in your body what position are you in?

_____

Kinetic Chain = the concept of overlapping segments connected by joints, muscles, ligaments, nerves, vessels & fascia creating a movement system where movement at one region affects movement at another region

Open kinetic chain - *distal* body part moves freely in space (eg. waving hello, picking up a weight, kicking a ball)

Closed kinetic chain - *proximal* body moves around planted limb (eg. sitting in a chair - squat, push-up or chin-up)

both actions are extension at the knee

Open Kinematic Chain   Closed Kinematic Chain

Muscle Manual page 21

MUSCLE MANUAL

prohealthsys

Introduction

Start with labeling the action, later progress to naming

☐ Muscles that cause action
☐ Nerves that cause action
☐ ROM in degrees
☐ Tissues stretched or compressed

Name: _____ %

1. _____

2. _____

3. _____

4. _____

5. _____

6. _____

7. _____

8. _____

9. _____

10. _____

11. _____

12. _____

13. _____

14. _____

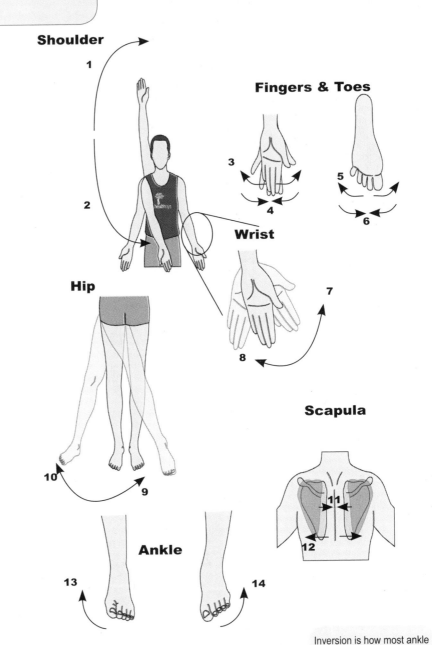

Shoulder

Fingers & Toes

Wrist

Hip

Scapula

Ankle

Inversion is how most ankle sprains occur

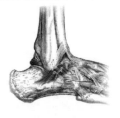

Muscle Manual page 22

Start with labeling the action, later progress to naming
- ☐ Muscles that cause action
- ☐ Nerves that cause action
- ☐ ROM in degrees
- ☐ Tissues stretched or compressed

Name: _____ %

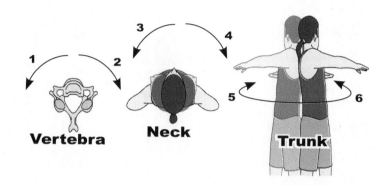

Vertebra   **Neck**   **Trunk**

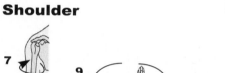
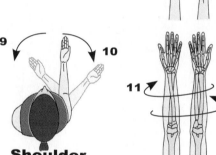

Shoulder   **Forearm**

Shoulder

Knee

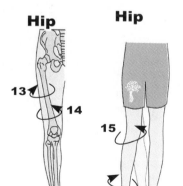

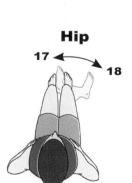

Hip   **Hip**   **Hip**

1. _____
2. _____
3. _____
4. _____
5. _____
6. _____
7. _____
8. _____
9. _____
10. _____
11. _____
12. _____
13. _____
14. _____
15. _____
16. _____
17. _____
18. _____
19. _____
20. _____

Muscle Manual page 19

prohealthsys

Start with labeling the action, later progress to naming
□ Muscles that cause action, □ Nerves that cause action,
□ ROM, □ Tissues stretched or compressed.

Name: _____ %

1. _____

2. _____

3. _____

4. _____

5. _____

6. _____

7. _____

8. _____

9. _____

10. _____

11. _____

12. _____

13. _____

14. _____

15. _____

16. _____

17. _____

18. _____

19. _____

20. _____

21. _____

22. _____

23. _____

24. _____

25. _____

26. _____

Trunk

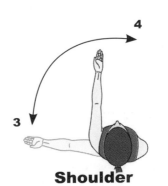

Shoulder

Hip

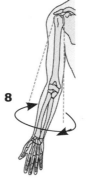

Scapula

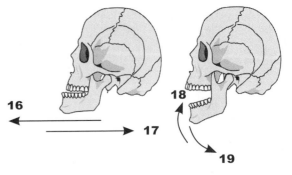

Hip & Pelvis

anterior   posterior

Temporomandibular Joint

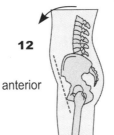

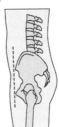 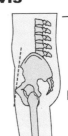

Forearm

Thumb (trapeziometacarpal joint)

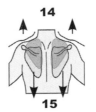

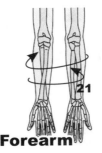

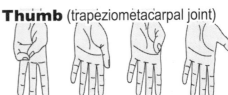

22   23   24   25   26

prohealthsys

1. Approximately how many skeletal muscle are in the body?
_____

Name: _____ %

2. What 3 factors determine muscle contraction strength?
a. _____
b. _____
c. _____

3. Through what range of motion do skeletal muscles have their maximum strength? _____

Name the Muscle Shape

1. _____
2. _____
3. _____
4. _____
5. _____
6. _____
7. _____
8. _____
9. _____
10. _____

Match the Definitions

Agonist | Antagonist | Concentric | Eccentric | Insertion | Isometric | Origin | Synergist | Tendon

1. _____: fibrous connective tissue that **connects muscle to bone, or muscle to muscle** and is designed to withstand tension (pulling force)

2. _____: attachment point of a muscle on a bone; usually more proximal/medial, or more fixed attachment (denoted **red** on anatomical drawings & models)

3. _____: attachment point for a muscle on a bone; usually more distal/lateral, or movable point of attachment on which the force of the muscle is applied (denoted grey or **blue** on anatomical drawings & models)

4. _____ **contraction:** muscle shortening contraction (muscle actions are given as concentric contractions). Insertion is brought closer to origin

5. _____ **contraction:** muscle lengthening contraction. Origin and insertion are taken away from each other

6. _____ **contraction:** muscle length stays the same, when tension is developed. Origin & insertion do not move

7. _____: muscle that creates primary movement in a joint by contracting. Also known as '**prime movers**' as they are primarily responsible for generating movement

8. _____: aids the action of a 'prime mover' by assisting the same movement or preventing undesirable movements by stabilizing joints across which the prime mover acts

9. _____: muscle acts in opposition the prime mover and returns a limb to its initial position

Muscle Strength Facts

- Muscles have **maximum strength in the mid-range** of active ROM
- As tissues begin to passively lengthen tension increases, this is felt as a muscle stretch
- Movement beyond anatomical limits results in fiber tears at the weakest point (strain, sprain or fracture)
- Injuries usually occur at the start of activity due to improper warm-up or end of activity due to fatigue
- **Muscle are mobilizers & ACTIVE stabilizers and ligaments are PASSIVE stabilizers** - when muscles or the nervous system become fatigued we rely more on ligaments for stabilization

Muscle Strength vs Length

prohealthsys

Start with labeling the muscles, then progress to naming
☐ actions, ☐ origins, ☐ insertions, ☐ nerves

Name: _____ %

1. _____

2. _____

3. _____

4. _____

5. _____

6. _____

7. _____

8. _____

9. _____

10. _____

11. _____

12. _____

13. _____

14. _____

15. _____

16. _____

17. _____

18. _____

19. _____

20. _____

21. _____

22. _____

23. _____

24. _____

25. _____

26. _____

27. _____

Muscle Manual page 26

Color this page

Start with labeling the muscles, then progress to naming
☐ actions, ☐ origins, ☐ insertions, ☐ nerves

Name: _____   %

1. _____

2. _____

3. _____

4. _____

5. _____

6. _____

7. _____

8. _____

9. _____

10. _____

11. _____

12. _____

13. _____

14. _____

15. _____

16. _____

17. _____

18. _____

19. _____

20. _____

21. _____

22. _____

23. _____

Muscle Manual page 27

Color this page

Introduction

Match the Terminology

Nerve: an enclosed, cable-like bundle of *axons* outside CNS & includes connective tissue coverings and blood vessels

Name: _____ %

- Most nerves and major branches of nerves have descriptive names. In the CNS bundles of axons are termed *tracts* rather than nerves
- Nerves may include both _____ (sensory) and _____ (motor) fibers

1. _____ : long, slender projection of a single nerve cell (neuron)

2. _____ : fatty sheath coating covering neuron axons that allows for the efficient conduction of nerve impulses. Myelin is produced by *oligodendrocytes* in the CNS and by *Schwann cells* in the PNS

3. _____ : where one neuron meets another neuron there is a small space between the cells (*synapse*), when a neuron meets a muscle it is called a *neuromuscular junction*. One neuron may synapse with hundreds of other neurons!

4. _____ : mass of cell bodies outside the CNS

5. _____ : network of nerves

6. _____ : bundle of axons within the CNS sharing common origin, destination and function

7. _____ : a group of tracts found within a specific region of the spinal cord

8. **Connective Tissue (_____) Coverings**

9. _____ : covers many fascicles or entire nerve

10. _____ : covers a bundle (fascicle) of axons

11. _____ : covers single axon

Afferent
Axon
Column
Efferent
Endoneurium
Epineurium
Fascial
Ganglion
Myelin
Perineurium
Plexus
Synapse
Tract

Label the Drawing

1. _____

2. _____

3. _____

4. _____

5. _____

6. _____

7. _____

8. _____

9. _____

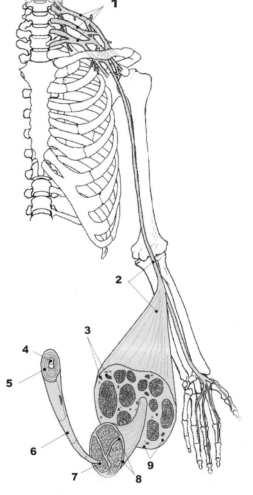

Muscle Manual page 38

What structures make up the central nervous system (CNS)

1. _____

2. _____

3. _____

Name: _____ %

Peripheral nervous system (PNS)

4. How many pairs of **spinal nerves are there?** _____ *pairs*

5. _____ (cervical)

6. _____ (thoracic)

7. _____ (lumbar)

8. _____ (sacral)

9. _____ (coccygeal)

10. How many pairs of **cranial nerves are there?** _____ *pairs*

Autonomic nervous system (ANS) (involuntary control) which is divided into

- **Sympathetic** division ('_____ or _____')
  - Actions:

11. _____

12. _____

13. _____
  - Exits the CNS from _____

- **Parasympathetic** division ('_____ & _____')
  - Actions:

14. _____

15. _____

16. _____
  - Exits the CNS through _____

Cerebrum

Midbrain

Pons

Cerebellum

Medulla

— Cervical

— Thoracic

Spinal cord

— Lumbar

— Sacral

transverse cut through thoracic spinal cord

Label the Drawing

1. _____

2. _____

3. _____

4. _____

5. _____

6. _____

7. _____

8. _____

9. _____

10. _____

Spinal Cord (CNS)

Somatic Neurons

SPINAL CORD

DORSAL ROOT

SPINAL NERVE

VENTRAL ROOT

SYMPATHETIC

Peripheral Nerves (PNS)

1 2 3 4 5 6 7 8 9 10

GI Tract (sensory & motor)

Skin or tendon (sensory)

skeletal muscle (motor)

Muscle Manual page 39

Name: _____ %

1. Ligaments *connect* _____ *to* _____ to form a _____ (tendons connect _____ *to* _____)

2. The term 'double-jointed' refers to people who have more _____ in their ligaments, allowing their joints to stretch & contort further. The medical term for describing such double-jointed persons is _____ which results in _____ (excess movement).

3. **Excessively stretched or torn ligaments (_____) can result in *instability* of the joint**; which over time can lead to wear of the cartilage & eventually to osteoarthritis. Because ligaments have a relatively poor blood supply, they can take a very long time to heal.

4. Ligaments that have gone into *contracture* can result in _____ of a joint, which can limit ROM & cause abnormal biomechanics.

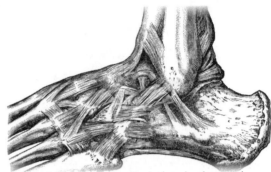

Left Lateral Ankle Ligaments (can be damaged following an inversion ankle sprain)

Ligament sprain healing occurs in 3 overlapping phases - duration varies depending on injury severity, general health, activity, nutrition & age of individual. Early return to full activity increases the likelihood of re-injury & development of chronic pain, repeat injury results in more scar tissue formation

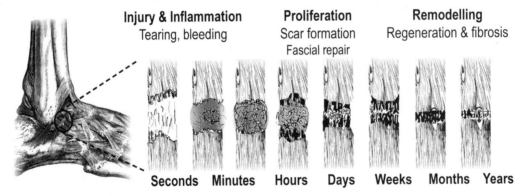

Injury & Inflammation
Tearing, bleeding

Proliferation
Scar formation
Fascial repair

Remodelling
Regeneration & fibrosis

Seconds   Minutes   Hours   Days   Weeks   Months   Years

Fill in the Blanks

Cartilage: type of dense connective tissue composed of collagen fibers and/or elastin fibers, and cells called *chondrocytes*, all of which are embedded in a firm gel-like ground substance called the *matrix*

Three main types of cartilage:

chondrocyte

matrix

1. _____ (articular cartilage) - most common cartilage, found lining the articular surfaces of bones in synovial joints

2. _____ (yellow cartilage) - found in the ear, larynx, nose, trachea

3. _____ (white cartilage) found in areas of high stress like the vertebral discs, meniscus of the knee & TMJ disc

• Because cartilage is mostly avascular, it has very limited repair capabilities; damaged cartilage is usually replaced by fibrocartilage scar tissue. _____ (OA) develops as the cartilage eventually is worn away & bone rubs on bone

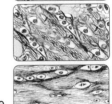

Muscle Manual page 16

Fascia: (Latin for 'band' or 'bandage') flat bands of dense irregular connective tissue below skin that covers the underlying tissues & separates layers of tissue. Fascia encloses muscles, organs, nerves, blood vessels, ligaments & bones; **it is found throughout the entire body**.

- Inflammation of the fascia is referred to as

  _____

- Increased blood pressure can sometimes occur in body regions enclosed with fascia resulting in a

  _____

- _____: located directly deep to skin & surrounds the entire body. It is filled with fat, nerves, blood vessels & other connective tissue

- _____: dense fibrous connective tissue that interpenetrates & surrounds the muscles, bones, nerves & blood vessels of the body; some muscle have origin & insertion directly on fascia (e.g. TFL, tib. anterior, glut. maximus)

  - _____ - a sheet-like fibrous membrane that binds muscles together or to connect muscle to bone or other fascia (e.g. abdominal _____)

Functions of Fascia:

- Fascia contains soft tissues & transmits mechanical tension generated by muscular activities or external forces throughout the body (**fascia glides & sticks together; failure of this basic principle = pathology**)

  - Provides a sliding & gliding environment for muscles (creates bursae)

  - Suspends organs in their proper place

  - Transmit movement from muscle to bones

  - Provide a supportive & movable wrapping for nerves & blood vessels as they pass through & between muscles

  - Superficial (subcutaneous) **fascia contains many nerve endings**, blood vessels & adipocytes (fat & vitamin storage)

    - May be the site of muscle attachment - (facial muscles, gluteus maximus, biceps brachii, tibialis anterior, palmaris longus)

    - Some sources suggest superficial fascia with skin as a human sex organ (a common source of pleasure is rubbing our skin/fascia against each other)

> **Muscles, fascia, ligaments, nerves and joint capsules attach to each other, creating myofascial connections & kinetic chains through the entire body!**

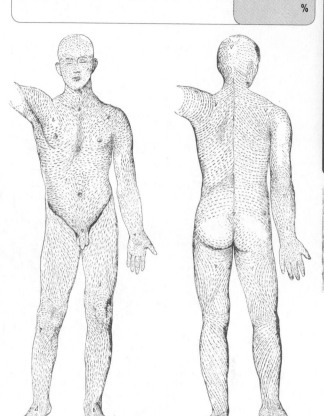

Name: _____   %

Image: general course of fascia determined by linear cleft made in skin with a round awl - similar to wood, this is the general 'grain' of the superficial fascia in the body (source: Gray's Anatomy). Superficial fascia is similar to a sweater in its covering of the body; Dysfunction in one part of the body it can influence function in other regions.

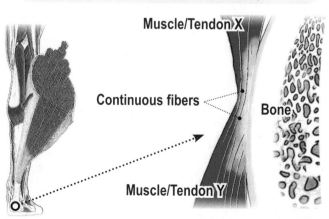

Muscle/Tendon X

Continuous fibers

Bone

Muscle/Tendon Y

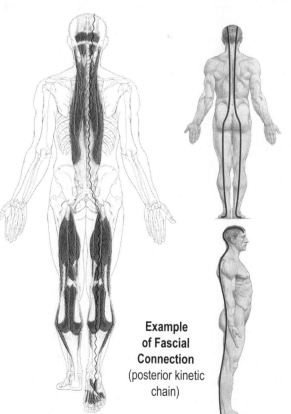

Example of Fascial Connection (posterior kinetic chain)

prohealthsys

Introduction

Name:

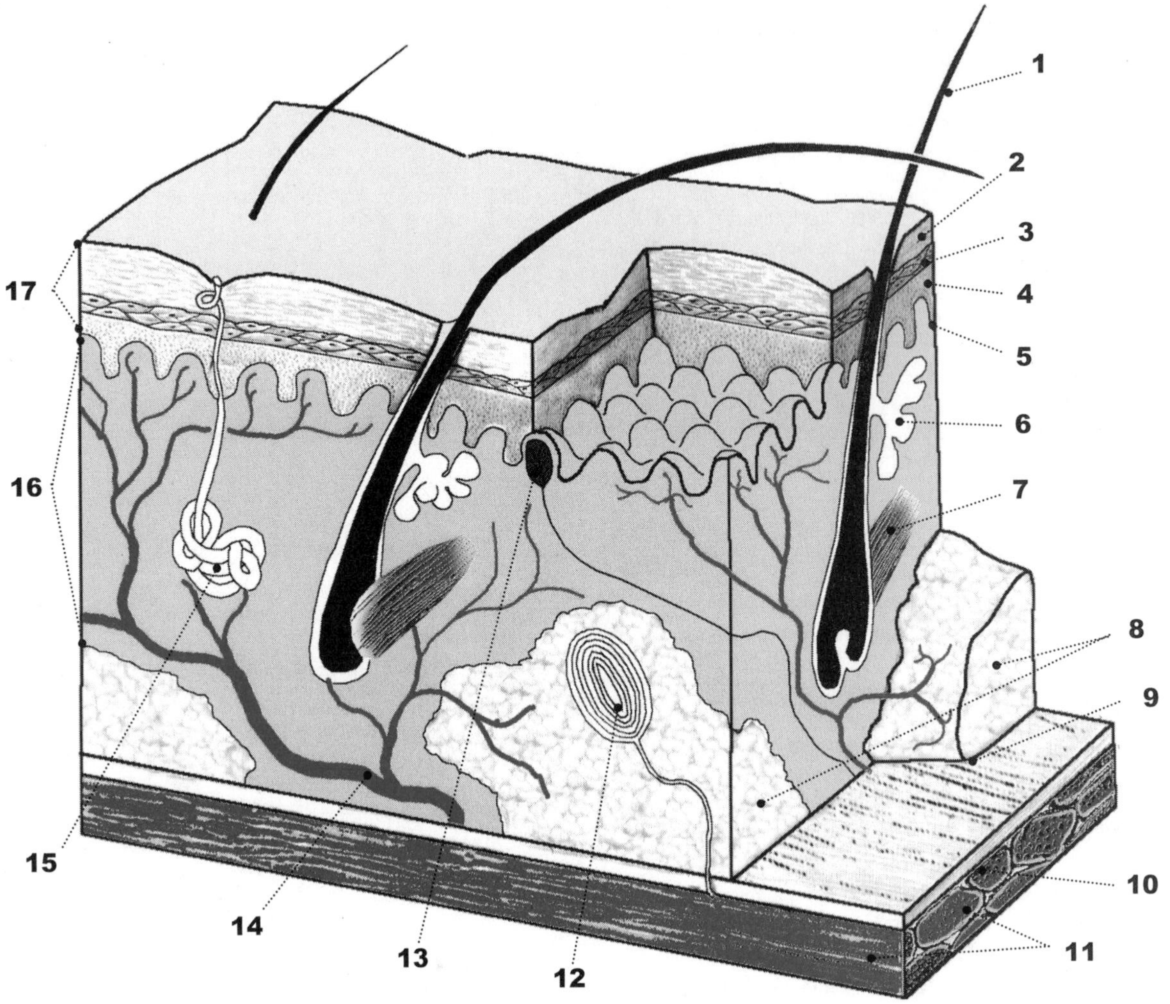

%

1

2

3

4

5

6

7

8

9

10

11

17

16

15

14

13

12

1. _____	10. _____
2. _____	11. _____
3. _____	12. _____
4. _____	13. _____
5. _____	14. _____
6. _____	15. _____
7. _____	16. _____
8. _____	17. _____
9. _____	

Muscle Manual page 43

Bonus - define the term Bursa:

prohealthsys

Name:

%

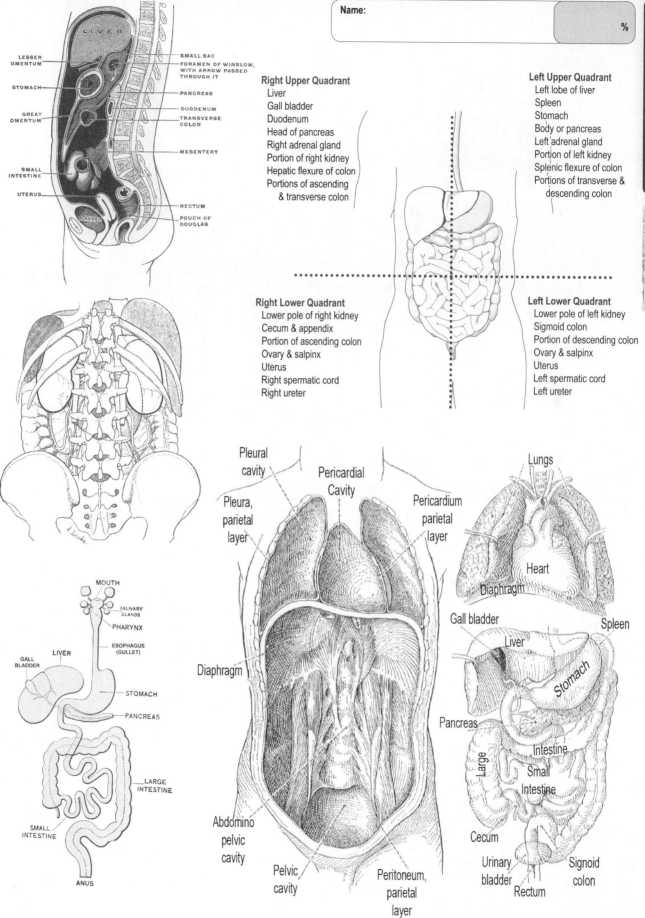

LIVER

LESSER OMENTUM
STOMACH
GREAT OMENTUM
SMALL INTESTINE
UTERUS
BLADDER

SMALL SAC
FORAMEN OF WINSLOW, WITH ARROW PASSED THROUGH IT
PANCREAS
DUODENUM
TRANSVERSE COLON
MESENTERY
RECTUM
POUCH OF DOUGLAS

XII

Right Upper Quadrant
Liver
Gall bladder
Duodenum
Head of pancreas
Right adrenal gland
Portion of right kidney
Hepatic flexure of colon
Portions of ascending
& transverse colon

Left Upper Quadrant
Left lobe of liver
Spleen
Stomach
Body or pancreas
Left adrenal gland
Portion of left kidney
Splenic flexure of colon
Portions of transverse &
descending colon

Right Lower Quadrant
Lower pole of right kidney
Cecum & appendix
Portion of ascending colon
Ovary & salpinx
Uterus
Right spermatic cord
Right ureter

Left Lower Quadrant
Lower pole of left kidney
Sigmoid colon
Portion of descending colon
Ovary & salpinx
Uterus
Left spermatic cord
Left ureter

MOUTH
SALIVARY GLANDS
PHARYNX
ESOPHAGUS (GULLET)
GALL BLADDER
LIVER
STOMACH
PANCREAS
LARGE INTESTINE
SMALL INTESTINE
ANUS

Pleural cavity
Pericardial Cavity
Pleura, parietal layer
Pericardium parietal layer
Diaphragm
Abdomino pelvic cavity
Pelvic cavity
Peritoneum, parietal layer

Lungs
Heart
Diaphragm
Gall bladder
Liver
Spleen
Stomach
Pancreas
Intestine
Large
Small
Intestine
Cecum
Urinary bladder
Rectum
Signoid colon

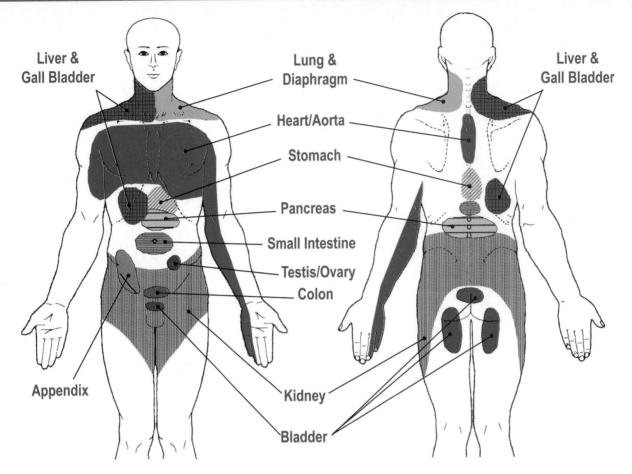

Introduction

Liver & Gall Bladder

Lung & Diaphragm

Heart/Aorta

Stomach

Pancreas

Small Intestine

Testis/Ovary

Colon

Liver & Gall Bladder

Appendix

Kidney

Bladder

All answers you need and more can be found on the corresponding pages of the '**Muscle Manual**'

Page1
1. Posterior
2. Anterior
3. Medial
4. Lateral
5. Proximal
6. Distal
7. Superior
8. Inferior
9. Coronal (frontal)
10. Sagittal
11. Transverse

1. Anterior: front of the body
2. Posterior: back of the body
3. Superior: toward head or upper part of a structure
4. Cephalad: towards the head
5. Inferior: away from head or lower part of a structure
6. Caudad: towards the tail
7. Medial: toward the midline
8. Lateral: away from midline
9. Proximal: closer to the point of origin of extremity
10. Distal: further away from the point of origin of extremity
11. Superficial: near the surface of the body
12. Deep: away from the surface of the body
13. External: located closer to the surface of the body
14. Internal: located away from the surface of the body
15. Ipsilateral: same side
16. Contralateral: opposite sides
17. Bilateral: both sides
18. Unilateral: one side
19. Supine: 'lay on spine' or back
20. Prone: lying on belly or front
Page 2

1. Upper lateral skull (parietal)
2. Base of skull (occipital) Neck (cervical)
3. Middle back (thoracic)
4. Loin (lumbar)
5. Tail bone (sacral)
6. Anal region (perineal) Shoulder (acromial)
7. Shoulder (deltoid)
8. Shoulder blade (scapular)
9. Arm (brachial)
10. Elbow (olecranon)*
11. Forearm (antebrachial)
12. Wrist (carpal)
13. Back of hand (dorsum)
14. Fingers (digits/pha-langes)
   Buttock (gluteal)
15. Thigh (femoral)
16. Back of knee (popliteal)
17. Calf (sural)
18. Heel (calcaneal)
19. Sole of foot (plantar)

Page 3
1. Forehead (frontal)
2. Eye (orbital)
3. Ear (auricular)
4. Nose (nasal)
5. Cheek (buccal)
6. Mouth (oral)
7. Chin (mental) Collar bone (clavicular)
8. Breast bone (sternal)
9. Breast (mammary)
10. Arm pit (axillary)
11. Shoulder (deltoid) Arm (brachial)
12. Cubital fossa
13. Forearm (antebrachial)
14. Wrist (carpal)
15. Base of thumb (thenar)
16. Palm (palmar)
17. Hypothenar eminence
18. Finger (digit/phalanges)

Epigastric
19. Navel (umbilical)
20. Groin (inguinal)
21. Pubic (pubis)
22. Genital (pudendal) Thigh (femoral)
23. Knee cap (patellar)
24. Shin (crural)
25. Ankle (tarsal)
26. Foot (pedal)

Page 4
1. Skull
2. Mandible
3. Cervical vertebrae (7)
4. Clavicle
5. Sternum
6. Scapula
7. Ribs (24) - costal
8. Humerus
9. Thoracic vertebrae (12)
10. Lumbar vertebrae (5)
11. Radius
12. Ulna
13. Ilium (os coxae)
14. Sacrum
15. Coccyx
16. Carpals (8 per wrist)
17. Metacarpals (5 per hand)
18. Phalanges (14 per hand)
19. Femur
20. Patella
21. Fibula
22. Tibia
23. Tarsals (7 per foot)
24. Metatarsals (5 per foot)
25. Phalanges (14 per foot)

Page 5
1. Skull
2. Mandible
3. Cervical vertebrae (7)
4. Clavicle
5. Sternum (not visible)
6. Scapula
7. Ribs (24) - costal

8. Humerus
9. Thoracic vertebrae (12)
10. Lumbar vertebrae (5)
11. Radius*
12. Ulna
13. Ilium (os coxae)
14. Sacrum
15. Coccyx
16. Carpals (8 per wrist)
17. Metacarpals (5 per hand)
18. Phalanges (14 per hand)
19. Femur
20. Patella (not visible)
21. Tibia
22. Fibula
23. Tarsals (7 per foot)
24. Metatarsals (5 per foot)
25. Phalanges (14 per foot)

Page 9
1. Carpal bones (8)
2. Scaphoid
3. Lunate
4. Triquetrum
5. Pisiform
6. Trapezium
7. Trapezoid
8. Capitate
9. Hamate
   Metacarpals
10. Proximal phalanges
11. Middle phalanges
12. Distal phalanges
Foot
1. Calcaneus
2. Talus
3. Navicular
4. Medial cuneiform
5. Intermediate cuneiform
6. Lateral cuneiform
7. Cuboid
8. Metatarsals
9. Proximal phalanges
10. Middle phalanges
11. Distal phalanges

Page 16
1. Frontalis
2. Orbicularis oculi
3. Orbicularis oris
4. Masseter
5. Platysma
6. Sternocleidomastoid
7. Trapezius
8. Deltoid
9. Pectoralis major
10. Serratus anterior
11. Biceps brachii
12. Brachioradialis
13. Forearm flexors
14. Thenar muscles
15. Hypothenar muscles
16. External oblique
17. Rectus abdominis
18. Iliopsoas
19. Pectineus
20. Sartorius
21. Gracilis
22. Rectus femoris
23. Vastus lateralis
24. Vastus medialis
25. Tibialis anterior
26. Fibularis longus
27. Extensor digitorum longus

page 17
1. Occipitalis
2. Sternocleidomastoid
3. Trapezius
4. Deltoid
5. Infraspinatus
6. Teres minor
7. Teres major
8. Rhomboids
9. Triceps brachii
10. Latissimus dorsi
11. Extensor carpi radialis longus
12. Forearm extensors
13. Thoracolumbar fascia
14. Gluteus maximus

15. Iliotibial band
16. Vastus lateralis
17. Biceps femoris
18. Semitendinosus
19. Semimembranosus
20. Gastrocnemius
21. Soleus
22. Fibularis longus
23. Calcaneal (Achilles) tendon

MUSCLE MANUAL

Tissue sensitivity to pain

Least sensitive
- Fibrocartilage
- Articular cartilage
- Synovium

- Cortical bone
- Muscle, fascia
- Viscera

- Tendons
- Ligaments
- Subchondral bone

- Fibrous capsule
- Periosteum
- Skin
Most sensitive

Learning Objectives

After completing this chapter, students will be able to:

1. Identify and palpate anatomy of the region (give a list of structures below their palpating hand) - sutures, joints, muscles, glands, eyes, ears, throat, tongue

2. Assess AROM, PROM & RROM

3. Describe biomechanics of the region

4. Perform detailed muscle testing and palpation

5. Discuss anatomical variation, ADLs and common injuries of the region

6. Summarize the cranial nerves (foramen they run through, functions, testing and lesions)

Skull & Upper Neck Bones	26
Skull	27
Mandible & TMJ	28
Joints of Skull	29
Cranial Vault & Foramen	30
Cranial Nerves	31
Muscles of Head & Face	32
Muscles of Facial Expression	34
Muscles of Mastication	39
Middle & Inner Ear	40
Muscles of Eye Movement	41
Tongue & Throat	42
Sagittal View	43
Answers	44

Surface anatomy

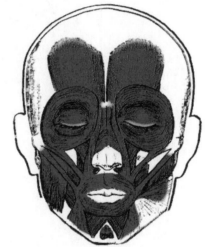

Myofascial

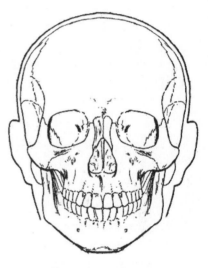

Bony Landmarks

Palpation Checklist

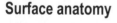
Video on prohealthsys

- ☐ Mandible
- ☐ TMJ
- ☐ Zygomatic arch/cheeks
- ☐ Masseter/Parotids
- ☐ Submandibular gland
- ☐ Submental gland
- ☐ Suprahyoid muscles
- ☐ Lymph nodes

- ☐ SCM
- ☐ Mastoid processes
- ☐ Temporal & carotid pulse
- ☐ Scalp & hair
- ☐ Ears & eyes lids
- ☐ Upper trapezius
- ☐ Occipitalis & EOP
- ☐ Splenius capitis

- ☐ Semispinalis capitis
- ☐ Suboccipitals
- ☐ Muscles of facial expression
- ☐ Muscles of mastication
- ☐ Oral cavity (gloved hand)
- ☐ . . . .
- ☐ . . . .
- ☐ . . . . Printable quiz on website

Name: _____ %

Head & Face

1. _____
  a. _____
  b. _____
  c. _____
2. _____
3. _____
  a. _____
4. _____
  a. _____
  b. _____
  c. _____
  d. _____
  e. _____
  f. _____
5. _____
6. _____
7. _____
8. _____
9. _____
  a. _____
  b. _____
  c. _____
  d. _____
  e. _____
10. _____
  a. _____
  b. _____
  c. _____
  d. _____
  e. _____
11. _____
12. _____
13. _____
  a. _____
  b. _____
  c. _____
  d. _____
  e. _____
  f. _____
  g. _____
14. _____
15. _____
16. _____

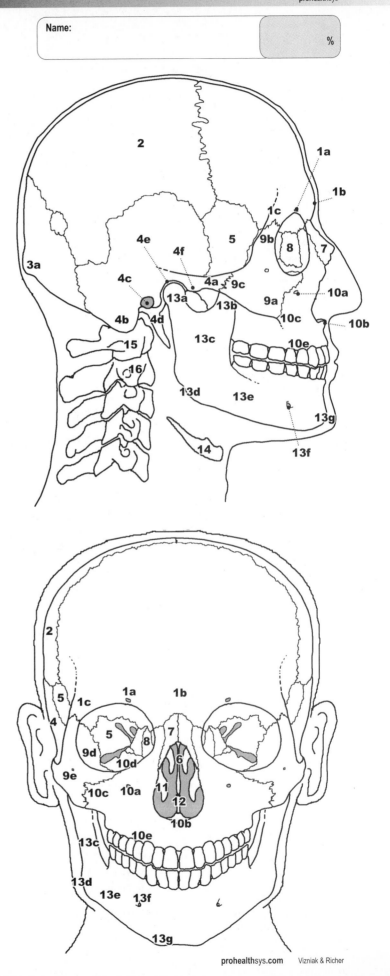

prohealthsys

1. _____

2. _____

3. _____

4. _____

5. _____

6. _____

7. _____

8. _____

   a. _____

   b. _____

   c. _____

   d. _____

   e. _____

9. _____

   a. _____

   b. _____

   c. _____

   d. _____

10. _____

   a. _____

   b. _____

11. _____

12. _____

13. _____

Name: _____ %

Head & Face

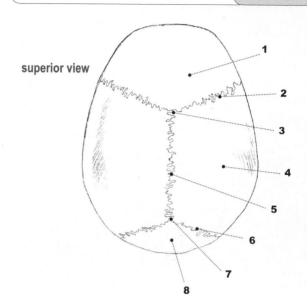
superior view

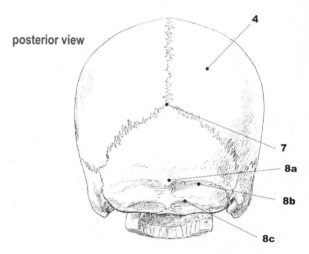
posterior view

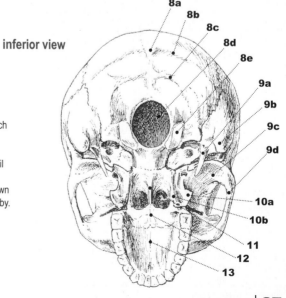
inferior view

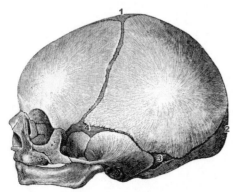

Skull at birth (below) showing fontanelles, which allow the head to pass through the birth canal and the brain to grow until skeletal maturity. The anterior fontanelle is known as the "soft spot" on a baby.

Fontanelles

1. Anterior
2. Posterior
3. Mastoid
4. Sphenoid

Mandible

Name:

%

1. ______________________
2. ______________________
3. ______________________
4. ______________________
5. ______________________
6. ______________________
7. ______________________
8. ______________________
9. ______________________
10. ______________________
11. ______________________
12. ______________________
13. ______________________
14. ______________________
15. ______________________
16. ______________________

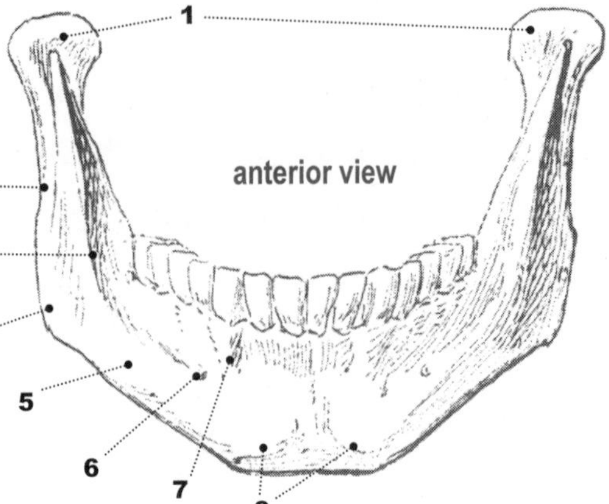

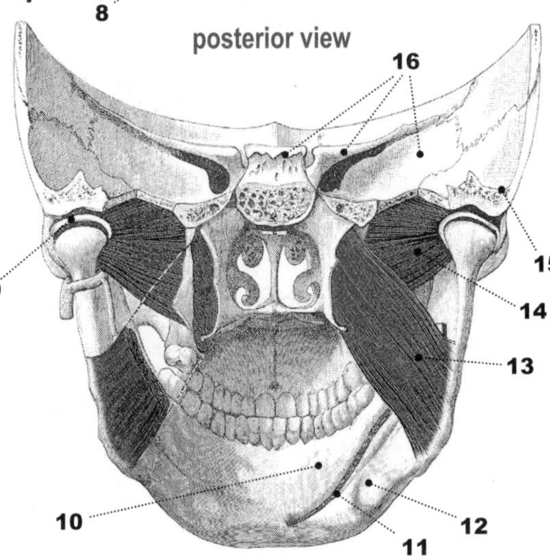

anterior view
1
2
3
4
5
6
7
8

posterior view
16
15
9
14
13
10
12
11

Left Temporomandibular Joint (TMJ)

medial view
6
2b
1c
2
5

lateral view
1
1a
1b
3
4
2a
2
2b

1. ______________________
   a. ______________________
   b. ______________________
   c. ______________________
2. ______________________
   2a. ______________________
   2b. ______________________
3. ______________________
4. ______________________
5. ______________________
6. ______________________

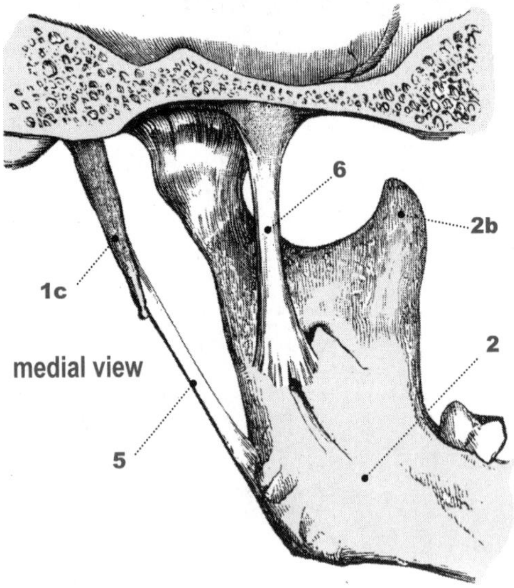

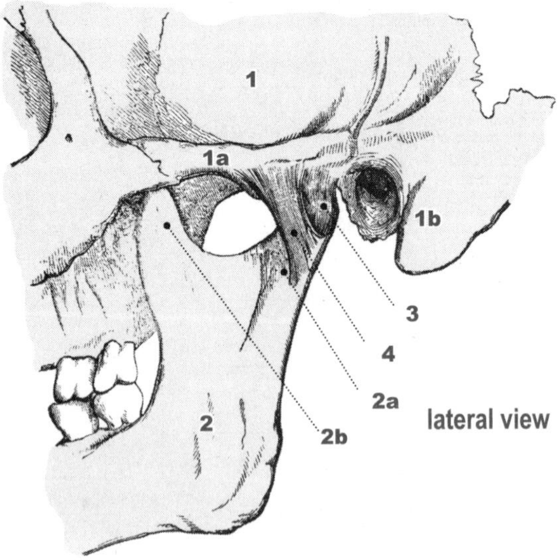

prohealthsys

Name: _____ %

anterior view

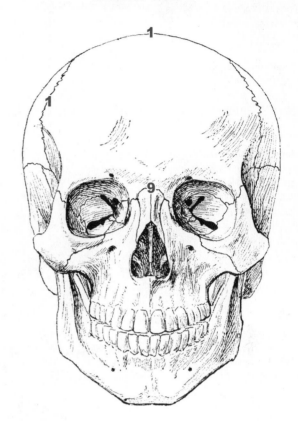

1. _____
2. _____
3. _____
4. _____
5. _____
6. _____
7. _____
8. _____
9. _____
10. _____
11. _____

lateral view

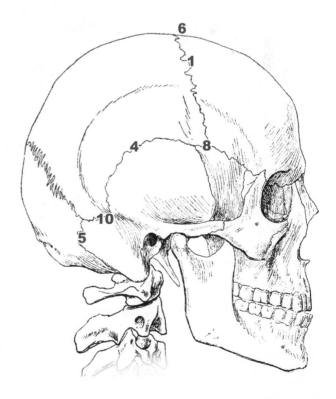

posterior view

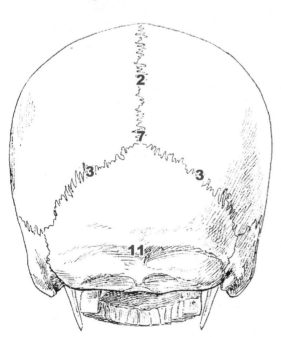

prohealthsys

Cranial Foramen & what passes through them

Name: _____ %

▶ youtube: vizniak skull

anterior

1. **Foramen cecum**
   ☐ emissary vein

2. **Cristae gali**

3. **Cribriform plate**
   ☐ CN-I Olfactory

4. **Optic canal**
   ☐ CN-II Optic
   ☐ opthalmic artery

5. **Superior orbital fissure**
   ☐ CN-III Oculomotor
   ☐ CN-IV Trochlear
   ☐ CN-V Trigeminal V$_1$ ophthalmic
   ☐ CN-VI Abducens
   ☐ Superior ophthalmic vein

6. **Foramen rotundum**
   ☐ CN-V Trigeminal V$_2$ maxillary

7. **Sella Turcica** (hypophyseal fossa)
   ☐ for pituitary gland

8. **Foramen ovale**
   ☐ CN-V Trigeminal V$_3$ mandibluar
   ☐ Accessory meningeal artery

9. **Foramen lacerum**

10. **Foramen spinosum**
    ☐ Middle meningeal artery & vein

11. **Carotid canal**
    ☐ Internal carotid artery & nerve plexus

12. **Internal acoustic meatus**
    ☐ CN-VII Facial
    ☐ CN-VIII Vestibulocochlear

13. **Jugular foramen**
    ☐ Sigmoid sinus
    ☐ CN-IX Glossopharyngeal
    ☐ CN-X Vagus
    ☐ CN-XI Accessory
    ☐ posterior menigeal artery

14. **Hypoglossal canal**
    ☐ CN-XII Hypoglossal

15. **Foramen magnum**
    ☐ Brain stem (medulla oblongata)
    ☐ Meninges (dura mater, arachnoid & pia mater)
    ☐ Vertebral arteries
    ☐ Spinal roots of CN-XI

16. **Occipital condyle**
    ☐ Atlas (C1) articulation

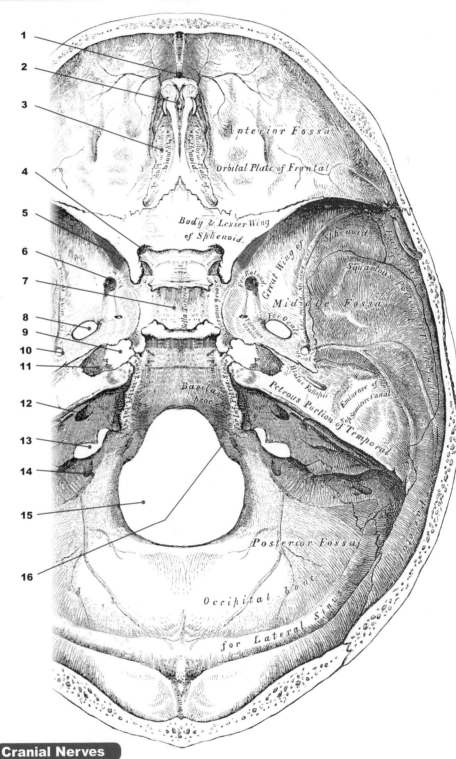

Cranial Nerves

I. Olfactory	Opt	VII. Facial	Feed
II. Optic	Out	VIII. Vestibulocochlear	Vegan
III. Oculomotor	Of	IX. Glossopharyngeal	Girls
IV. Trochlear	Trouble,	X. Vagus	Vegetables
V. Trigeminal	Try	XI. Accessory (spinal)	At
VI. Abducens	And	XII. Hypoglossal	Home

Cranial nerves exit the CNS though cranial foramen

Name: _____

_____ %

Nerve	Function	Lesion/Pathology	Test
I Olfactory (s)	sensory: smell	anosmia (loss of smell)	Ask patient to smell - Scent (coffee, mint)
II Optic (s)	sensory: vision	visual field deficits	Visual acuity (eye chart), Visual fields Pupillary constriction (III) Fundiscopic exam (look in back of eye)
III Oculomotor (m)	motor: superior, inferior & medial rectus muscles; inferior oblique, levator palpebra parasympathetic: constrictor pupillae, cillary muscles (lens shape)	dilated pupil, ptosis, eye turned down & lateral loss of pupillary light reflex on lesion side	Patient holds head still - tracking 'H' pattern with eye movement only
IV Trochlear (m)	motor: superior oblique	inability to look down when eye is adducted	Patient holds head still - tracking 'H' pattern with eye movement only
V Trigeminal (b)	sensory: V1(ophthalmic), V2(maxillary), V3(mandibular), sensation anterior 2/3 tongue motor: V3 - masseter, temporalis, lat & med pterygoid, anterior belly digastric, mylohyoid, tensor tympani/ veli palatini	paresthesia (pain & touch) over face mandible deviation to side of lesion when mouth is opened masseter & temporalis do not contract	Motor: pterygoids = lateral deviation of the jaw against resistance - masseters = palpation of masseters while patient clenches jaw or patient 'bites down' Sensory: sensory perception of the face & buccal mucosa - bilaterally equal? Sensory: test afferent fibers of the **corneal reflex** • Examiner lightly brushes cotton across surface of the patient's cornea
VI Abducens (m)	motor: lateral rectus muscle	no abduction if ipsilateral eye medial strabismus, diplopia	Patient holds head still - tracking 'H' pattern with eye movement only - Smooth tracking & nystagmus? - Finish with convergence & observe pupil constriction
VII Facial (b)	sensory: taste – anterior 2/3 of tongue motor: frontalis, occipitalis, orbicularis, buccinator, zygomaticus, mentalis, post. belly digastric, stapedius, stylohyoid parasympathetic: lacrimal, nasal & palatine, sublingual, lingual subman- dibular, labial	loss of taste anterior 2/3 tongue paralysis of facial muscles, hyperacousis (stapedius paralysis) ↓ salivation, lacrimation	Motor: all voluntary & involuntary movements of the face - does not include jaw movements; includes elevation of the eyebrows, wrinkle forehead, smile, frown, grimace, puff out cheeks with air Sensory: taste anterior 2/3 of tongue Note: VII also innervates lacrimal glands, submandibular & submaxillary glands; these are not routinely tested, but be aware of presence or absence of saliva & tears
VIII Acoustic (s) (*vestibulocochlear*)	sensory: hearing & equilibrium	unilateral hearing loss balance problems	Vestibular division tested with Romberg's & tandem walk - Cochlear division: auditory acuity; Weber & Rinne
IX Glossopharyn- geal (b)	sensory: sensation & taste posterior 1/3 of tongue, pharynx, tympanic cavity, carotid baro/chemo receptors motor: stylopharyngeus muscle parasympathetic: parotid gland	loss of taste on posterior 1/3 of tongue loss of sensation on affected side of soft palate ↓ salivation	Often tested with Vagus; taste to posterior 1/3 of tongue; motor: stylopharyngeus muscle Gag reflex: general sensation, tonsillar & pharyngeal mucosa
X Vagus (b)	sensory: pinna of ear, GI distension motor: muscles of palate, pharynx & larynx parasympathetic: heart, esophagus, GI tract up to distal 2/3 of transverse colon	ipsilateral: uvula deviates to opposite side of lesion, dyspnea, hoarse voice bilateral: death	Motor: palate, pharynx contracting muscles Vagus function: patient says 'Ahhhh'; examiner observes for palate elevation & symmetry Normal: symmetrical elevation of palate & contraction of pharyngeal muscles Lesion: palate & uvula deviate to unaffected side
XI Accessory (m) (*spinal accessory*)	motor: SCM, trapezius	paralysis of SCM & superior fibers of trapezius → drooping of shoulder	Motor: Trapezius & SCM strength against slight resis- tance (muscle tests)
XII Hypoglossal (m)	motor: intrinsic muscles of tongue, ge- nioglossus, styloglossus, hyoglossus	tongue deviates toward side of lesion on protrusion (action of genioglossus)	Check for tongue deviation toward affected side with protrusion, fasciculations Check tongue ROM, muscle tone; patient pushes tongue against cheek or 'stick out tongue'

mnemonic - (I) **O**pt, **O**ut, **O**f, **T**rouble, **T**ry, **A**nd, **F**eed, **V**egan, **G**irls, **V**egetables, **A**t, **H**ome (XII)

s = sensory, m = motor, b = both - (I) **s**ome **s**ay **m**arry **m**oney **b**ut **m**y **b**rother **s**ays **b**ig **b**rains **m**atter **m**ore (XII)

Start with labeling the muscles, then progress to naming
□ actions,   □ origins,   □ insertions,   □ nerves

Name:

%

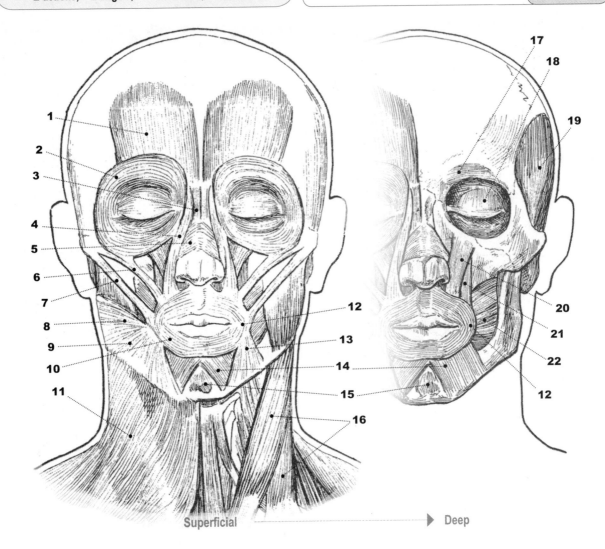

Superficial ▷ Deep

1. _____

2. _____

3. _____

4. _____

5. _____

6. _____

7. _____

8. _____

9. _____

10. _____

11. _____

12. _____

13. _____

14. _____

15. _____

16. _____

17. _____

18. _____

19. _____

20. _____

21. _____

22. _____

Start with labeling the muscles, then progress to naming
□ actions, □ origins, □ insertions, □ nerves

Name:

%

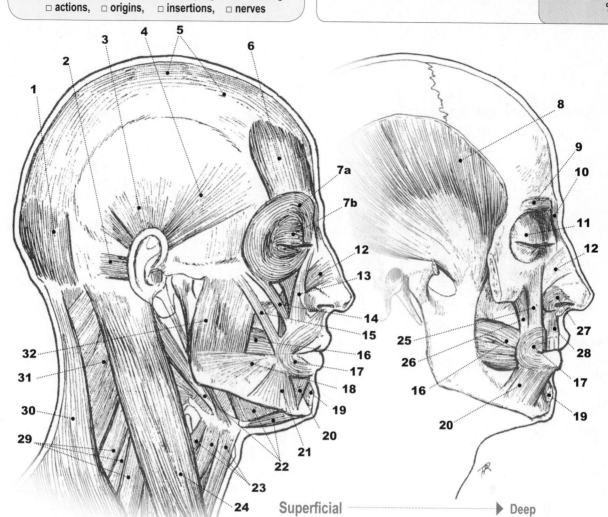

Superficial ----------------------► Deep

Head & Face

1. _____

2. _____

3. _____

4. _____

5. _____

6. _____

7. _____

   a. _____

   b. _____

8. _____

9. _____

10. _____

11. _____

12. _____

13. _____

14. _____

15. _____

16. _____

17. _____

18. _____

19. _____

20. _____

21. _____

22. _____

23. _____

24. _____

25. _____

26. _____

27. _____

28. _____

29. _____

30. _____

31. _____

32. _____

prohealthsys

Name: [   ] %

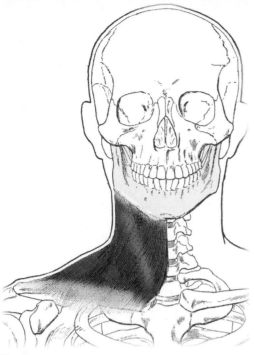

Name:

O
I
A
C

Name:

O
I
A
C

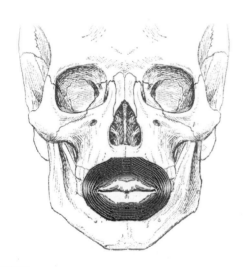

Name:

O
I
A
C

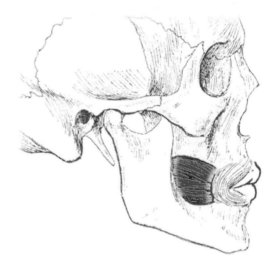

Name:

O
I
A
C

prohealthsys.com   Vizniak & Richer

Name: _____ %

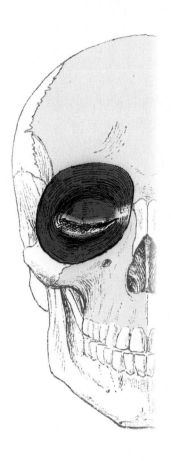
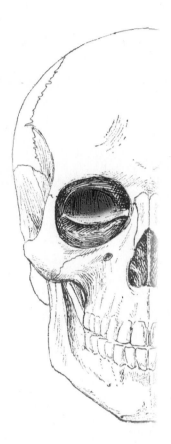
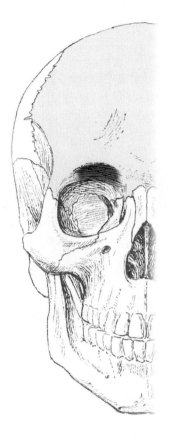
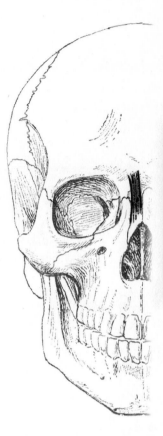

Name:

O
I
A
C

Name:

O
I
A
C

Name:

O
I
A
C

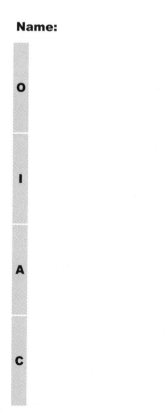

Name:

O
I
A
C

prohealthsys

Name: _____ %

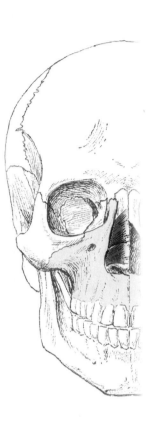

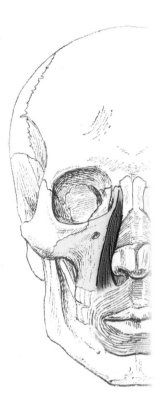

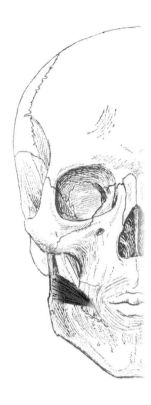

Head & Face

Name:

O

I

A

C

Name:

O

I

A

C

Name:

O

I

A

C

Name:

O

I

A

C

prohealthsys.com   Vizniak & Richer

Name: _____ %

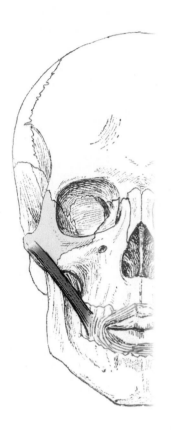

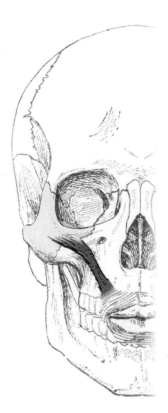

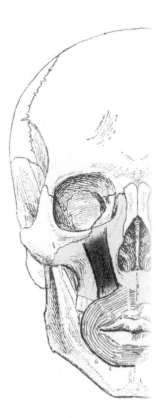

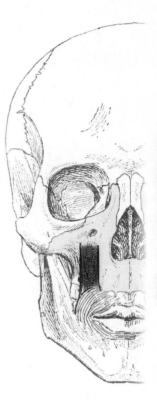

Name:

O

I

A

C

Name:

O

I

A

C

Name:

O

I

A

C

Name:

O

I

A

C

prohealthsys

Head & Face

Name: _____ %

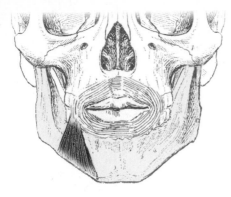

Name:

O

I

A

C

Name:

O

I

A

C

Name:

O

I

A

C

Name:

O

I

A

C

Name:

O

I

A

C

prohealthsys

Name:

%

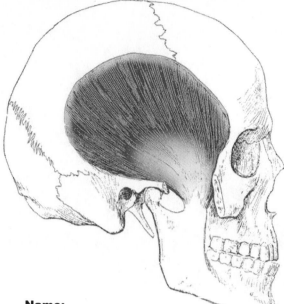

Name:

O

I

A

C

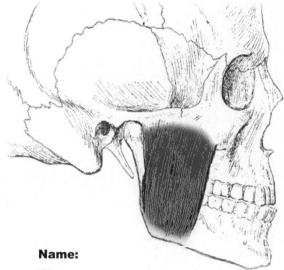

Name:

O

I

A

C

Head & Face

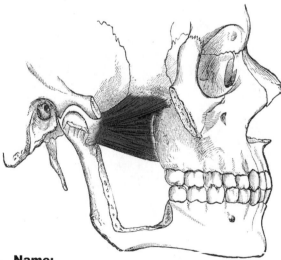

Name:

O

I

A

C

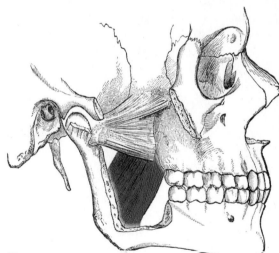

Name:

O

I

A

C

Head & Face

Name:

%

coronal

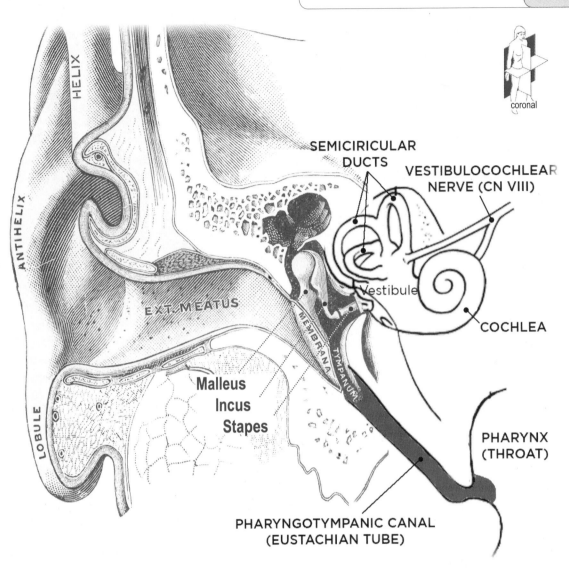

HELIX

ANTIHELIX

EXT. MEATUS

MEMBRANA

TYMPANUM

LOBULE

Malleus
Incus
Stapes

SEMICIRICULAR DUCTS

VESTIBULOCOCHLEAR NERVE (CN VIII)

Vestibule

COCHLEA

PHARYNX (THROAT)

PHARYNGOTYMPANIC CANAL (EUSTACHIAN TUBE)

External Right Ear

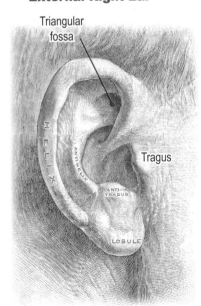

Triangular fossa

HELIX

ANTIHELIX

ANTI-TRAGUS

Tragus

LOBULE

Right Tympanic Membrane

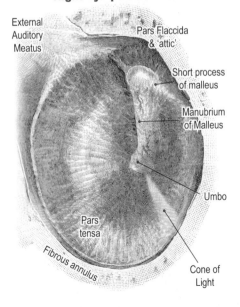

External Auditory Meatus

Pars Flaccida & 'attic'

Short process of malleus

Manubrium of Malleus

Umbo

Pars tensa

Fibrous annulus

Cone of Light

Name: _____ [ ] %

Lateral view of right eye

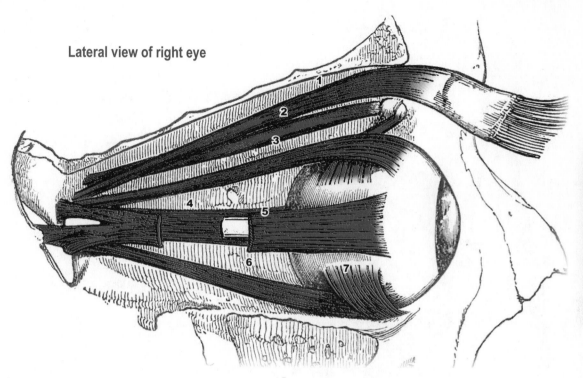

1. _____   5. _____
2. _____   6. _____
3. _____   7. _____
4. _____

Muscle	Origin	Insertion	Action	Nerve

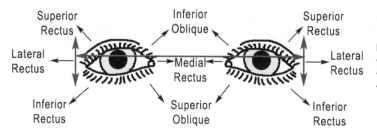

Extra-ocular movements (H-pattern)
- Ask patient to follow finger with out moving their head
- Note presence of *nystagmus* (fluttering of the eyes)
- Ask patient: did you note any *double vision*?

Head & Face *(side tab)*

prohealthsys

Name: _____ %

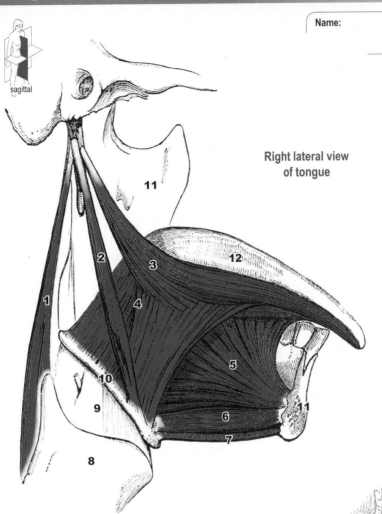

Right lateral view of tongue

1. stylopharyngeus
2. stylohyoid
3. styloglossus
4. hyoglossus
5. geniohyoglossus
6. geniohyoid
7. mylohyoid
8. thyroid cartilage
9. thyrohyoid membrane
10. hyoid bone
11. mandible

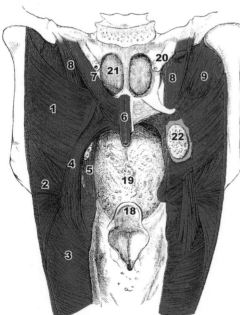

Posterior view with pharynx reflected

coronal

1. superior pharyngeal constrictor
2. middle pharyngeal constrictor
3. inferior pharyngeal constrictor
4. palato-pharyngeus
5. palato-glossus
6. musculus uvulae
7. levator veli palatini
8. tensor tympany
9. lateral pterygoid
10. mylohyoid
11. depressor anguli inferioris
12. buccinator
13. orbicularis oris
14. esophagus
15. trachea
16. thyroid cartilage
17. hyoid bone
18. epiglottis
19. tongue (posterior)
20. eustatchian tube
21. posterior naris (nasal avity)
22. tonsil

sagittal

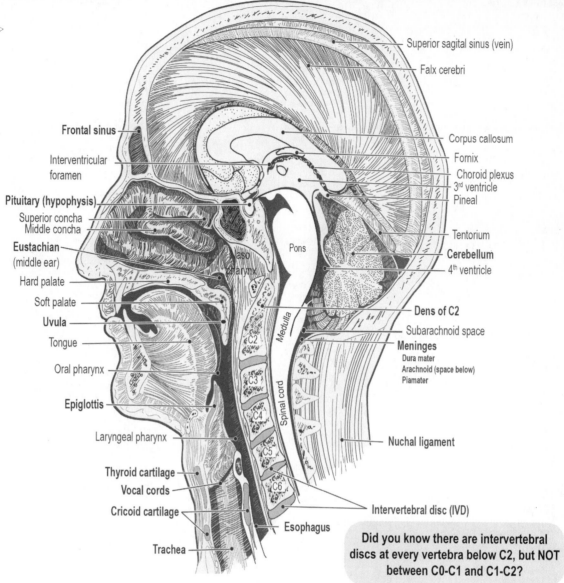

Superior sagittal sinus (vein)

Falx cerebri

Frontal sinus

Interventricular foramen

Corpus callosum

Fornix

Choroid plexus

3rd ventricle

Pineal

Pituitary (hypophysis)

Superior concha

Middle concha

Tentorium

Eustachian (middle ear)

Pons

Cerebellum

4th ventricle

Hard palate

Soft palate

Dens of C2

Uvula

Subarachnoid space

Meninges
Dura mater
Arachnoid (space below)
Piamater

Tongue

Oral pharynx

Epiglottis

Laryngeal pharynx

Nuchal ligament

Medulla

Spinal cord

Thyroid cartilage

Vocal cords

Cricoid cartilage

Intervertebral disc (IVD)

Esophagus

Trachea

Naso pharynx

C2

C3

C4

C5

C6

Did you know there are intervertebral discs at every vertebra below C2, but NOT between C0-C1 and C1-C2?

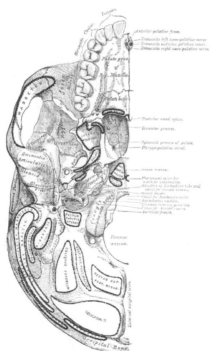

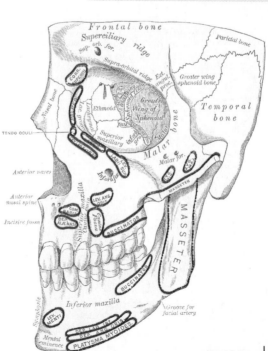

Head & Face

Head & Face

Page 26 Skull & Neck Bones
1. Frontal bone
   a. Supraorbital foramen
   b. Glabella
   c. Zygomatic process
2. Parietal bone
3. Occipital bone
   a. External occipital protuberance (EOP)
4. Temporal bone
   a. Zygomatic process
   b. Mastoid process
   c. External auditory meatus
   d. Styloid process
   e. Mandibular fossa
   f. Articular tubercle
5. Sphenoid bone
6. Ethmoid bone
7. Nasal bone
8. Lacrimal bone
9. Zygomatic bone
   a. Maxillary process
   b. Frontal process
   c. Temporal process
   d. Orbital surface
   e. Zygomaticofascial foramen
10. Maxilla
   a. Infraorbital foramen
   b. Anterior nasal spine
   c. Zygomatic process
   d. Orbital plate
   e. Alveolar process
11. Inferior Nasal Conchae
12. Vomer
13. Mandible
   a. Condylar process
   b. Coronoid process
   c. Ramus
   d. Angle
   e. Body
   f. Mental foramen
   g. Mental tubercle
14. Hyoid bone
15. C1 (Atlas)
16. C2 (Axis)

Page 27 Skull
1. Frontal bone
2. Coronal suture
3. Bregma
4. Parietal bone
5. Saggital suture
6. Lambdoidal suture
7. Lambda
8. Occipital bone
   a. External occipital protuberance (EOP)
   b. Superior nuchal line
   c. Inferior nuchal line
   d. Foramen magnum
   e. Occipital condyle
9. Temporal bone
   a. Styloid process
   b. Mastoid process
   c. Mandibular fossa
   d. Zygomatic process
10. Sphenoid bone
   a. Lateral pterygoid plate
   b. Medial pterygoid plate
11. Vomer
12. Palatine bone
13. Maxilla

Page 28 Mandible & TMJ
Mandible
1. **Condylar process**
2. **Ramus**
3. **Oblique line**
4. **Angle**
5. **Body**
6. **Mental foramen**
7. **Alveolar process**
8. **Mental tubercle**
9. **TMJ Disc**
10. **Sublingual fossa**
11. **Mylohyoid line**
12. **Submandibular fossa**
13. **Medial pterygoid muscle**
14. **Lateral pterygoid muscle**
15. **Temporal bone**
16. **Sphenoid bone**

TMJ
1. Temporal bone
   a. Zygomatic process
   b. Mastoid process
   c. Styloid process
2. Mandible
   2a. Condylar process
   2b. Coronoid process
3. TMJ Capsule
4. Lateral temporomandibular ligament
5. Stylomandibular ligament
6. Sphenomandibular ligament

Page 29 Joints of Skull
1. Coronal suture
2. Sagittal suture
3. Lambdoidal suture
4. Squamosal suture
5. Occipitomastoid suture
6. Bregma - junction of coronal & sagittal sutures
7. Lambda - junction of sagittal & lamdoidal sutures
8. Pterion - junction of temporal, parietal, frontal & sphenoid bones
9. Nasion - junction of nasal suture & frontal bone
10. Asterion - junction of occipital, parietal & temporal bones
11. Inion - external occipital protuberance (EOP)

Page 32 Muscles of Face
1. Frontalis (epicranius)
2. Orbicularis oculi
3. Procerus
4. Levator labii superioris alaeque nasi
5. Nasalis
6. Zygomaticus minor
7. Zygomaticus major
8. Risorius
9. Parotid fascia
10. Orbicularis oris
11. Platysma
12. Modiolus - attachment point for muscles at angle of mouth
13. Depressor anguli oris
14. Depressor labii inferioris
15. Mentalis
16. Sternocleidomastoid
17. Corrugator supercilii
18. Levator palpebrae superioris
19. Temporalis
20. Levator labii superioris
21. Levator anguli oris
22. Buccinator

Page 33 Muscles of Face
1. Occipitalis (epicranius)
2. Auricularis posterior
3. Auricularis superior
4. Temporoparietalis
5. Galea aponeurotica
6. Frontalis (epicranius)
7. Orbicularis oculi
   a. Orbital part
   b. Palpebral part
8. Temporalis
9. Corrugator supercilii
10. Procerus
11. Levator palpebrae superioris
12. Nasalis
13. Levator labii superioris alaeque nasi
14. Zygomaticus minor
15. Zygomaticus major
16. Buccinator
17. Orbicularis oris
18. Risorius
19. Mentalis
20. Depressor labii inferioris
21. Depressor anguli oris
22. Suprahyoid muscles
23. Infrahyoid muscles
24. Sternocleidomastoid
25. Levator labii superioris
26. Levator anguli oris
27. Nasalis (dilator naris)
28. Depressor septi nasi
29. Scalenes
30. Trapezius
31. Splenius capitis
32. Masseter

Where is the brain located?

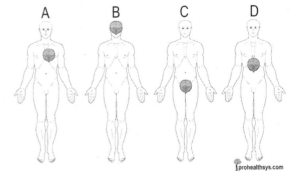

A   B   C   D

prohealthsys.com
Dr. Nikita Vizniak

For specific muscle information use
the Muscle Manual Text, Muscle Tables
Chapter, or on-line resources

Learning Objectives

After completing this chapter, students will be able to:

1. Identify and palpate structures of the region (give a list of structures below their palpating hand)

2. Assess AROM, PROM & RROM

3. Describe biomechanics & kinesiology of the neck

4. Perform detailed muscle testing and palpation

5. Discuss anatomical variation, ADLs and common injuries of the body region

6. Develop a set of strength and flexibility exercises for the cervical spine & neck

Neck Kinematics..46
   AROM 47
   PROM 48
   RROM 49
Bones of the Neck 50
Cervical Ligaments..52
Cervical Musculature 54
Cervical Myofascial Layers...........................55
Posterior Neck Muscles 56
Anterior Neck Muscles 57
Neck Superficial...58
Suboccipital Muscles 59
Suprahyoid Muscles......................................60
Infrahyoid Muscles 61
Deep Anterior Neck 62
Scalene Muscles 63
Answers..64

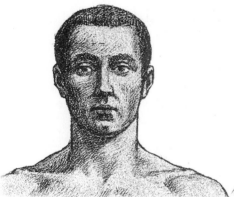

Surface anatomy

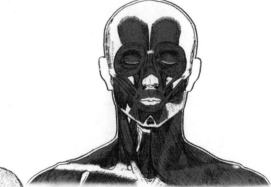

Myofascial

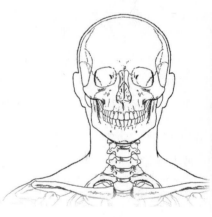

Bony Landmarks

Palpation Checklist

 Printable quiz on website

- ☐ Mandible & TMJ
- ☐ Masseter/Parotids
- ☐ Submandibular gland
- ☐ Submental gland
- ☐ Hyoid bone
- ☐ Trachea & larynx
- ☐ Thyroid gland
- ☐ Lymph nodes

- ☐ Clavicle/SC joint
- ☐ Suprasternal notch
- ☐ Scalenes/brachial plexus
- ☐ SCM & mastoid
- ☐ Carotid pulse
- ☐ Upper trapezius
- ☐ Levator scapulae
- ☐ Splenius cervicis

- ☐ Semispinalis cerv./cap.
- ☐ Suboccipitals
- ☐ Facet joints / Articular pillars
- ☐ Spinous processes (C2-C7)
- ☐ T1 SP & upper rib motion
- ☐ . . . .
- ☐ . . . .
- ☐ . . . .

 Video on proCentral

Joint types:

Gliding (zygapophyseal joints)

Pivot (atlantoaxial joint C1-C2)

Fibrocartilaginous (intervertebral joints)

Hinge & gliding (TMJ)

Articular surfaces

Atlanto-occipital joint: *convex* (occipital condyles of occiput) on *concave* (superior articular facets of atlas)

Atlantoaxial: *concave* (articular facet for dens on atlas) *on convex* (anterior facet of dens on axis)

Zygapophyseal: facets are oriented 45°

Intervertebral discs: horizontal plane

TMJ: *convex* (mandibular condyle & disc) *on concave* (mandibular fossa of temporal bone)

Active range of motion

Flexion	80-90°
Extension	60-70°
Lateral Flexion	20-45°
Rotation	70-90°
TMJ	35-50 mm opening

Main muscle actions

Flexion: sternocleidomastoid (SCM), longus coli, longus capitis, rectus capitis anterior

Extension: trapezius, splenius cervicis & capitis, longissimus capitis, suboccipitals

Lateral flexion: splenius capitis & cervicis, levator scapula, trapezius, longissimus capitis, scalenes, rectus capitis lateralis

Rotation: SCM, longus capitis & coli, rotatores, splenius, suboccipitals

Resting position: slight extension

Close packed position: full extension

Normal end feel: tissue stretch

Abnormal end feel
Early myospasm → muscle/ligament tear
Late myospasm → instability
Empty → ligament rupture
Hard → bone approximation (osteophyte)

Coupled motions - pure rotation and pure lateral flexion do not occur at any region in the spine below C2

For C2-~T5 vertebral segments

- Ipsilateral flexion & lateral flexion are coupled
- **Left lateral flexion coupled with left rotation**
- **Right lateral flexion coupled with right rotation**
- **Coupled motions are determined by the shape of the facet joints**

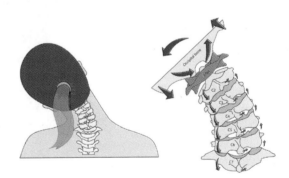

Cervical Facet Angles

Line of gravity

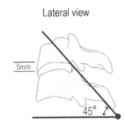

Lateral view

5mm

45°

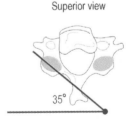

Superior view

35°

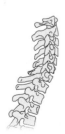

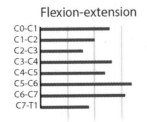

Flexion-extension

C0-C1	
C1-C2	
C2-C3	
C3-C4	
C4-C5	
C5-C6	
C6-C7	
C7-T1	

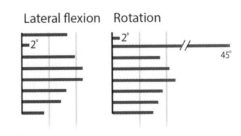

Lateral flexion   Rotation

2°   2°

45°

Depending numerous factors, functional AROM can vary greatly (anatomical variation, bone/joint shape, flexibility, muscle mass, training adaptation, scar tissue, injury, pain, contracture, posture, ADLs, genetics) - Adapted from: White, A & Panjabi, M. Clinical Biomechanics of the Spine. Lippincott, 1978. Hoppenfeld, S. Physical Examination of the Spine & Extremities. New York: Appleton-Century Crofts, 1976. Kapandji, LA. Physiology of the Joints. Vols. 1& 2, second edition. Demeter et al. Disability Evaluation. American Medical Association, Mosby 2003. American Academy of Orthopedic Surgeons 2018.

Introduction statement: "Try and move as far as possible, if any of the actions or movements are painful please let me know, do not do any action you feel will cause you further injury."

Flexion

Muscles Activated: sternocleidomastoid (SCM), longus cervicis, longus capitis, rectus capitis anterior; *eccentric* contraction of upper trapezius, splenius, semispinalis, longissimus capitis

Tissue Stretched: trapezius, splenius cervicis & capitis, longissimus capitis, suboccipitals, nuchal ligament, interspinous ligament, posterior IVD, posterior facet joint capsule

Tissue Compressed: anterior neck muscles, trachea, esophagus, carotid arteries

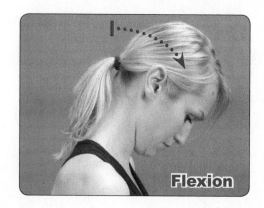

Flexion

Extension

Muscles Activated: trapezius (upper), splenius cervicis & capitis, longissimus capitis, suboccipitals

Tissue Stretched: anterior neck muscles, anterior longitudinal ligament, anterior IVD, trachea, esophagus, carotid arteries

Tissue Compressed: posterior neck muscles, posterior intervertebral discs, facet (z-joints) joints, vertebral arteries

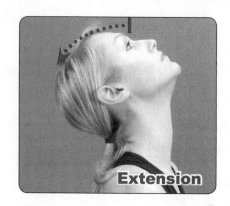

Extension

Lateral Flexion

Muscles Activated: *ipsilateral:* trapezius (upper), splenius cervicis & capitis, longissimus capitis, levator scapulae, suboccipitals

Tissue Stretched: *contralateral:* trapezius (upper), longissimus capitis, SCM, lateral IVD, carotid artery, z-joints

Tissue Compressed: *ipsilateral:* trapezius (upper), longissimus capitis, SCM, lateral IVD, carotid artery, z-joints

Lateral Flexion

Rotation

Muscles Activated: *ipsilateral:* splenius cervicis & capitis, suboccipitals; *contralateral:* SCM

Tissue Stretched: *contralateral:* splenius cervicis & capitis, suboccipitals; *ipsilateral:* SCM

Tissue Compressed: *ipsilateral:* splenius cervicis & capitis, suboccipitals; *contralateral:* SCM

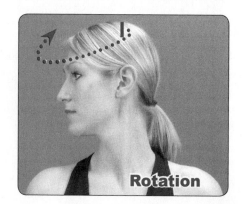

Rotation

Neck

Neck

Compare bilaterally; if possible palpate joint during PROM & use the shortest lever possible, apply over pressure at end ROM; introduction statement:
"If any of the actions or movements are painful or uncomfortable please let me know."

PROM may be performed with the patient seated or supine

▶ youtube: vizniak cervical exam

| Seated | Supine |

Flexion

Tissue Stretched: upper trapezius, splenius cervicis & capitis, longissimus capitis, suboccipitals, nuchal ligament, interspinous ligament, posterior IVD, posterior facet joint capsule

Tissue Compressed: anterior neck muscles, trachea, esophagus, carotid arteries

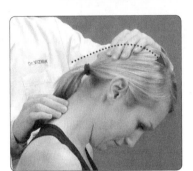

Extension

Tissue Stretched: anterior neck muscles, anterior longitudinal ligament, anterior IVD, trachea, esophagus, carotid arteries

Tissue Compressed: posterior neck muscles, posterior intervertebral discs, facet (z-joints) joints, vertebral artery

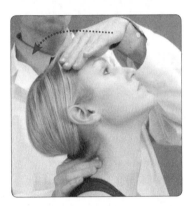

Lateral Flexion

Tissue Stretched: *contralateral:* trapezius (upper), longissimus capitis, SCM, lateral IVD, carotid artery, z-joints

Tissue Compressed: *ipsilateral:* trapezius (upper), longissimus capitis, SCM, lateral IVD, carotid artery, z-joints

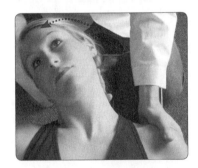

Rotation

Tissue Stretched: *contralateral:* splenius cervicis & capitis, suboccipitals; *ipsilateral:* SCM

Tissue Compressed: *ipsilateral:* splenius cervicis & capitis, suboccipitals

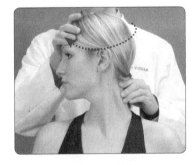
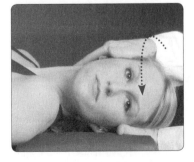

prohealthsys

Compare bilaterally, patient instructions for assessing general muscle strength:
"I am going to try and move you in _____ direction, don't let me do it" or "resist my force"

Flexion

Muscles Activated: sternocleidomastoid (SCM), longus cervicis, longus capitis, rectus capitis anterior

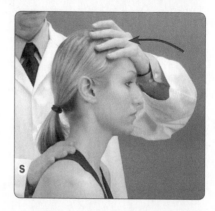

Extension

Muscles Activated: trapezius (upper), splenius cervicis & capitis, semispinalis capitis, longissimus capitis, suboccipitals

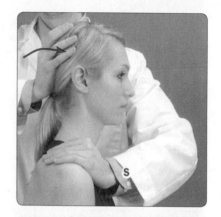

Lateral Flexion

Muscles Activated: *ipsilateral:* trapezius (upper), splenius cervicis & capitis, longissimus capitis, levator scapulae, suboccipitals

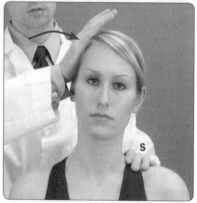

Rotation

Muscles Activated: *ipsilateral:* splenius cervicis & capitis, suboccipitals; *contralateral:* SCM

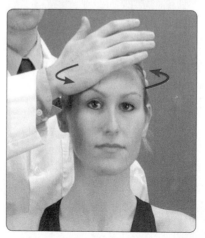

Neck

Name: _____ %

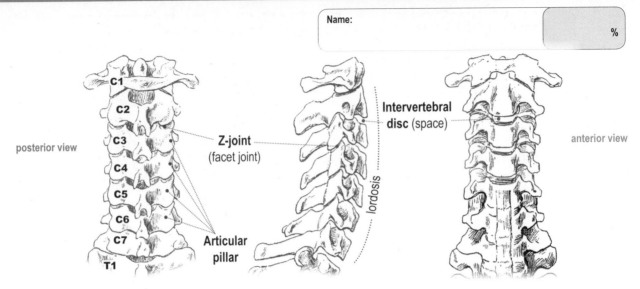

posterior view

C1
C2
C3
C4
C5
C6
C7
T1

Z-joint (facet joint)

Intervertebral disc (space)

lordosis

anterior view

Articular pillar

1. _____
2. _____
3. _____
4. _____
5. _____
6. _____
7. _____
8. _____
9. _____
10. _____

1. _____
2. _____
3. _____
4. _____
5. _____
6. _____
7. _____
8. _____
9. _____
10. _____

1. _____
2. _____
3. _____
4. _____
5. _____
6. _____
7. _____
8. _____
9. _____
10. _____

Neck

Atlas (C1)

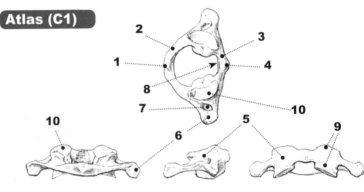

Axis (C2)

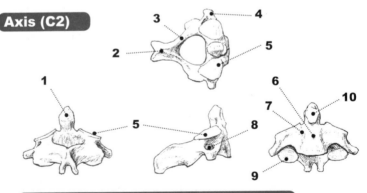

Typical Cervical Vertebra (C3-C6)

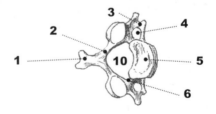

prohealthsys.com   Vizniak & Richer

Name: _____ %

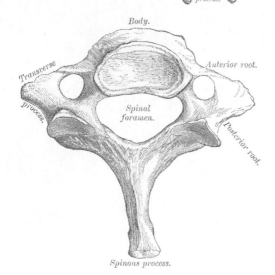

Anterior tubercle of transverse process.

Costal cartilage.

Costo-transverse foramen for vertebral artery and vein and sympathetic plexus.

Posterior tubercle of transverse process.

Body

Transverse process.

Pedicle

Spinal Foramen

Superior articular process.

Inferior articular process.

Lamina

Spinous process.

Body.

Transverse process.

Anterior root.

Spinal foramen.

Posterior root.

Spinous process.

Segmental ROM

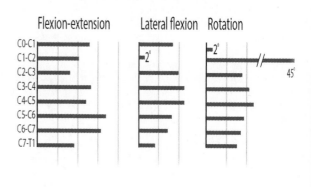

	Flexion-extension	Lateral flexion	Rotation
C0-C1		2°	2°
C1-C2			
C2-C3			
C3-C4			45°
C4-C5			
C5-C6			
C6-C7			
C7-T1			

Neutral

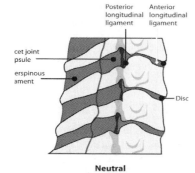

Interspinous ligament

Impact

During Impact

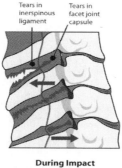

Hyperextension

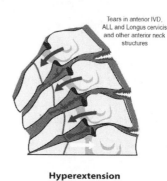

Hyperflexion

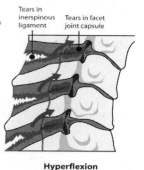

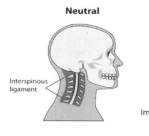

Posterior longitudinal ligament

Anterior longitudinal ligament

cet joint psule

erspinous ament

Disc

Neutral

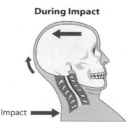

Tears in inerspinous ligament

Tears in facet joint capsule

During Impact

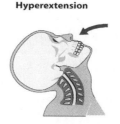

Tears in anterior IVD, ALL and Longus cervicis and other anterior neck structures

Hyperextension

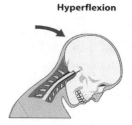

Tears in inerspinous ligament

Tears in facet joint capsule

Hyperflexion

In whiplash injuries be aware that clinical presentation & perceived severity of injury do not correlate! - lower speed impacts often result in more significant & potentially chronic injuries. Damage or tearing of soft tissue around the cervical spine and resulting inflammation

- Tearing of muscles/ligaments (ALL, nuchal, longus cervicis, SCM, scalenes)
- Cervical facet capsular ligaments (z-joints) and disc injury
- Muscles attached to periosteum contract causing myofascial pain
- Often involves reversal or straightening of cervical lordosis (protective myospasm of deep neck flexors)

prohealthsys

Name: _____ %

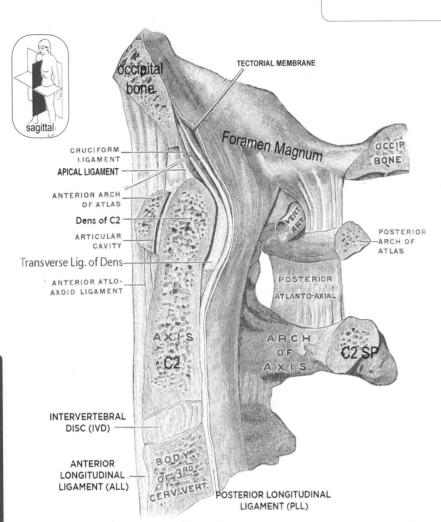

sagittal

occipital bone

TECTORIAL MEMBRANE

Foramen Magnum

OCCIP BONE

CRUCIFORM LIGAMENT
APICAL LIGAMENT
ANTERIOR ARCH OF ATLAS
Dens of C2
ARTICULAR CAVITY
Transverse Lig. of Dens
ANTERIOR ATLO-AXOID LIGAMENT

VERT ART

POSTERIOR ARCH OF ATLAS

POSTERIOR ATLANTO-AXIAL

AXIS C2

ARCH OF AXIS

C2 SP

INTERVERTEBRAL DISC (IVD)

ANTERIOR LONGITUDINAL LIGAMENT (ALL)

BODY OF 3RD CERV. VERT.

POSTERIOR LONGITUDINAL LIGAMENT (PLL)

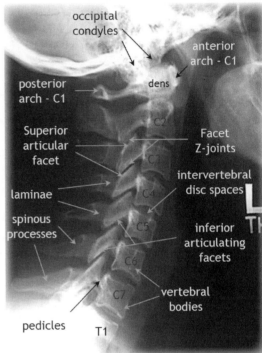

occipital condyles

posterior arch - C1

anterior arch - C1

dens

Superior articular facet

Facet Z-joints

intervertebral disc spaces

laminae

spinous processes

inferior articulating facets

vertebral bodies

pedicles

T1

Ligament	Attaches (origin/insertion)	Function
Anterior longitudinal	Anterior vertebral body & disc to next vertebrae	Resists neck extension
Annulus fibrosus	Vertebral bodies from C3-S1	Shock absorption, resists all spinal motions - **MAIN spinal stabilizer**
Posterior longitudinal	Posterior vertebral body & disc to next vertebrae	Resists neck flexion
Z-joint capsule	Facet below to facet above	Resist flexion & lateral flexion of neck
Ligamentum flavum	Laminae to laminae	Resists trunk flexion, elasticity assists extension
Interspinous	Spinous process to spinous process	Resists flexion of trunk, & shear forces on vertebrae
Supraspinous	Spinous process to SP above	Resists trunk flexion & forward shear force on spine
Nuchal	EOP to C7-T1 SPs	Resists flexion, attachment point for muscles
Alar	Apex of dens to medial occipital	Resists lateral flexion & rotation of head; holds dens into atlas
Apical	Apex of dens to front foramen magnum	Holds dens into atlas & skull
Cruciform (*transverse lig. of dens*)	Odontoid bone to arch of atlas (C1-2 stability) Transverse lig connects lateral masses	Stabilizes C1-C2, resists anterior translation of C1 on C2 (prevents brainstem compression)

Name: _____ %

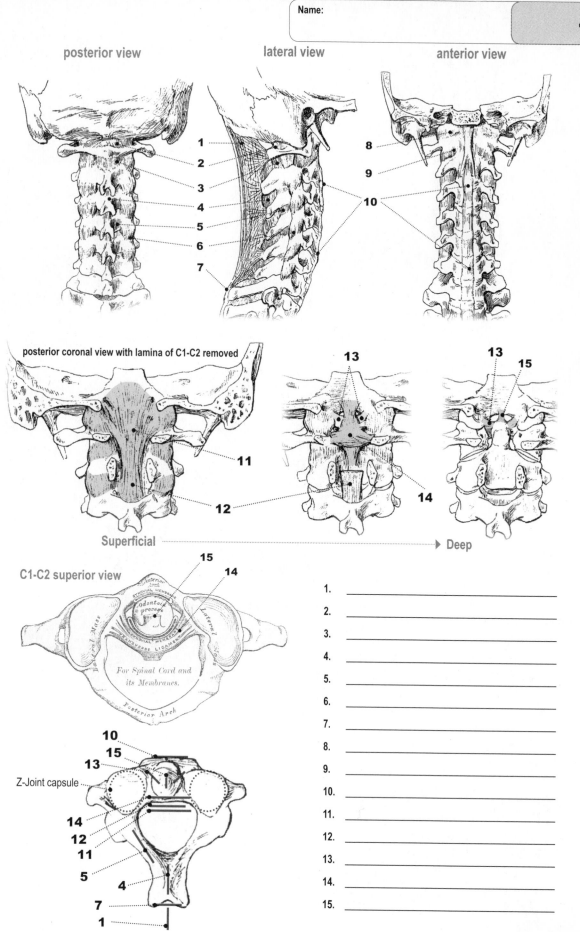

posterior view

lateral view

anterior view

1
2
3
4
5
6
7

8
9
10

posterior coronal view with lamina of C1-C2 removed

11
12

13
14

13
15

Superficial ──────────────────────────▶ Deep

C1-C2 superior view

Anterior Arch
Synovial Membrane
Odontoid process
Lateral Mass
Lateral Mass
Synovial Membrane
Transverse Ligament
For Spinal Cord and its Membranes.
Posterior Arch

15
14

10
15
13

Z-Joint capsule

14
12
11
5
4
7
1

1. _____
2. _____
3. _____
4. _____
5. _____
6. _____
7. _____
8. _____
9. _____
10. _____
11. _____
12. _____
13. _____
14. _____
15. _____

Neck

Name: _____ %

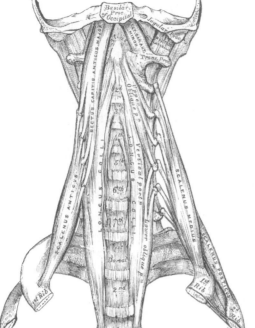

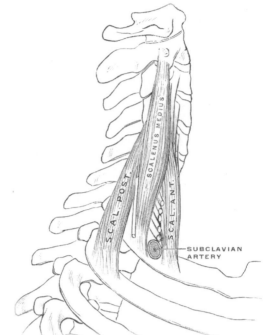

SUBCLAVIAN ARTERY

Neck

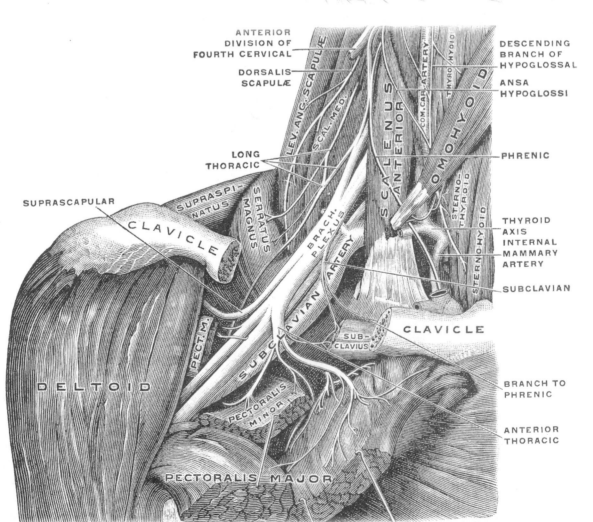

ANTERIOR DIVISION OF FOURTH CERVICAL

DORSALIS SCAPULÆ

LONG THORACIC

SUPRASCAPULAR

CLAVICLE

SUPRASPINATUS

SERRATUS MAGNUS

LEV. ANG. SCAPULÆ

SCAL. MED.

BRACH. PLEXUS

SCALENUS ANTERIOR

COM. CAR. ARTERY

THYRO-HYOID

OMOHYOID

STERNO-THYROID

STERNOHYOID

DESCENDING BRANCH OF HYPOGLOSSAL

ANSA HYPOGLOSSI

PHRENIC

THYROID AXIS

INTERNAL MAMMARY ARTERY

SUBCLAVIAN

CLAVICLE

PECT. M.

DELTOID

SUBCLAVIAN ARTERY

SUB-CLAVIUS

PECTORALIS MINOR

PECTORALIS MAJOR

BRANCH TO PHRENIC

ANTERIOR THORACIC

Name:

%

Name: Sternocleidomastoid (SCM)

O

I

A

C

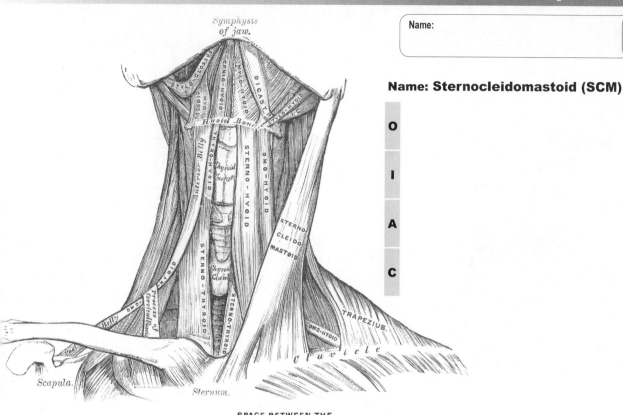

Symphysis of jaw.

STYLO-GLOSS

HYO-GLOSSUS

GENIO-HYOID

MYLO-HYOID

DIGASTRIC

STYLO-HYOID

T.C.

Hyoid Bone

Anterior Belly

TETRO-THYROID

STERNO-HYOID

OMO-HYOID

Thyroid Cartilage

STERNO-CLEIDO-MASTOID

Thyroid Gland

STERNO-THYROID

STERNO-THYROID

DIGASTRIC

Process of Cervical Vert.

OMO-HYOID

Post. Belly

OMO-HYOID

TRAPEZIUS.

clavicle

Scapula.

Sternum.

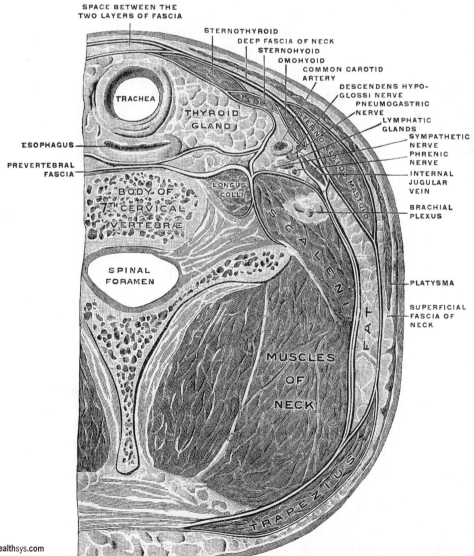

SPACE BETWEEN THE
TWO LAYERS OF FASCIA

STERNOTHYROID

DEEP FASCIA OF NECK

STERNOHYOID

OMOHYOID

COMMON CAROTID
ARTERY

DESCENDENS HYPO-
GLOSSI NERVE

PNEUMOGASTRIC
NERVE

LYMPHATIC
GLANDS

SYMPATHETIC
NERVE

PHRENIC
NERVE

INTERNAL
JUGULAR
VEIN

BRACHIAL
PLEXUS

PLATYSMA

SUPERFICIAL
FASCIA OF
NECK

TRACHEA

THYROID
GLAND

ESOPHAGUS

PREVERTEBRAL
FASCIA

BODY OF
7TH CERVICAL
VERTEBRÆ

LONGUS
COLLI

STERNO-CLEIDO-MASTOID

SCALENI

SPINAL
FORAMEN

FAT

MUSCLES
OF
NECK

TRAPEZIUS

prohealthsys

Start with labeling the muscles, then progress to naming
☐ actions, ☐ origins, ☐ insertions, ☐ nerves

Name: _____ %

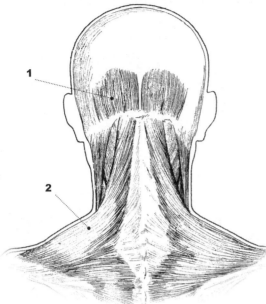

1. _____
2. _____
3. _____
4. _____
5. _____
6. _____
7. _____
8. _____
9. _____
10. _____
11. _____
12. _____
13. _____
14. _____

Neck

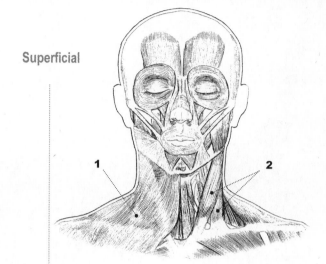

Start with labeling the muscles, then progress to naming
□ actions, □ origins, □ insertions, □ nerves

Name:

%

Superficial

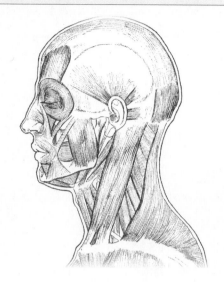

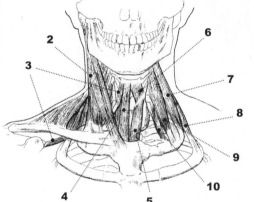

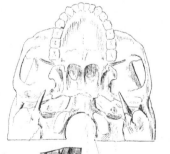

1. _____

2. _____

3. _____

4. _____

5. _____

6. _____

7. _____

8. _____

9. _____

10. _____

11. _____

12. _____

13. _____

14. _____

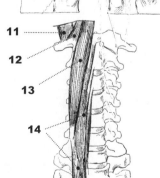

Deep

Neck

prohealthsys

prohealthsys

Name: _____ %

Neck

Name: _____

O

I

A

C

Name: _____

O

I

A

C

Name: _____

O

I

A

C

Name: _____

O

I

A

C

prohealthsys.com   Vizniak & Richer

prohealthsys

Lateral view   Posterior view

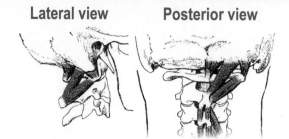

Name:

%

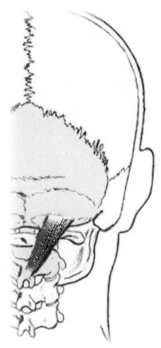

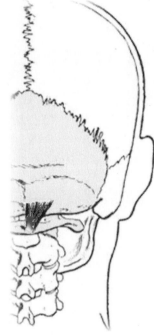

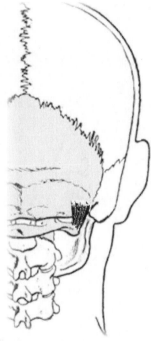

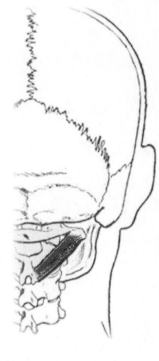

Neck

Name:

O

I

A

C

Name:

O

I

A

C

Name:

O

I

A

C

Name:

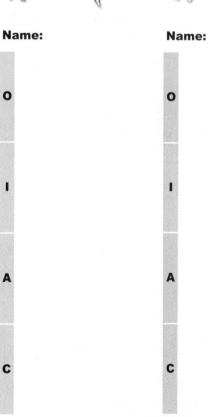

O

I

A

C

prohealthsys

Name: _____ %

Neck

Name:

O

I

A

C

Name:

O

I

A

C

Name:

O

I

A

C

Name:

O

I

A

C

Name: _____ %

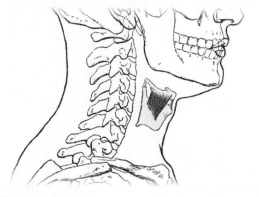

Name:

O

I

A

C

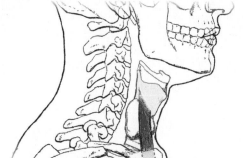

Name:

O

I

A

C

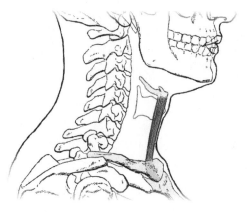

Name:

O

I

A

C

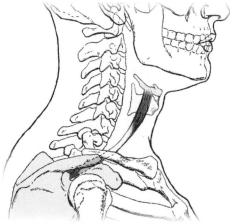

Name:

O

I

A

C

Neck

prohealthsys

Name: [_____] %

Neck

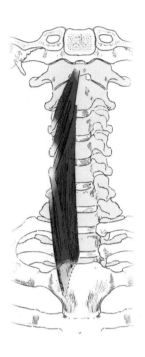
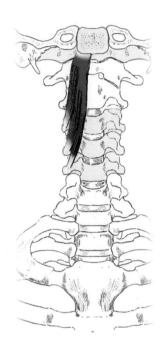
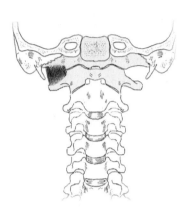
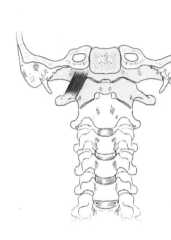

Name:

O

I

A

C

Name:

O

I

A

C

Name:

O

I

A

C

Name:

O

I

A

C

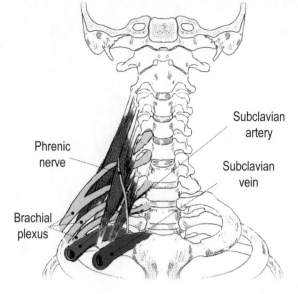

Phrenic
nerve

Subclavian
artery

Subclavian
vein

Brachial
plexus

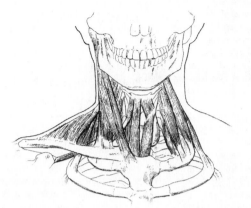

Name:

%

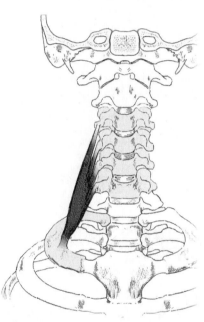

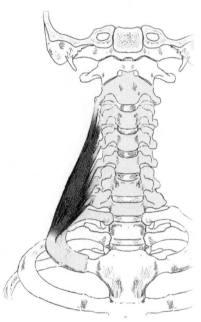

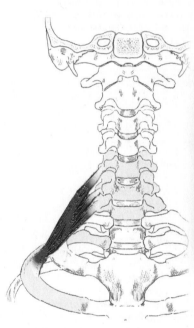

Name:

O

I

A

C

Name:

O

I

A

C

Name:

O

I

A

C

Page 50, Bones of the neck

C1-Atlas
1. Posterior tubercle (no spinous process)
2. Posterior arch
3. Anterior arch
4. Anterior tubercle
5. Lateral mass (no body)
6. Transverse process
7. Transverse foramen
8. Articular facet for dens
9. Articular process (superior & inferior)
10. Superior articular facet

C2-Axis
1. Dens (odontoid process)
2. Spinous process (bifid)
3. Lamina
4. Transverse process
5. Superior articular facet
6. Body
7. Pedicle
8. Transverse foramen
9. Inferior articular facet
10. Facet for anterior arch of C1

Typical cervical vertebra
1. Spinous process (bifid)
2. Lamina
3. Transverse process
4. Transverse foramen
5. Body
6. Pedicle
7. Superior articular facet
8. Inferior articular process
9. Uncinate process (uncus)
10. Vertebral canal (spinal cord)

Hyoid bone
1. Greater cornu
2. Lesser cornu
3. Body

Page 53 Cervical Ligaments
4. Nuchal ligament
5. Posterior atlanto-occipital membrane
6. Posterior atlantoaxial membrane
7. Interspinous Ligament
8. Ligamentum flavum
9. Capsular ligs (zygapophyseal)
10. Supraspinous ligament
11. Anterior atlanto-occipital membrane
12. Anterior atlantoaxial membrane
13. Anterior longitudinal ligament
14. Tectorial membrane
15. Posterior longitudinal ligament
16. Alar ligaments (off dens)
17. Cruciform ligament (transverse ligament of dens)
18. Apical ligament (off dens)

Page 56 Posterior Neck Muscles
1. Occipitalis
2. Trapezius (upper fibers)
3. Splenius capitis
4. Splenius cervicis
5. Levator scapulae
6. Rhomboid minor
7. Spinalis capitis
8. Semispinalis capitis
9. Longissimus capitis
   Suboccipital muscles*
10. Rectus capitis posterior minor*

11. Rectus capitis posterior major*
12. Obliquus capitis inferior*
13. Obliquus capitis superior*
14. Interspinalis

Page 57 Anterior Neck Muscles
1. Platysma
2. Sternocleidomastoid
   Infrahyoid muscles
3. Omohyoid
4. Sternohyoid
5. Sternothyroid
6. Thyrohyoid

   Lateral neck (paravertebrals)
7. Middle scalene
8. Posterior scalene
9. Anterior scalene
10. Scalenus minimus
    Deep Anterior (prevertebrals)
11. Rectus capitis lateralis
12. Rectus capitis anterior
13. Longus capitis
14. Longus cervicis

For specific muscle information use the Muscle Manual Text, eBooks, Flashcards, Muscle Tables Chapter or on-line resources

Video on proCentral

Neck

Learning Objectives

After completing this chapter, students will be able to:

1. Identify and palpate anatomy of the region (give a list of structures below their palpating hand)
2. Assess AROM, PROM & RROM
3. Describe biomechanics of the lumbar region
4. Perform detailed muscle testing and palpation
5. Discuss anatomical variation, ADLs and common injuries of the low back and pelvis
6. Summarize the importance of pelvic floor muscles

Printable quiz on prohealthsys

Spinal Kinematics..............................66
   AROM..67
   PROM..68
   RROM..69
Bones of the Trunk.............................70
Thoracic Vertebra & Ribs.....................72
Lumbar Vertebra & Sacrum..................73
Ligaments of the Spine.......................74
Spinal Bones....................................75
Muscles of Spine...............................76
Abdominal Muscles............................78
Superficial Back Muscles....................80
Deep Back Muscles............................81
Anterior Trunk Muscles.......................82
Back Muscles....................................83
Erector Spinae..................................85
Transversospinalis.............................86
Self Test Fun....................................87
Intercostal Muscles............................88
Diaphragm & Pelvic Floor...................89
Answers...90

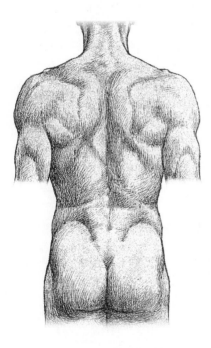

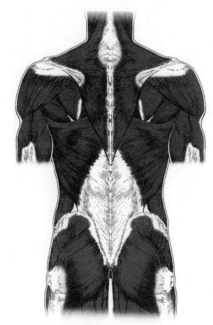

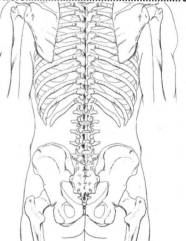

Palpation Checklist

Video on proCentral

- ☐ SPs & TPs T1-L5
- ☐ Erector spinae
- ☐ Upper ribs
- ☐ Lower ribs
- ☐ Scapulae
- ☐ Trapezius
- ☐ Rhomboids
- ☐ Latissimus dorsi

- ☐ Quadratus lumborum
- ☐ Sternum / clavicle
- ☐ Supraclavicular fossa
- ☐ Axilla (anterior & posterior)
- ☐ Lymph nodes
- ☐ Pectoralis major/minor
- ☐ Sternoclavicular joint
- ☐ Sternocostal joints

- ☐ Abdominal muscles
- ☐ Diaphragm
- ☐ Abdominal viscera
- ☐ Abdominal aorta
- ☐ Ilium & sacrum
- ☐ . . . .
- ☐ . . . .
- ☐ . . . .

Torso & Back

Joint types:
- Gliding (zygapophyseal/facet joints)
- Gliding (costal & transverse costal)
- Fibrocartilaginous (intervertebral joints)

Articular surfaces
- **Thoracic:** facets are oriented in coronal plane
- **Lumbar:** facet oriented in sagittal plane
- **Sacroiliac:** facets oriented ~45°

Active range of motion (thoracic)
Flexion..............**20-45°** *(Adam's sign scoliosis)*
Extension..........**25-45°**
Lateral flexion...**20-40°**
Rotation.............**35-50°**

Active range of motion (lumbar)
Flexion ....**40-60°**
Extension ....**20-35°**
Lateral Flexion ....**15-20°**
Rotation ....**5-20°**

Active range of motion (SI)
Flexion/Extension ......**0-10°**
Int./external rotation ..**0-10°**

Main muscle actions
- **Flexion:** iliopsoas, rectus abdominis, internal/external oblique
- **Extension:** erector spinae, multifidi
- **Lateral flexion:** erector spinae, semispinalis, rectus abdominis, internal/external oblique
- **Rotation:** internal/external oblique, rotatores, multifidi, semispinalis, erector spinae

Resting position
- **T-spine:** mid way between flexion & extension
- **L-spine:** mid way between flexion & extension

Close packed position: full extension

Normal end feel: tissue stretch

Abnormal end feel
- **Early myospasm** → muscle/ligament tear
- **Late myospasm** → instability
- **Empty** → ligament rupture
- **Hard** → bone approximation (osteophyte)

Coupled motions

T6-L5 vertebral segments*
- Left lateral flexion coupled with right rotation
- Right lateral flexion coupled with left rotation
- *this is the opposite coupling that occurs in the cervical & upper thoracic spine (rotation & lateral flexion occur to the same side)

Lumbar motion is coupled with sacral motion
- **Lumbar extension** (hyperlordosis) is coupled with sacral *nutation* (anterior sacral tilting or "nod")
- **Lumbar flexion** (hypolordosis) is coupled with sacral *counter-nutation* (posterior sacral tilting) when standing
- Once the lumbar spine flexes past ~45° the sacrum nutates relative to the ilium to assist with bending forward (touching toes)

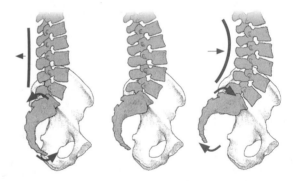

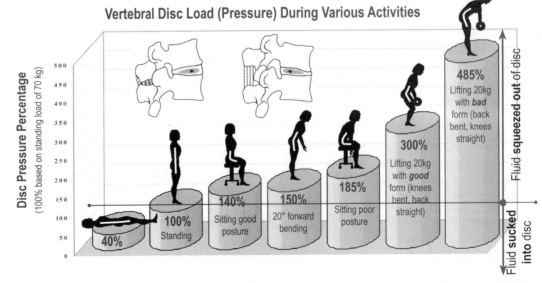

Vertebral Disc Load (Pressure) During Various Activities

Graph shows the intervertebral disc pressure involved with different activities & lifting techniques. More pressure results in an increased chance of injury; proper biomechanics are required to minimize the frequency & severity of injury. **Flexing twisting actions cause the most stress & greatest chance of injury.**

Disc Pressure Percentage (100% based on standing load of 70 kg)

- **40%**
- **100%** Standing
- **140%** Sitting good posture
- **150%** 20° forward bending
- **185%** Sitting poor posture
- **300%** Lifting 20kg with *good* form (knees bent, back straight)
- **485%** Lifting 20kg with *bad* form (back bent, knees straight)

Fluid **squeezed out of disc**

Fluid **sucked into disc**

Torso & Back

Compare bilaterally; prior to ROM examiner should make an introduction statement:
"Try and move as far as possible, if any of the actions or movements are painful or uncomfortable please let me know, do not do any action you feel will cause you further injury."

Flexion

Muscles Activated: *eccentric* contraction of erector spinae

Tissue Stretched: erector spinae, supraspinous & interspinous ligaments, posterior IVD, posterior facet joint capsule

Tissue Compressed: anterior lumbar structures, anterior longitudinal ligament, anterior IVD, intestines, aorta

Extension

Muscles Activated: *concentric* contraction of erector spinae & multifidi (transversospinalis), *eccentric* contraction of rectus abdominis & abdominal obliques

Tissue Stretched: rectus abdominis, anterior longitudinal ligament, aorta, abdominal obliques

Tissue Compressed: erector spinae, supraspinous & interspinous ligaments, posterior IVD, posterior facet joint capsule

Lateral Flexion

Muscles Activated: *eccentric* contraction of *contralateral* erector spinae, transversospinalis & quadratus lumborum

Tissue Stretched: *contralateral* erector spinae, transverso-spinalis, QL, IVD, z-joints

Tissue Compressed: *ipsilateral:* erector spinae, transverso-spinalis, QL, IVD, z-joints

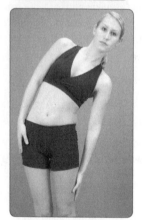

Rotation *

Muscles Activated: *contralateral* external oblique & transverso-spinalis, *ipsilateral* internal oblique

Tissue Stretched: *ipsilateral* external oblique & transverso-spinalis, *contralateral* internal oblique

Tissue Compressed: abdominal contents

* to reduce sacroiliac and lower extremity movement consider assessing lumbar rotation and other motions in the seated position

Torso & Back

> **Compare bilaterally; if possible palpate joint during PROM & use the shortest level possible, apply over pressure at end ROM; introduction statement:**
> "If any of the actions or movements are painful or uncomfortable please let me know."

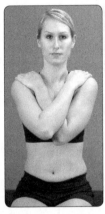 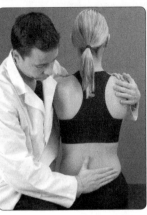  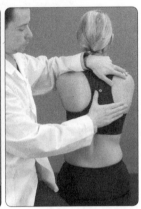

Starting position
Patient arms crossed

Thenar spinous contact
to assess motion

Alternate finger-tip
spinous contact

Alternate patient
contact with forearm-
shoulder stabilization

Flexion

Tissue Stretched: erector spinae, supraspinous & interspinous ligaments, posterior IVD, posterior facet joint capsule

Tissue Compressed: anterior lumbar structures, anterior longitudinal ligament, anterior IVD, intestines, aorta

Extension

Tissue Stretched: rectus abdominis, anterior longitudinal ligament, aorta, abdominal obliques

Tissue Compressed: erector spinae, supraspinous & interspinous ligaments, posterior IVD, posterior facet joint capsule

Lateral Flexion

Tissue Stretched: *contralateral* erector spinae, transverso-spinalis, QL, IVD, z-joints

Tissue Compressed: *ipsilateral:* erector spinae, transverso-spinalis, QL, IVD, z-joints

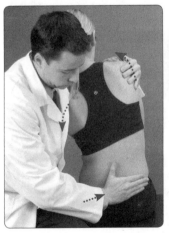
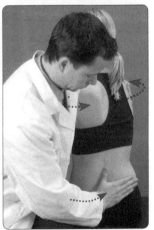

Rotation

Tissue Stretched: *ipsilateral* external oblique & transverso-spinalis, *contralateral* internal oblique

Tissue Compressed: abdominal contents

Torso & Back

Patient instructions for assessing general muscle strength:
"I am going to try and move you in _____ direction, don't let me do it" or "resist my force"

Flexion
Muscles Activated: *isometric or eccentric* contraction of erector spinae & transversospinalis

youtube: Vizniak Lumbar Exam

Extension
Muscles Activated: *isometric or eccentric* contraction of rectus abdominis & abdominal obliques

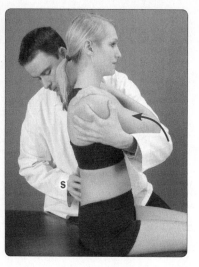

Lateral Flexion
Muscles Activated: *eccentric* contraction of *contralateral* erector spinae, transversospinalis & quadratus lumborum, & abdominal muscles

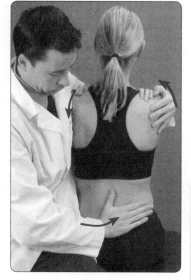

Rotation
Muscles Activated: *contralateral* external oblique & transversospinalis, *ipsilateral* internal oblique

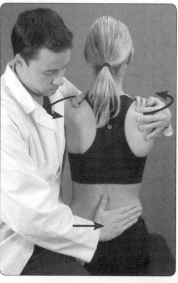

Torso & Back

prohealthsys

Name:

%

Sternum

1. _____
2. _____
3. _____
4. _____
5. _____

Ribs

6. _____
7. _____
8. _____
9. _____
10. _____
11. _____

Vertebrae

12. _____
13. _____
14. _____
15. _____
16. _____

17. Name the true ribs _____
18. Name the false ribs _____
19. Name the floating ribs _____

Bonus: can you label the joints on the drawing?

Acromioclavicular (AC), Sternoclavicular joint (SC), Sternomanubrial joint,
Sternocostal joint, Xiphisternal joint, Costovertebral joint

Intervertebral joint, Zygapophyseal (facet) joint, Sacroiliac (SI) joint

Torso & Back

Name: _____ %

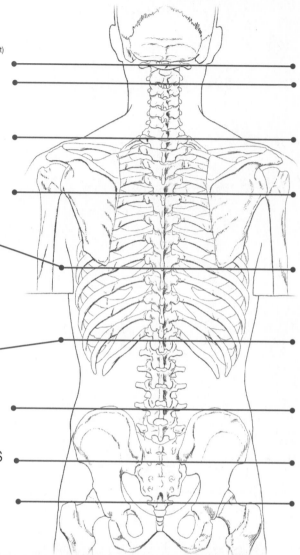

> **Realize that normal anatomical variation in bone size & shape may alter exact spinal levels being palpated**

- **C1** - palpate TP anterior & inferior to mastoid process (difficult)

- **C2** - first palpable SP below the occipital bone

- **C7 or T1** - most prominent SP at base of neck (C7 will usually move from a palpating finger with cervical flexion/extension)

- **T4** - level with the root of the spine of scapula or apex of axillary fold

- **T7-T8** - level with the inferior angle of scapula

> **Thoracic TP palpation Rule of 3s**
> - **T1-T3 TPs:** at level of corresponding SP
> - **T4-T6 TPs:** ~½ segment *above* SP
> - **T7-T9 TPs:** ~1 segment *above* SP
> T10-T12 have TP's that project from a position similar to T9 & rapidly regress until T12 is like T1

- **T12** - level with the head of the 12th rib

- **L4** - level with the superior border of the iliac crest

- **PSIS & S2** - level with the most inferior portion of the PSIS

- **Sacral Apex** - level with upper greater trochanter (rotate patient hip to locate trochanter)

Structure	Location
EOP	midline of occipital base
C1 TP	~1 cm (½" inch) anterior & inferior to mastoid process (under ear lobe)
C2 SP	1st prominent SP below EOP
C4 SP	hyoid bone
C5 SP	thyroid cartilage
C7 SP	usually second most prominent SP, slides anterior during cervical extension
T1 SP	most prominent SP (usually)
T7-T8 SP	inferior angle of scapula with patient standing (~T7 SP, T8 body)
L4 SP	level of iliac crest
S2 SP	level of the most inferior portion of PSIS
PSIS	follow iliac crest to dimples on back (usually ~2-3 cm long)
Ischial tuberosity	~5 cm (2") inferior & lateral to apex of coccyx (covered by glut. max standing)

TP = transverse process, SP = spinous process, thoracic TP palpation rule of 3s is a guideline more than a strict rule

Torso & Back

Name: _____ %

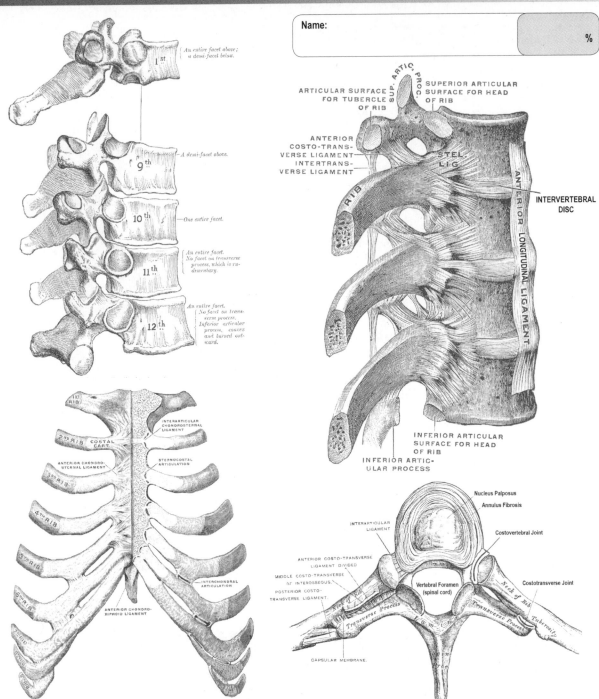

Ligament	Attaches (origin/insertion)	Function
Anterior longitudinal	Anterior vertebral body & disc to next vertebrae	Resists spinal extension
Annulus fibrosus	Vertebral bodies from C3-S1	Shock absorption, resists all spinal motions **MAIN SPINAL STABILIZER**
Posterior longitudinal	Posterior vertebral body & disc to next vertebrae	Resists spinal flexion
Z-joint capsule	Facet below to facet above	Resist flexion & lateral flexion of trunk
Ligamentum flavum	Laminae to laminae	Resists flexion of trunk, elasticity assists extension of trunk
Interspinous	Spinous process to SP	Resists flexion of trunk, & shear forces on vertebrae
Supraspinous	Spinous process to SP above on tips	Resists trunk flexion & forward shear force on spine
Intertransverse	Transverse process to TP	Resists lateral flexion of trunk
Costotransverse	Tubercles of ribs to transverse process of vertebrae	Supports rib attachment to thoracic vertebrae
Radiate	Head of ribs to body of vertebrae	Maintains ribs to thoracic vertebrae

Torso & Back

prohealthsys

Name: _____

_____ %

Erect standing posture load

45% 50% 5%   20% 40% 40%

Normal disc   Degenerated disc

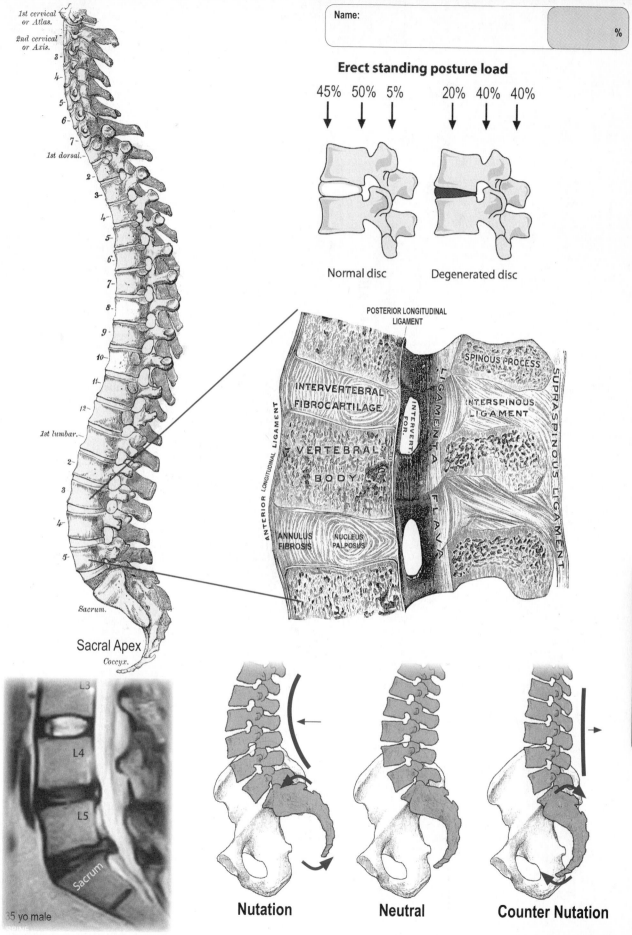

POSTERIOR LONGITUDINAL LIGAMENT

INTERVERTEBRAL FIBROCARTILAGE

ANTERIOR LONGITUDINAL LIGAMENT

VERTEBRAL BODY

ANNULUS FIBROSIS

NUCLEUS PALPOSUS

INTERVERT. FOR.

LIGAMENTA FLAVA

SPINOUS PROCESS

INTERSPINOUS LIGAMENT

SUPRASPINOUS LIGAMENT

1st cervical or Atlas.
2nd cervical or Axis.
3
4
5
6
7
1st dorsal.
2
3
4
5
6
7
8
9
10
11
12
1st lumbar.
2
3
4
5
Sacrum.
Sacral Apex
Coccyx.

L3
L4
L5
Sacrum
35 yo male

Nutation   **Neutral**   **Counter Nutation**

Torso & Back

prohealthsys

Name:

%

anterior view   lateral view   posterior view

1. _____

2. _____

3. _____

4. _____

5. _____

6. _____

7. _____

8. _____

9. _____

10. _____

11. _____

12. _____

lordosis

kyphosis

lordosis

1. _____

2. _____

3. _____

4. _____

5. _____

6. _____

7. _____

8. _____

9. _____

10. _____

11. _____

Torso & Back

prohealthsys.com   Vizniak & Richer

Name:

%

Thoracic Vertebra

1. _____
2. _____
3. _____
4. _____
5. _____
6. _____
7. _____
8. _____
9. _____
10. _____
11. _____
12. _____

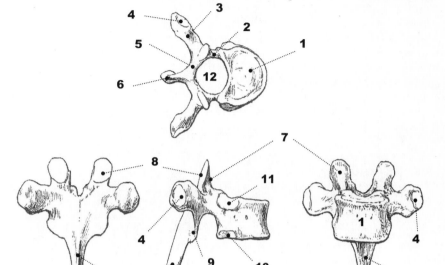

Lumbar Vertebra

1. _____
2. _____
3. _____
4. _____
5. _____
6. _____
7. _____
8. _____
9. _____
10. _____

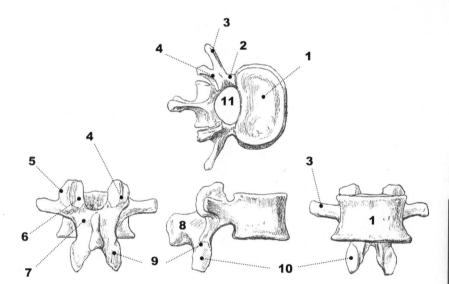

Sacrum & Coccyx

1. _____
2. _____
3. _____
4. _____
5. _____
6. _____
7. _____
8. _____

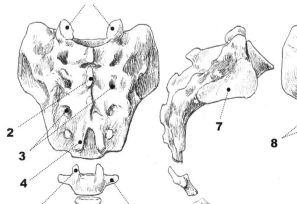
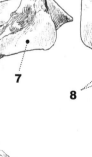
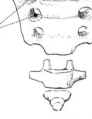

Vizniak & Richer   prohealthsys.com

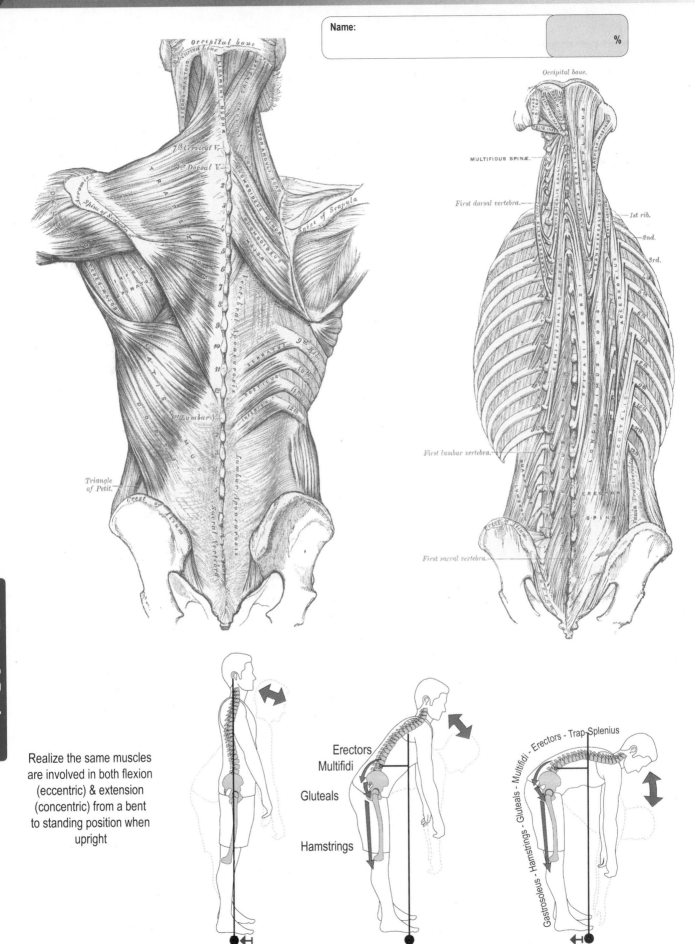

Name: _____ %

Realize the same muscles are involved in both flexion (eccentric) & extension (concentric) from a bent to standing position when upright

Erectors
Multifidi

Gluteals

Hamstrings

Gastrosoleus - Hamstrings - Gluteals - Multifidi - Erectors - Trap-Splenius

Torso & Back

Name:

%

scoliosis

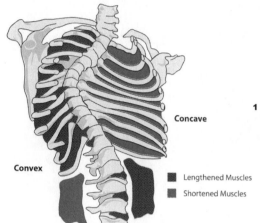

Concave

Convex

Lengthened Muscles
Shortened Muscles

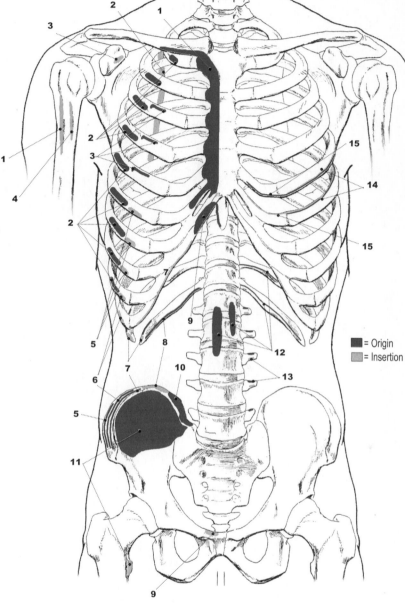

= Origin
= Insertion

1. _____

2. _____

3. _____

4. _____

5. _____

6. _____

7. _____

8. _____

9. _____

10. _____

11. _____

12. _____

13. _____

14. _____

15. _____

Start with labeling the muscles, then progress to naming
☐ actions, ☐ origins, ☐ insertions, ☐ nerves

Name: _____ %

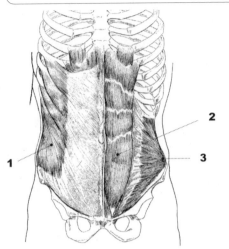

1. _____

2. _____

3. _____

4. _____

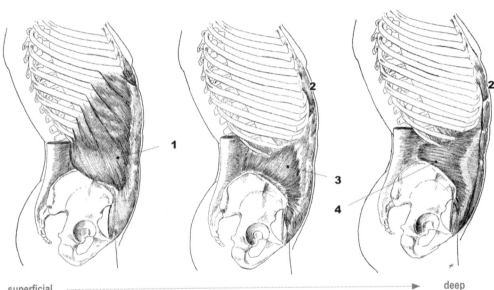

superficial ————————————————➤ deep

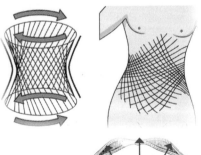

Transverse section through ~L3

RECTUS
EXTERNAL OBLIQUE
INTERNAL OBLIQUE
TRANSVERSALIS
LATIS DORSI
PSOAS
QUADR. LUMB.
ERECTOR SPINE

Core body stabilizers
'the abdominal corset'
protects your back & prevent injury

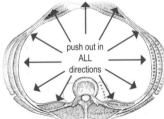

push out in ALL directions

Name:

%

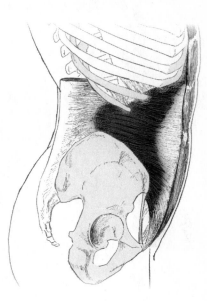

Name:

O

I

A

C

Name:

O

I

A

C

Name:

O

I

A

C

Name:

O

I

A

C

Start with labeling the muscles, then progress to naming
☐ actions, ☐ origins, ☐ insertions, ☐ nerves

Name:

%

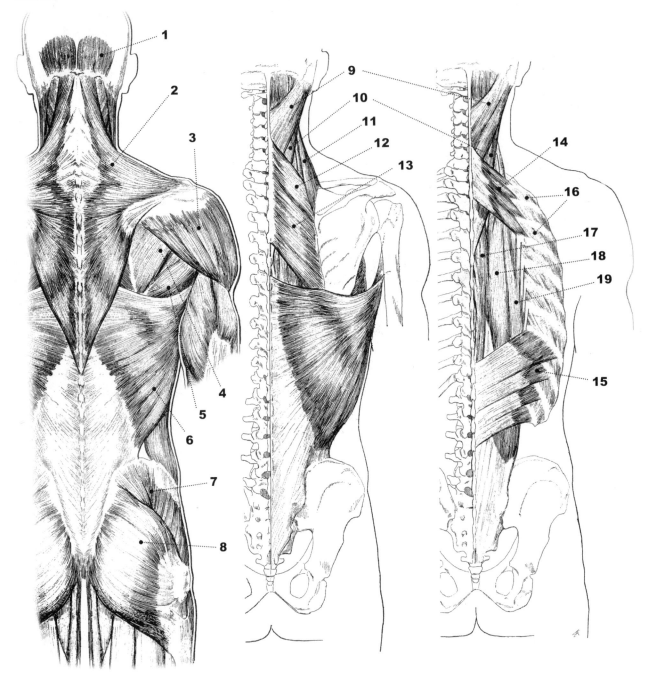

1. _____

2. _____

3. _____

4. _____

5. _____

6. _____

7. _____

8. _____

9. _____

10. _____

11. _____

12. _____

13. _____

14. _____

15. _____

16. _____

17. _____

18. _____

19. _____

Torso & Back

prohealthsys

Start with labeling the muscles, then progress to naming
☐ actions, ☐ origins, ☐ insertions, ☐ nerves

Name:

%

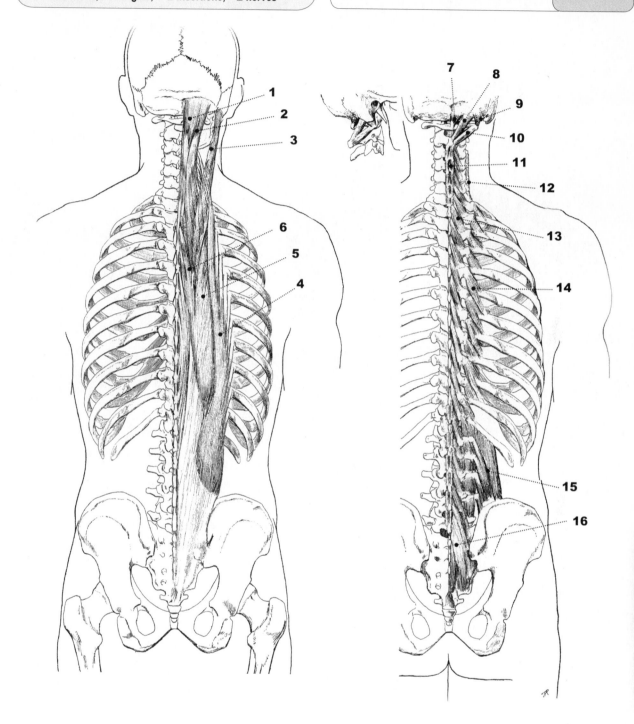

1. _____

2. _____

3. _____

4. _____

5. _____

6. _____

7. _____

8. _____

9. _____

10. _____

11. _____

12. _____

13. _____

14. _____

15. _____

16. _____

Name: _____ %

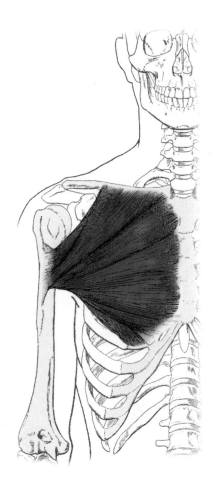

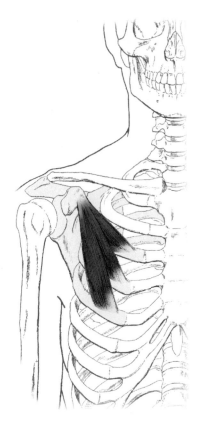

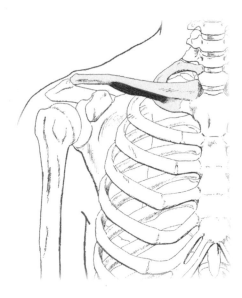

Torso & Back

Name:

O

I

A

C

Name:

O

I

A

C

Name:

O

I

A

C

Name: _____ %

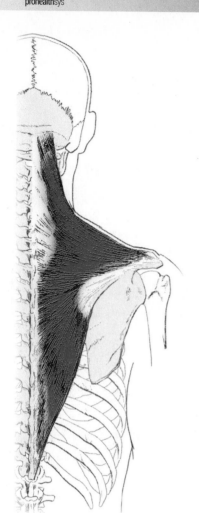

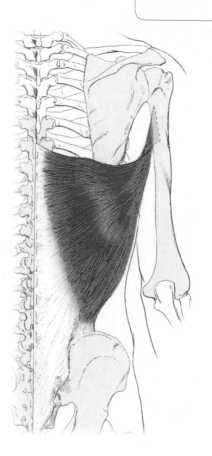

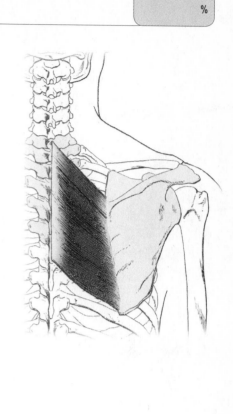

Name: _____

O

I

A

C

Name: _____

O

I

A

C

Name: _____

O

I

A

C

prohealthsys

Name: _____ %

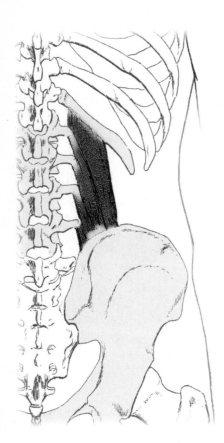
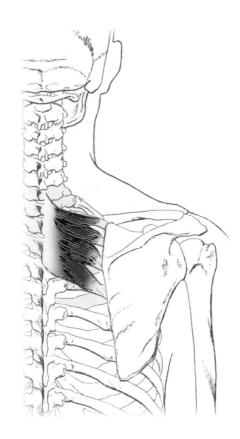
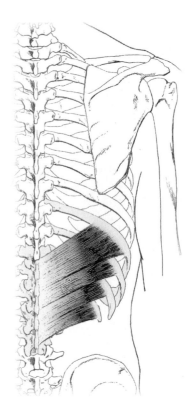

Name:

O

I

A

C

Name:

O

I

A

C

Name:

O

I

A

C

prohealthsys

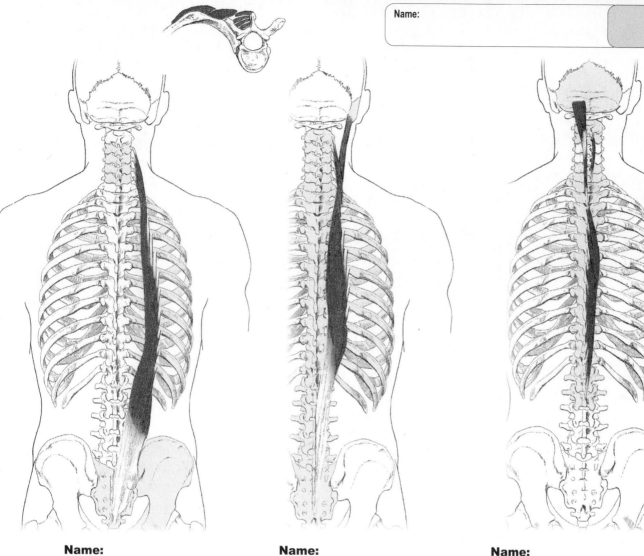

Name:

O

I

A

C

Name:

O

I

A

C

Name:

O

I

A

C

prohealthsys

Name: [   ] %

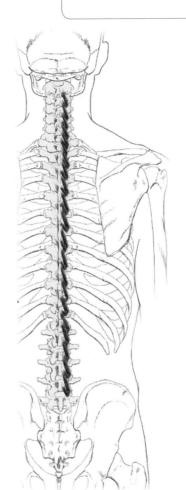

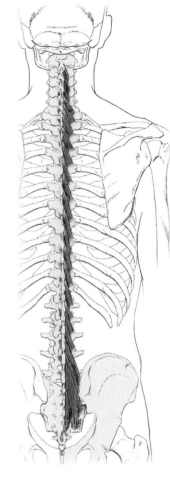

Name:

O

I

A

C

Name:

O

I

A

C

Name:

O

I

A

C

prohealthsys

Start with labeling the bones, then progress to drawing
□ muscles, □ ligaments, □ Os & Is, □ nerves, □ vessels

Name: _____ %

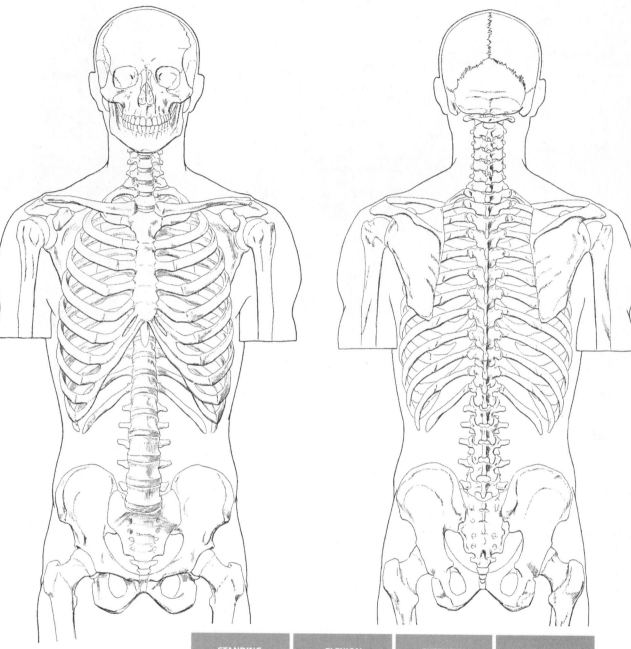

You have been
studying too long, get
up and move ☺

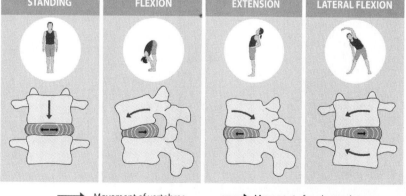

| STANDING | FLEXION | EXTENSION | LATERAL FLEXION |

➡ Movement of vertebrae   ➡ Movement of nucleus pulposus

Torso & Back

Name:

%

1. External intercostal
2. Internal intercostal
3. Transversus abdominis
4. Rectus abdominis
5. Sternohyoid
6. Sternothyroid
7. Innermost intercostals
8. Transversus thoracis
9. Diaphragm

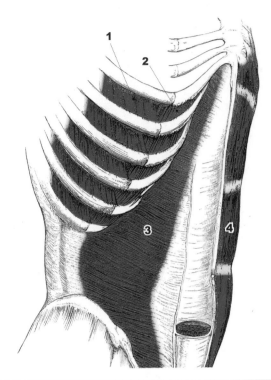

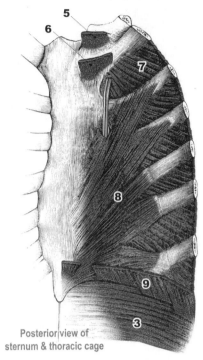

Posterior view of
sternum & thoracic cage

Muscle	Origin	Insertion	Action	Nerve
external intercostal	inferior border of ribs	superior border of ribs	elevation of ribs; fix intercostal spaces during respiration	intercostal nerves
internal intercostal	inferior border of ribs	superior border of ribs below	depression of ribs during expiration; fix intercostal spaces during expiration	
innermost intercostal	interior inferior border of ribs above	interior superior border of ribs below	depression of ribs during expiration; fix intercostal spaces during expiration	
subcostalis	internal surface ribs 10-12	internal surface of ribs 8-10	depression ribs of 10-12	
transversus thoracis (sternocostalis)	inferior 1/3 of inner aspect of sternum, xiphoid process & costosternal junctions of ribs 4-7	costal cartilage of ribs 2-6	depresses upper ribs	

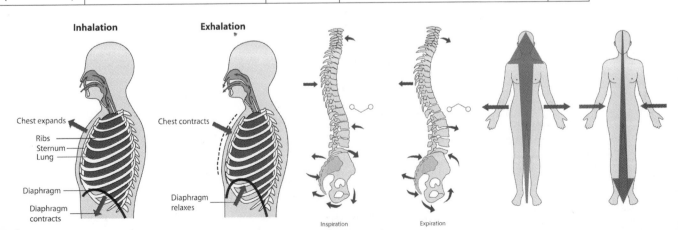

Inhalation

Chest expands
Ribs
Sternum
Lung
Diaphragm
Diaphragm contracts

Exhalation

Chest contracts
Diaphragm relaxes

Inspiration

Expiration

Torso & Back

Name: _____ _____ %

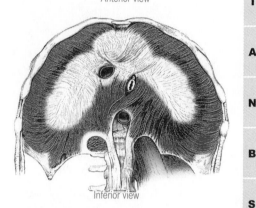

Anterior view

Inferior view

O
I
A
N
B
S

left side pelvic floor

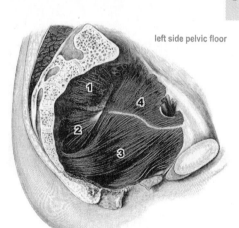

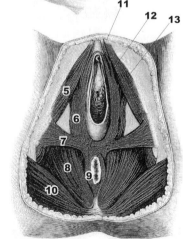

female pelvic floor

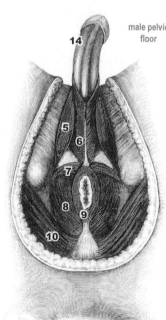

14

male pelvic floor

1. _____
2. _____
3. _____
4. _____
5. _____
6. _____
7. _____
8. _____
9. _____
10. _____
11. _____
12. _____
13. _____
14. _____

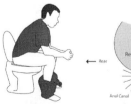

Rectum

Anal Canal

Rectum

the pelvic equator: squatty potty

Page 70, Torso Bones
Sternum
1. Suprasternal / jugular notch
2. Manubrium
3. Sternal angle
4. Body / corpus
5. Xiphoid process
   Ribs
6. Head
7. Neck
8. Tubercle
9. Angle
10. Body
11. Costal cartilages
    Vertebrae
12. Cervical
13. Thoracic
14. Lumbar
15. Sacrum
16. Coccyx
17. 1-8 true ribs
18. 9-12 false ribs
19. 11-12 floating ribs

Page 74, Ligaments of Spine
Spine
1. Posterior atalntooccipital membrane
2. Posterior atalntoaxial membrane
3. Nuchal ligament
4. Zygapophyseal joint
5. Annulus fibrosus (disc)
6. Intervertebral foramen
7. Costal facet (for rib head)
8. Anterior longitudinal ligament
9. Posterior longitudinal ligament
10. Supraspinous ligament
11. Interspinous ligament
12. Ligamentum flavum
Sacroiliac articulations
1. Anterior longitudinal ligament
2. Iliolumbar ligaments
3. Anterior sacroiliac ligaments
4. Inguinal ligament
5. Obturator membrane
6. Iliofemoral ligament
7. Sacrospinous ligament
8. Posterior sacroiliac ligament
9. Long posterior sacroiliac ligament
10. Sacrotuberous ligament
11. Acetabulofemoral joint capsule

Page 75 Vertebra, Sacrum
Thoracic Vertebra
1. Body
2. Pedicle
3. Transverse process
4. Transverse costal facet
5. Lamina
6. Spinous process
7. Superior articular process
8. Superior articular facet
9. Inferior articular process
10. Inferior costal facet
11. Superior costal facet
12. Vertebral canal
Lumbar Vertebra
1. Body
2. Pedicles
3. Transverse process
4. Superior articular process
5. Mammilary process
6. Superior articular facet
7. Lamina
8. Spinous process
9. Inferior articular process
10. Inferior articular facet
11. Vertebral canal
Sacrum & Coccyx
1. Superior articular facet
2. S2 tubercle
3. Posterior sacral foramen
4. Cornu of sacrum
5. Cornu of coccyx
6. Transverse process
7. Articular surface for ilium
8. Anterior sacral foramen

Page 77, Trunk origins & Insertions
1. Pectoralis major
2. Serratus anterior
3. Pectoralis minor
4. Latissimus dorsi
5. External abdominal oblique
6. Internal abdominal oblique
7. Transversus abdominis
8. Quadratus lumborum
9. Rectus abdominis
10. Erector spinae
11. Iliacus (iliopsoas)
12. Diaphragm
13. Intertransversarius
14. External intercostal
15. Internal intercostal

Page 78 Abdominal Muscles
1. External oblique
2. Rectus abdominis
3. Internal oblique
4. Transversus abdominus

Page 80 Superficial Back Muscles
1. Occipitalis
2. Trapezius
3. Deltoid
4. Infraspinatus
5. Teres minor & major
6. Latissimus dorsi
7. Gluteus medius
8. Gluteus maximus
9. Splenius capitis
10. Splenius cervicis
11. Levator scapulae
12. Rhomboid minor
13. Rhomboid major
14. Serratus posterior superior
15. Serratus posterior inferior
16. Intercostal muscles
    Erector spinae (deep layer)
17. Spinalis
18. Longissimus
19. Iliocostalis

Page 81 Deep Back Muscles
1. Spinalis capitis
2. Semispinalis capitis
3. Longissimus capitis
   Erector spinae muscle group
4. Iliocostalis
5. Longissimus
6. Spinalis
   Sub occipitals
7. Rectus capitis posterior minor
8. Rectus capitis posterior major
9. Obliquus capitis superior
10. Obliquus capitis inferior

11. Interspinalis
12. Intertransversarius
13. Multifidi
14. Levator costarum
15. Quadratus lumborum
16. Multifidi lumborum

Page 89, Diaphragm & Pelvic Floor
1. Piriformis
2. Coccygeus
3. Levator ani
4. Obturator internus
5. Ischiocavernosus
6. Bulbospongiosus
7. Transversus pernei
8. Levator ani
9. External anal sphincter
10. Gluteus maximus
11. Clitoris
12. Urethra
13. Vagina
14. Penis

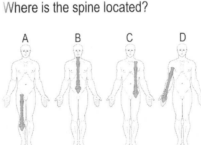

Where is the spine located?

A   B   C   D

prohealthsys.com

Video on proCentral

Torso & Back

Learning Objectives

After completing this chapter, students will be able to:

1. Identify and palpate structures of the region (give a list of structures below their palpating hand)
2. Assess AROM, PROM & RROM
3. Describe biomechanics & kinesiology of the shoulder including scapulohumeral rhythm
4. Perform detailed muscle testing and palpation
5. Discuss anatomical variation, ADLs and common injuries of the body region
6. Select appropriate stretch and strengthen exercises for the body region

Shoulder Kinematics 92
  AROM 93
  PROM 94
  RROM (muscle testing) 95
Scapulohumeral Rhythm 96
Elbow Kinematics 98
  AROM, PROM, RROM 99
Clavicle & Scapula 100
Humerus 101
Shoulder Bones 102
Shoulder/Elbow Ligaments 103
SC & GH Joint 104
Shoulder & Arm Attachments 105
Shoulder Muscles 106
Arm Muscles 107
Shoulder 108
Rotator Cuff 109
Anterior Arm Muscles 110
Posterior Arm Muscles 111
Answers 112

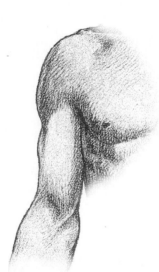

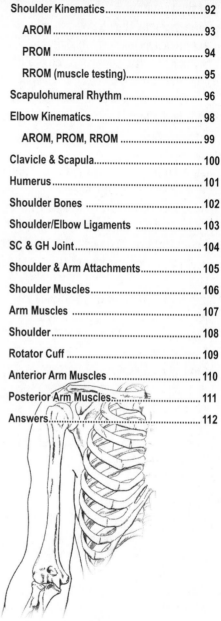

Surface anatomy   **Myofascial**   **Bony Landmarks**

Palpation Checklist

Video on prohealthsys.com

- ☐ Trapezius & rhomboids
- ☐ Levator scapulae
- ☐ Scalenes
- ☐ Thoracic outlet
- ☐ C-spine, T-spine & ribs
- ☐ Deltoid muscle
- ☐ Supraspinatus
- ☐ Infraspinatus

- ☐ Teres minor
- ☐ AC & SC joint
- ☐ GH joint / rotator cuff
- ☐ Teres major
- ☐ Latissimus dorsi
- ☐ Subscapularis
- ☐ Serratus anterior
- ☐ Triceps brachii

- ☐ Pectoralis major & minor
- ☐ Coracoid process
- ☐ Coracobrachialis
- ☐ Biceps brachii & brachialis
- ☐ Bicipital groove
- ☐ Radial groove
- ☐ . . . .
- ☐ . . . .

Joint type: synovial
Glenohumeral (ball & socket)
Acromioclavicular joint (gliding)
Scapulothoracic - not considered a true joint, but is the space between the scapula & thoracic cage & consists of muscle, connective tissue & bursa that allow for gliding-type motions

Articular surfaces
Glenohumeral: *convex* (head of humerus) on *concave* (glenoid fossa)
Acromioclavicular: *convex* (acromion) *on convex* (lateral clavicle)
Scapulothoracic: *concave* (subscapular fossa) *on convex* (posterior ribs)

Active range of motion (shoulder)
Flexion .... 160-180°
Extension .... 50-60°
Medial rotation .... 60-100°
Lateral rotation .... 80-90°
Abduction .... 170-180°
Adduction .... 35°
Horizontal Add./Abd. .130°/45°
Scapulohumeral (humerus: scapula)
  120°:60° (2:1)

Main muscle actions
Flexion: anterior deltoid, biceps brachii, coracobrachialis, pectoralis major
Extension: posterior deltoid, latissimus dorsi, triceps brachii, teres major
Abduction: middle deltoid, supraspinatus
Adduction: latissimus dorsi, teres major, pectoralis major

Horizontal adduction: pectoralis major, coracobrachialis, anterior deltoid
Horizontal abduction: posterior deltoid, teres major
Internal rotation: subscapularis, pectoralis major, latissimus dorsi
External rotation: infraspinatus, teres minor

Resting position
Glenohumeral: 55°-70° abduction, 30° horizontal adduction
Acromioclavicular: arm at side
Sternoclavicular: arm at side

Close packed position
Glenohumeral: maximal abduction & lateral rot.
Acromioclavicular: 90° abduction
Sternoclavicular: full elevation

Normal end feel
Flexion: soft tissue stretch, capsular
Abduction: soft tissue stretch, capsular
Extension: **elastic** soft tissue stretch, capsular
IR / ER: soft tissue stretch, capsular
Horizontal adduction: soft tissue approximation
Horizontal abduction: soft tissue stretch

Abnormal end feel
Empty → severe instability
Hard capsular → frozen shoulder
Late myospasm → instability

Shoulder & Arm

Compare bilaterally, examiner should make an introduction statement:
"Try and move as far as possible, if any of the actions or movements are painful or uncomfortable please let me know, do not do any action you feel will cause you further injury."

Flexion

Muscles Activated: deltoid (anterior fibers), biceps brachii, pectoralis major & coracobrachialis (1st 60° only)

Tissue Stretched: latissimus dorsi, teres major, pectoralis major (lower fibers), triceps brachii (long head), inferior GH capsule, conoid ligament

Tissue Compressed: supraspinatus tendon, subdeltoid bursa, upper GH joint capsule

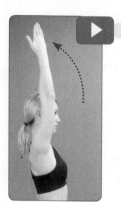 youtube: **Vizniak Shoulder**

Extension

Muscles Activated: deltoid (posterior fibers), latissimus dorsi, teres major/minor, infraspinatus, triceps brachii

Tissue Stretched: deltoid (anterior fibers), biceps brachii, pectoralis major, anterior GH capsule

Tissue Compressed: posterior GH capsule, quadrangular space

Abduction

Muscles Activated: supraspinatus, deltoid (middle fibers), trapezius, serratus anterior

Tissue Stretched: latissimus dorsi, teres major, pectoralis major (lower fibers), triceps brachii (long head), inferior GH capsule, conoid ligament

Tissue Compressed: supraspinatus tendon, subdeltoid bursa, upper GH joint capsule

Adduction

Muscles Activated: deltoid (anterior fibers), pectoralis major, latissimus dorsi, teres major, coracobrachialis, trapezius

Tissue Stretched: deltoid (middle fibers), posterior GH capsule

Tissue Compressed: pectoralis major, AC & SC joint, anterior GH capsule

Lateral Rotation

Muscles Activated: infraspinatus, teres minor, posterior deltoid

Tissue Stretched: pectoralis major, subscapularis, anterior GH capsule

Tissue Compressed: posterior GH capsule

Medial Rotation

Muscles Activated: pec major, subscapularis, anterior deltoid, teres major, latissimus dorsi

Tissue Stretched: infraspinatus, teres minor, posterior deltoid posterior GH capsule

Tissue Compressed: anterior GH capsule

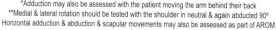
*Adduction may also be assessed with the patient moving the arm behind their back
**Medial & lateral rotation should be tested with the shoulder in neutral & again abducted 90°
Horizontal adduction & abduction & scapular movements may also be assessed as part of AROM

 Shoulder & Arm

Compare bilaterally; if possible palpate joint during PROM & use the shortest level possible, start with unaffected; apply over pressure at end ROM; introduction statement:
"If any of the actions or movements are painful or uncomfortable please let me know."

Flexion

Tissue Stretched: latissimus dorsi, teres major, pectoralis major (lower fibers), triceps brachii (long head), inferior GH capsule, conoid ligament

Tissue Compressed: supraspinatus tendon, subdeltoid bursa, upper GH joint capsule

Extension

Tissue Stretched: deltoid (anterior fibers), biceps brachii, pectoralis major, anterior GH capsule

Tissue Compressed: posterior GH capsule

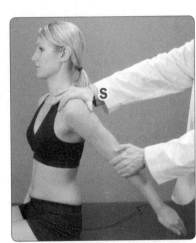

Abduction

Tissue Stretched: latissimus dorsi, teres major, pectoralis major (lower fibers), triceps brachii (long head), inferior GH capsule, conoid ligament

Tissue Compressed: supraspinatus tendon, subdeltoid bursa, upper GH joint capsule

Adduction

Tissue Stretched: deltoid (middle fibers), posterior GH capsule

Tissue Compressed: pectoralis major, AC & SC joint, anterior GH capsule

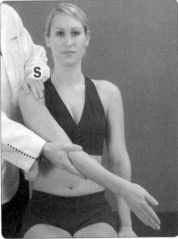

Medial Rotation

Tissue Stretched: infraspinatus, teres minor, posterior deltoid posterior GH capsule

Tissue Compressed: anterior GH capsule

Lateral Rotation

Tissue Stretched: pectoralis major, subscapularis, anterior GH capsule

Tissue Compressed: posterior GH capsule

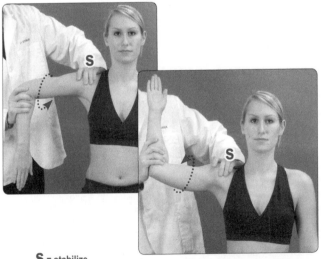

*shoulder PROM may also be assessed with the patient supine

S = stabilize

Shoulder & Arm

prohealthsys

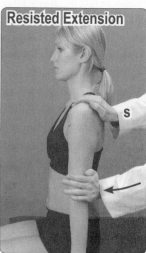

Patient instructions for assessing general muscle strength testing:
"I am going to try and move you in _____ direction, don't let me do it" or "resist my force"

Flexion

Muscles Activated: deltoid (anterior fibers), biceps brachii, pectoralis major & coracobrachialis

Extension

Muscles Activated: deltoid (posterior fibers), latissimus dorsi, teres major/minor, infraspinatus, triceps brachii

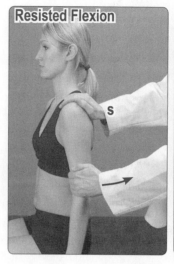

Resisted Flexion · Resisted Extension · S

Adduction

Muscles Activated: deltoid (anterior fibers), pectoralis major, latissimus dorsi, teres major, coracobrachialis, trapezius

Abduction

Muscles Activated: supraspinatus, deltoid (middle fibers), trapezius, serratus anterior

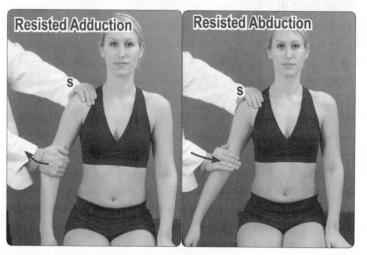

Resisted Adduction · Resisted Abduction · S

Medial Rotation

Muscles Activated: pectoralis major, subscapularis, anterior deltoid, teres major, latissimus dorsi

Lateral Rotation

Muscles Activated: infraspinatus, teres minor, posterior deltoid

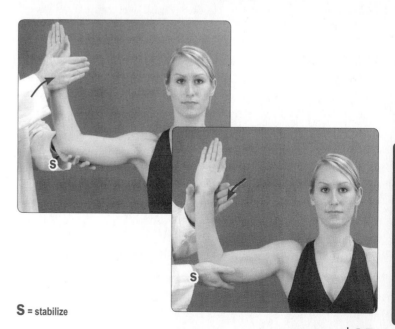

S = stabilize

Shoulder & Arm

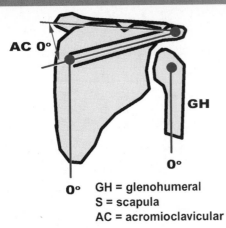

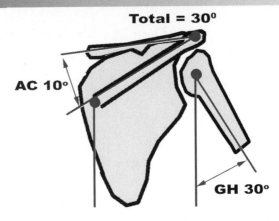

GH = glenohumeral
S = scapula
AC = acromioclavicular

Resting phase (neutral)	Phase 1 (0°-30°)
Shoulder ROM is measured from standard anatomical position	**Important abductors** Deltoid (60%-70%) Supraspinatus (30%-40%) When arm is externally rotated, long head of biceps will help in abduction (coracobrachialis & biceps short head help with GH flexion when the arm externally rotated)
Shoulder hiking (elevation) in phase 1 may indicate shoulder pathology	
Clavicle follows the humerus	
The inferior capsule folds like an accordion, & unfolds for abduction, loss of this motion = *"frozen shoulder" or adhesive capsulitis*	**Rotator cuff as a group** Depresses humerus*, cancels superior translation by deltoid
Most important shoulder girdle stabilizer is serratus anterior	**GH:** 15°-20°, superior roll with inferior slide
Rotator cuff = SITS muscles	**Scapula:** 10°-15°, external rotation Serratus anterior is the major stabilizer, at this point, of the shoulder girdle. Upper & lower trapezius are minor stabilizers at this point
Supraspinatus	
Infraspinatus	
Teres minor	**SC:** Distal end elevates 10°-15° Superior roll with inferior glide (same as GH) Upper trapezius is not very active
Subscapularis	

GH = glenohumeral joint, AC = acromioclavicular joint, SC = sternoclavicular joint
*note that the action of supraspinatus is not to directly depress the humerus, rather the space occupied by the muscle helps keep the humerus inferior, following a full supraspinatus rupture it is possible to observe the humerus in an elevated position relative to the glenoid fossa on MRI or X-ray

Scapulohumeral rhythm serves at least two purposes:

1. It preserves the length-tension relationships of the glenohumeral muscles; the muscles do not shorten as much as they would without the scapula's upward rotation, so they can sustain their force production through a larger portion of the range of motion

2. It prevents impingement between the humerus & the acromion. Because of the difference in size between the glenoid fossa & the humeral head, subacromial impingement can occur unless relative movement between the humerus & scapula is limited. Simultaneous movement of the humerus & scapula during shoulder elevation limits relative (arthrokinematic) movement between the two bones

> ## Total Motion = 180°, 2:1 (GH : Scapula)
> **GH:** 120° **Shoulder Girdle** (Scap./SC/AC): 60°
> Suspect a capsular issue if the ratio approaches 1:1 (frozen shoulder)

Shoulder & Arm

prohealthsys

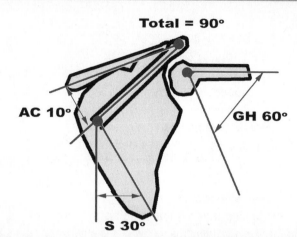

Total = 90°

AC 10°

GH 60°

S 30°

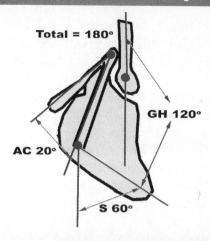

Total = 180°

GH 120°

AC 20°

S 60°

Phase 2 (30°-90°)	**Phase 3 (90°-180°)**

GH: 40°-45° (55°-65° total)

Superior roll with inferior slide

Deltoid & supraspinatus - abduction

Rotator cuff - depress & externally rotate

Greatest impingement: 70°-120°

Scapula: 15°-20° (30° total)

Externally rotates

Serratus anterior prevents winging

Upper & lower trapezius - forces couple & cancel each other out

SC: 15°-20° (30° total)

Elevation of distal clavicle due to superior roll & inferior glide

At end of 1st 30° the coracoclavicular ligaments (conoid & trapezoid) become taut & stop the superior roll & inferior slide that make up the hinge action, this will cause rotation in the 3rd phase

AC: twisting/rotation: 0°-5° (10°-15° total) AC: 5°-10° scapula rotation

---

Phase 3 (90°-180°)

GH: 60° (120° total)

Deltoid & supraspinatus still active, but biceps join in after 90°; above 90° rotator cuff & ligaments act to depress, externally rotate & stabilize the joint

Biceps also help depress the humerus

Triceps long head tendon resists inferior translation

Pectoralis major & subscapularis reinforce anterior capsule & resists anterior translation & dislocation

Inferior glenohumeral ligament most important anterior capsule ligament

Structures that resist abduction: inferior capsule, latissimus dorsi, pectoralis major, teres major, subscapularis, inferior GH ligament, long head of triceps (resist inferior translation)

Scapula: 30° (60° total) upper more than lower trapezius, serratus anterior externally rotates scapula

Structures that limit external rotation; rhomboids (esp. if tight), lower trapezius, upper trapezius

SC: rotates externally & points upwards

Crank-shaped clavicle allows elevation at distal end, while proximal rotates, this causes a 30° elevation at the distal clavicle due to taut coracoclavicular ligaments, which stop the hinge & cause rotation, this is resisted by costoclavicular ligaments from the 1st rib & eccentric contraction of the subclavius

AC: 10° (20° total) final 10° rotation during phase 1-2

the AC rotation is due to scapular rotation; the AC is the weak link in abduction

---

Shoulder Stability

Muscles provide a full 50% of the GH joint stability (bone shape, glenoid labrum, synovial fluid surface tension & ligaments provide the other 50%)

Throwing

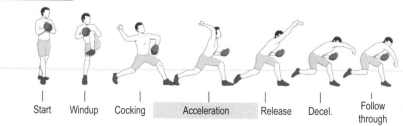

Start   Windup   Cocking   Acceleration   Release   Decel.   Follow through

Foot down   Max external rotation & weight transfer forward

Maximum speed and power are a result of a full body kinetic chain and energy transfer into the projectile

Shoulder & Arm

Joint type: synovial
Hinge (humeroulnar & humeroradial)
Pivot (proximal radioulnar & humeroradial)

Articular surfaces
Humeroulnar: *concave* (trochlear notch of ulna) *on convex* (trochlea of humerus)
Humeroradial: *concave* (radial head) *on convex* (capitilum of humerus)
Proximal radioulnar: *convex* (radial head) *on concave* (radial notch of ulna)

Active range of motion (elbow)
Flexion ....140-150°
Extension ....0-10°
Pronation ....80-90°
Supination ....90°

Main muscle actions
Flexion: brachialis, biceps brachii, brachioradialis
Extension: triceps brachii, anconeus
Pronation: pronator teres, pronator quadratus
Supination: biceps brachii, supinator

Resting position
Humeroulnar: 70° flexion
Humeroradial: full extension & supination
Proximal radioulnar: 70° flexion, 35° supination

Close packed position
Humeroulnar: full extension
Humeroradial: 90° flexion, 5° supination
Proximal radioulnar: 5° supination, 90° flexion

Normal end feel
Flexion: soft tissue approximation
Extension: bony approximation
Pronation: bony approx. or ligamentous
Supination: ligamentous

Abnormal end feel
Boggy → joint effusion
Early myospasm → acute injury
Late myospasm → instability
Springy block → loose body (osteochondritis dissecans)

Open kinetic chain
Humeroulnar & humeroradial:
Flexion: radius & ulna roll & glide anterior on humerus
Extension: radius & ulna roll & glide posterior on humerus
Proximal radioulnar:
Pronation: radius spins medially on ulna
Supination: radius spins laterally on ulna

Closed kinetic chain
Humeroulnar & humeroradial:
Flexion: humerus rolls & glides anterior on radius & ulna
Extension: humerus roll & glide posterior on radius & ulna
Proximal radioulnar:
Pronation: ulna spins laterally on radius
Supination: ulna spins medially on radius

Carrying angle of the elbow
Normal = 5°-15° - angle permits the forearms to clear the hips in swinging movements during walking & is important when carrying objects
Cubitus valgum - angle greater than 15°
Cubitus varum - angle less than 5°

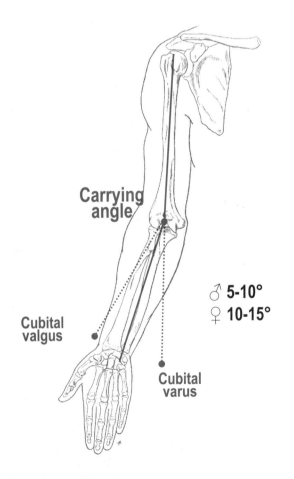

Carrying angle

♂ **5-10°**
♀ **10-15°**

Cubital valgus

Cubital varus

Shoulder & Arm

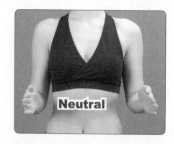

Compare bilaterally, examiner should make an introduction statement:
"Try and move as far as possible, if any of the actions or movements are painful or uncomfortable please let me know, do not do any action you feel will cause you further injury."

PROM

Flexion
Muscles Activated: brachialis, biceps brachii, brachioradialis
Tissue Stretched: triceps brachii, posterior elbow joint capsule, ulnar nerve
Tissue Compressed: forearm flexors, median nerve, anterior joint capsule

Extension
Muscles Activated: triceps brachii, anconeus
Tissue Stretched: brachialis, biceps brachii, brachioradialis, median nerve
Tissue Compressed: posterior joint capsule

Supination
Muscles Activated: biceps brachii, supinator
Tissue Stretched: pronator teres, pronator quadratus

Pronation
Muscles Activated: pronator teres, pronator quadratus
Tissue Stretched: biceps brachii, supinator, brachioradialis

Neutral

Supination

Pronation

PROM

Flexion
Tissue Stretched: triceps brachii, posterior elbow joint capsule, ulnar nerve
Tissue Compressed: forearm flexors, median nerve, anterior joint capsule

Extension
Tissue Stretched: brachialis, biceps brachii, brachioradialis, median nerve
Tissue Compressed: posterior joint capsule

Supination
Tissue Stretched: pronator teres, pronator quadratus
Tissue Compressed:

Pronation
Tissue Stretched: biceps brachii, supinator, brachioradialis
Tissue Compressed:

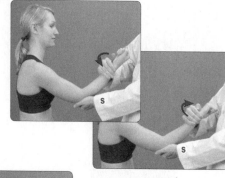

Elbow Muscle Testing

Flexion
Muscles Activated: brachialis, biceps brachii, brachioradialis

Extension
Muscles Activated: triceps brachii, anconeus

Supination
Muscles Activated: biceps brachii, supinator

Pronation
Muscles Activated: pronator teres, pronator quadratus

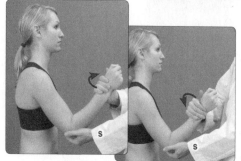

Shoulder & Arm

Name: _____

_____ %

Clavicle

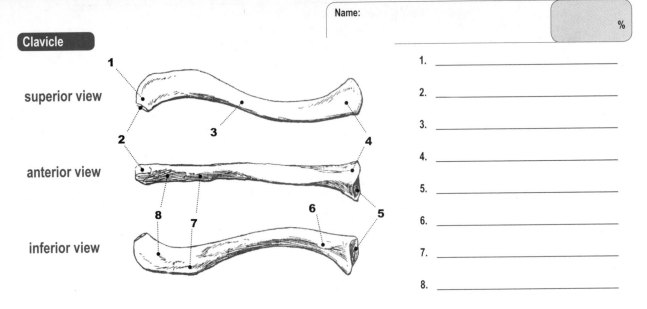

superior view

anterior view

inferior view

1. _____
2. _____
3. _____
4. _____
5. _____
6. _____
7. _____
8. _____

Scapula

superior view

posterior view

anterior view

lateral view

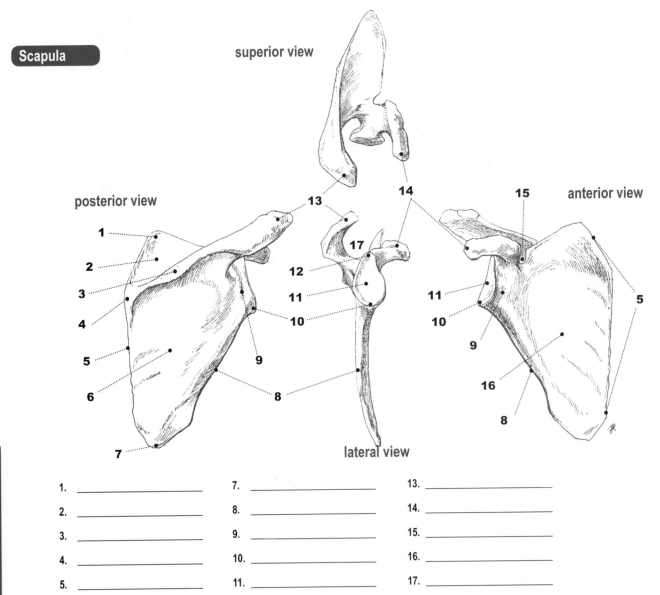

1. _____
2. _____
3. _____
4. _____
5. _____
6. _____

7. _____
8. _____
9. _____
10. _____
11. _____
12. _____

13. _____
14. _____
15. _____
16. _____
17. _____

Shoulder & Arm

Name: _____ %

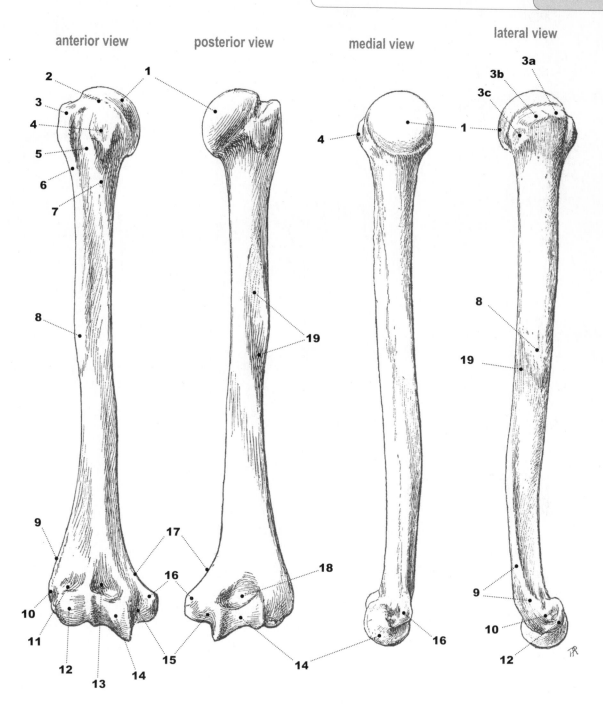

anterior view   posterior view   medial view   lateral view

2
3
4
5
6
7
1
8
9
10
11
12
13
14
17
16
15
18
19
14
4
1
16
3a
3b
3c
1
8
19
9
10
12

1. _____

2. _____

3. _____
   a. _____
   b. _____
   c. _____

4. _____

5. _____

6. _____

7. _____

8. _____

9. _____

10. _____

11. _____

12. _____

13. _____

14. _____

15. _____

16. _____

17. _____

18. _____

19. _____

prohealthsys

Name:

%

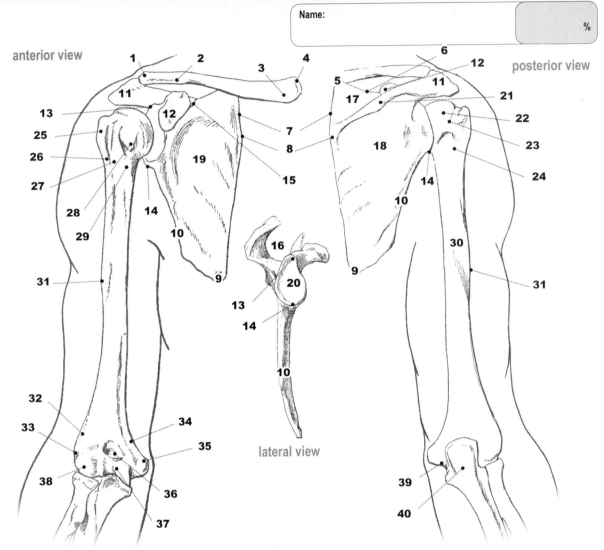

anterior view

1
2
3
4
11
13
12
25
26
27
28
29
31
32
33
38
34
35
36
37
14
10
9
19
7
8
15

posterior view

6
12
5
11
17
21
22
23
24
18
14
10
30
31
9
39
40

lateral view

16
13
20
14
10

Clavicle

1. _____

2. _____

3. _____

4. _____

Scapula

5. _____

6. _____

7. _____

8. _____

9. _____

10. _____

11. _____

12. _____

13. _____

14. _____

15. _____

16. _____

17. _____

18. _____

19. _____

20. _____

21. _____

Humerus

22. _____

23. _____

24. _____

25. _____

26. _____

27. _____

28. _____

29. _____

30. _____

31. _____

32. _____

33. _____

34. _____

35. _____

36. _____

37. _____

38. _____

39. _____

40. _____

prohealthsys

Name: _____ %

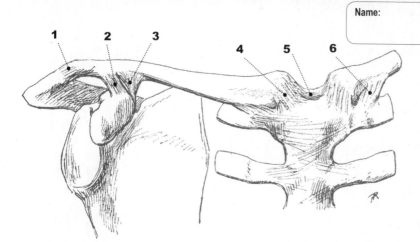

anterior view

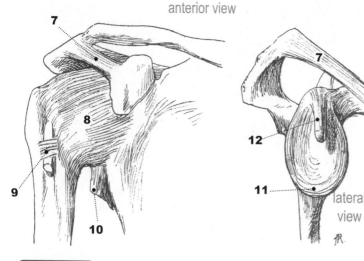

lateral view

1. _____

Coracoclavicular ligaments

2. _____

3. _____

Sternoclavicular (SC) joint

4. _____

5. _____

6. _____

Glenohumeral (GH) joint

7. _____

8. _____

9. _____

10. _____

11. _____

12. _____

Right Elbow

Right medial view

Right lateral view

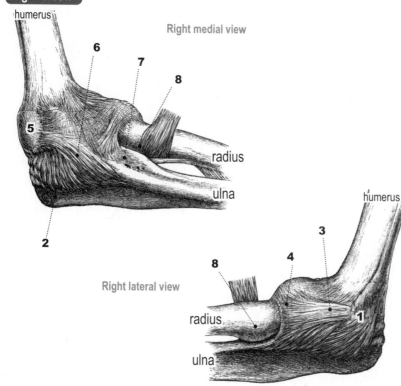

Elbow joint

1. _____

2. _____

3. _____

4. _____

5. _____

6. _____

7. _____

8. _____

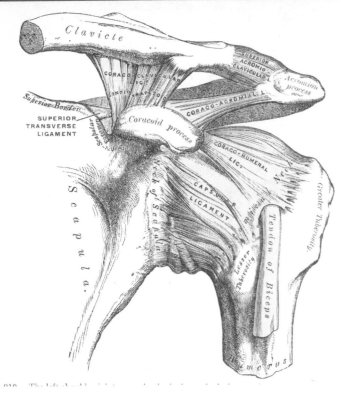

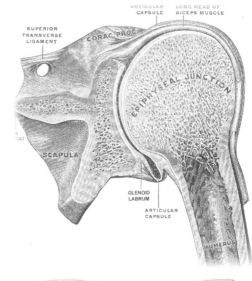

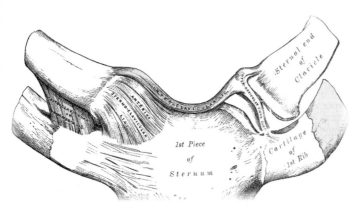

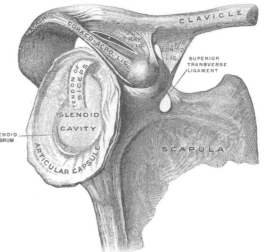

Ligamevnt	Attaches (origin/insertion)	Function
Acromioclavicular	Acromion process to clavicle	Resists AC joint separation
Coracoacromial	Coracoid process to acromion	Forms arch over shoulder
Coracoclavicular Trapezoid Conoid	Coracoid process to clavicle	Resists anterior and posterior scapula movements & upward/downward movements of clavicle on scapula
Coracohumeral	Coracoid process to greater and lesser tuberosity on humerus	Resists upward humeral head movement & external rotation Supports weight of arm
Costoclavicular	Clavicle to 1st rib	Resists clavicle elevation, anterior, posterior, and lateral movement Supports weight of arm
GH - Superior Middle Inferior	Upper, anterior edge of glenoid to over, in front, and below humeral head	Tight with external rotation & abduction past 100° Prevents anterior dislocation of humerus; resists clavicular motion, supports weight of arm
Interclavicular	Clavicle to clavicle	Checks motion of clavicle, supports arm weight
Transverse Humeral	Bicipital grove lateral to medial lip	Hold biceps long head in intertubercular groove

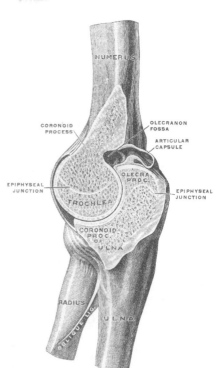

Name:

%

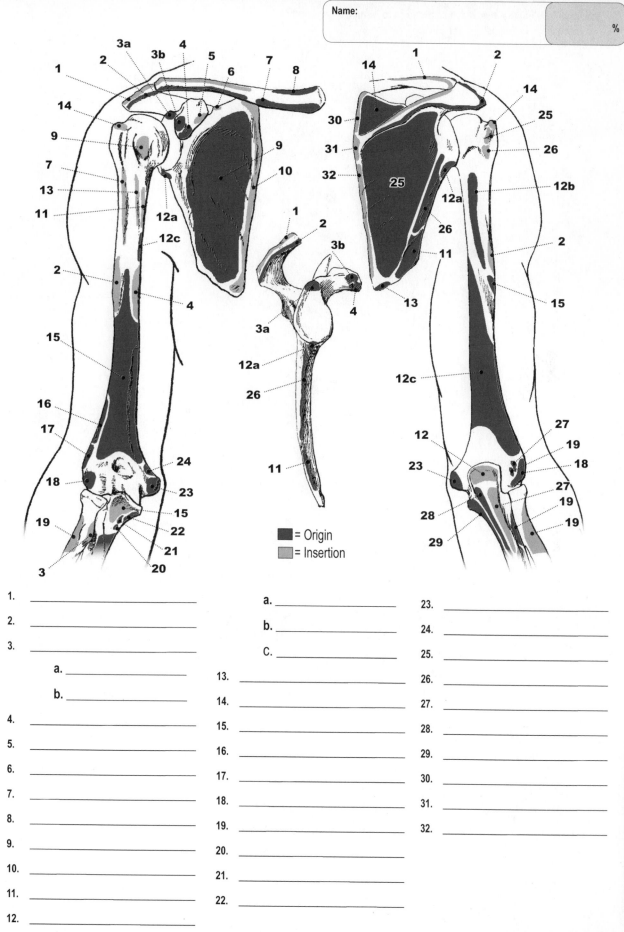

= Origin
= Insertion

1. _____
2. _____
3. _____
   a. _____
   b. _____
4. _____
5. _____
6. _____
7. _____
8. _____
9. _____
10. _____
11. _____
12. _____

a. _____
b. _____
c. _____
13. _____
14. _____
15. _____
16. _____
17. _____
18. _____
19. _____
20. _____
21. _____
22. _____

23. _____
24. _____
25. _____
26. _____
27. _____
28. _____
29. _____
30. _____
31. _____
32. _____

Start with labeling the muscles, then progress to naming
□ actions, □ origins, □ insertions, □ nerves

Name: _____ %

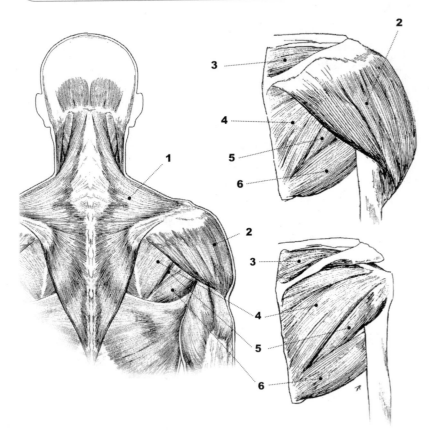

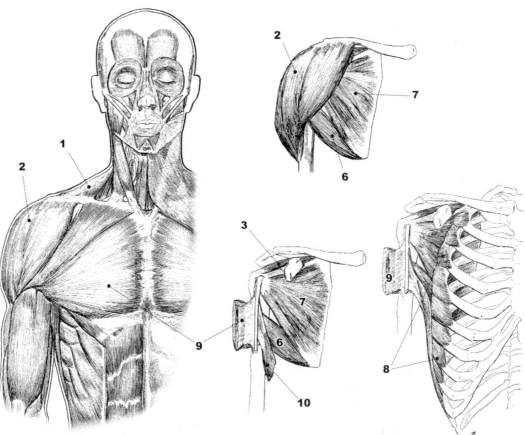

1. _____

2. _____

3. _____

4. _____

5. _____

6. _____

7. _____

8. _____

9. _____

10. _____

Shoulder & Arm

prohealthsys

Start with labeling the muscles, then progress to naming
☐ actions, ☐ origins, ☐ insertions, ☐ nerves

Name:

%

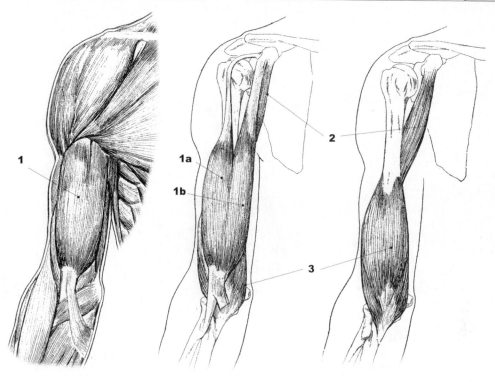

Superficial ....➤ Deep

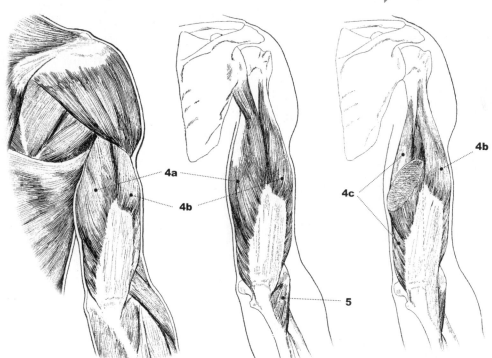

1. _____
   a. _____
   b. _____
2. _____
3. _____

4. _____
   a. _____
   b. _____
   c. _____
5. _____

Shoulder & Arm

prohealthsys

Name:
%

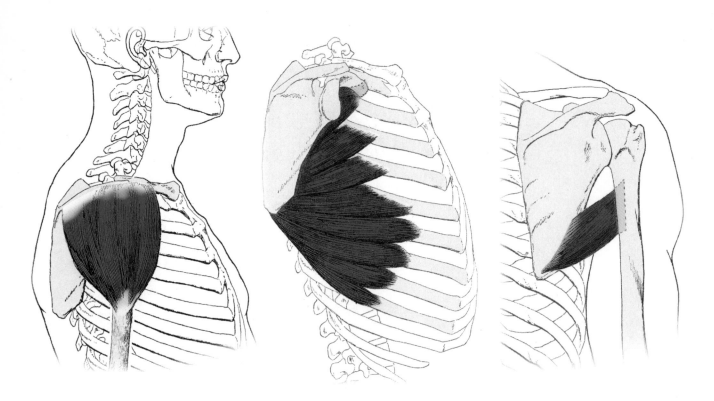

Name:

O

I

A

C

Name:

O

I

A

C

Name:

O

I

A

C

Shoulder & Arm

prohealthsys

Name: [   ] [%]

Name:

O

I

A

C

Name:

O

I

A

C

Name:

O

I

A

C

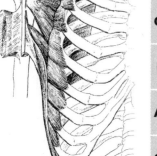

Name:

O

I

A

C

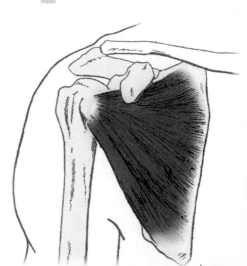

Shoulder & Arm

prohealthsys

Name: _____ %

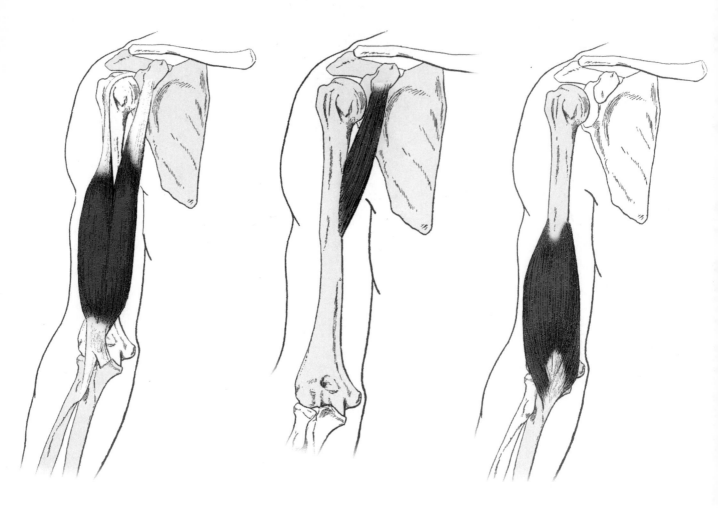

Name:

O

I

A

C

Name:

O

I

A

C

Name:

O

I

A

C

prohealthsys.com   Vizniak & Richer

Name: _____ %

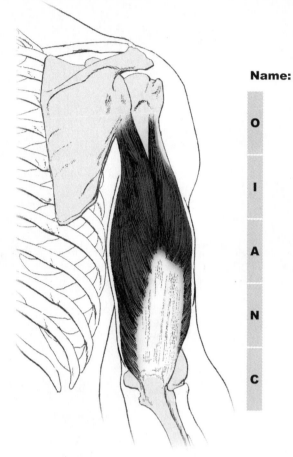

Name:

O

I

A

N

C

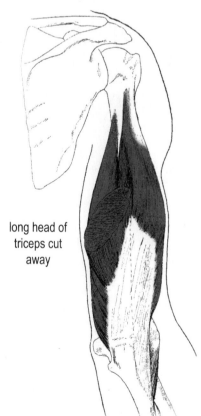

long head of
triceps cut
away

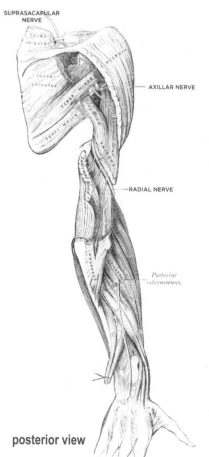

SUPRASACAPULAR
NERVE

AXILLAR NERVE

RADIAL NERVE

Posterior
interosseons.

posterior view

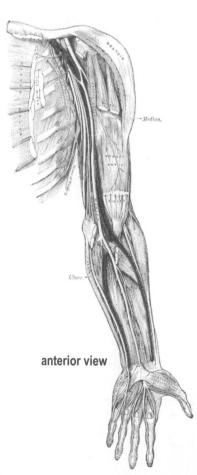

anterior view

prohealthsys

Page 100, Clavicle & Scapula
1. Acromial end
2. Acromial facet
3. Shaft (body)
4. Sternal end
5. Sternal facet
6. Tuberosity
7. Conoid tubercle
8. Trapezoid ligament attachment

Scapula
1. Superior angle
2. Supraspinous fossa
3. Spine of scapula
4. Medial angle
5. Medial border
6. Infraspinous fossa
7. Inferior angle
8. Lateral border
9. Neck
10. Infraglenoid tubercle
11. Glenoid fossa
12. Supraglenoid tubercle
13. Acromion
14. Coracoid process
15. Suprascapular notch
16. Subscapular fossa
17. Spinoglenoid notch

Page 101 Humerus
1. Head of Humerus
2. Anatomical neck
3. Greater tubercle
   a. Superior facet
   b. Middle facet
   c. Inferior facet
4. Lesser tubercle
5. Intertubercular sulcus (bicipital groove)
6. Crest of greater tubercle (lateral lip)
7. Crest of lesser tubercle (medial lip)
8. Deltoid tuberosity
9. Lateral supracondylar ridge
10. Lateral epicondyle
11. Radial fossa
12. Capitulum
13. Coronoid fossa
14. Trochlea
15. Groove for ulnar nerve
16. Medial epicondyle
17. Medial supracondylar ridge
18. Olecranon fossa
19. Radial groove

Page 102 Shoulder Bones
Clavicle
1. Acromial end
2. Conoid tubercle
3. Costal tubercle
4. Sternal end
   Scapula
5. Superior angle
6. Superior border
7. Medial (vertebral) border
8. Medial angle
9. Inferior angle
10. Lateral (axillary) border
11. Acromion
12. Coracoid process
13. Supraglenoid tubercle
14. Infraglenoid tubercle
15. Suprascapular notch
16. Spinoglenoid notch
17. Supraspinous fossa
18. Infraspinous fossa

19. Subscapular fossa
20. Glenoid fossa
21. Spine of the scapula
Humerus
22. Head
23. Anatomical neck
24. Surgical neck
25. Greater tubercle
26. Crest of greater tubercle
27. Intertubercular sulcus (bicipital groove)
28. Lesser tubercle
29. Crest of lesser tubercle
30. Radial/spiral groove
31. Deltoid tuberosity
32. Lateral supracondylar ridge
33. Lateral epicondyle
34. Medial supracondylar ridge
35. Medial epicondyle
36. Coronoid fossa
37. Trochlea
38. Capitulum
39. Notch for the ulnar nerve
40. Olecranon

Page 103 Shoulder/Elbow ligaments
Shoulder
1. Acromioclavicular (AC) joint
Coracoclavicular ligaments
2. Trapezoid ligament
3. Conoid ligament
Sternoclavicular (SC) joint
4. Anterior SC ligament
5. Interclavicular ligament
6. Costoclavicular ligament
Glenohumeral (GH) joint
7. Coracoacromial ligament
8. GH ligaments (joint capsule)
9. Transverse humeral ligament
10. Triceps brachii long head tendon
11. Glenoid labrum

Biceps long head tendon Elbow
1. Lateral epicondyle
2. Olecranon
3. Radial collateral ligament
4. Annular ligament
5. Medial epicondyle
6. Ulnar collateral ligament
7. Ulnar tuberosity
8. Radial tuberosity

Page 105, Shoulder & Arm Attachments
1. Trapezius
2. Deltoid
3. Biceps brachii
   a. Long head
   b. Short head
4. Coracobrachialis
5. Pectoralis minor
6. Omohyoid
7. Pectoralis major
8. Sternocleidomastoid
9. Subscapularis
10. Serratus anterior
11. Teres major
12. Triceps brachii
   a. Long head
   b. Lateral head
   c. Deep (medial) head
13. Latissimus dorsi
14. Supraspinatus
15. Brachialis
16. Brachioradialis
17. Extensor carpi radialis longus
18. Common extensor tendon

19. Supinator
20. Flexor pollicis longus
21. Pronator teres (ulnar head)
22. Flexor digitorum superficialis
23. Common flexor tendon
24. Pronator teres (humeral head)
25. Infraspinatus
26. Teres minor
27. Anconeus
28. Flexor carpi ulnaris
29. Flexor digitorum profundus
30. Levator scapulae
31. Rhomboid minor
32. Rhomboid major
33.

Page 106 Shoulder Muscles
1. **Trapezius**
2. **Deltoid**
3. **Supraspinatus**
4. **Infraspinatus**
5. **Teres minor**
6. **Teres major**
7. **Subscapularis**
8. **Serratus anterior**
9. **Pectoralis major**
10. **Latissimus dorsi**

Page 107 Arm Muscles
1. **Biceps brachii**
   a. **Long head**
   b. **Short Head**
2. **Coracobrachialis**
3. **Brachialis**
4. **Triceps brachii**
   a. **Long head**
   b. **Lateral head**
   c. **Deep (medial) head**
5. 5. **Anconeus**

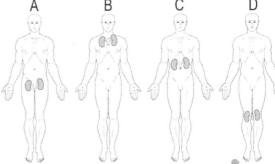

Where are the kidneys located? What about the 'kid knees'?

A   B   C   D

prohealthsys.com
Dr. Nikita Vizniak

For specific muscle information use the Muscle Manual Text, Muscle Tables Chapter or on-line resources

▶ Video on proCentral

Learning Objectives

After completing this chapter, students will be able to:

1. Identify and palpate structures of the region (give a list of structures below their palpating hand)
2. Assess AROM, PROM & RROM
3. Describe biomechanics & kinesiology of the shoulder including scapulohumeral rhythm
4. Perform detailed muscle testing and palpation
5. Discuss anatomical variation, ADLs and common injuries of the body region
6. Select appropriate stretch and strengthen exercises for the body region

Wrist & Hand Kinematics 114

Wrist & Hand AROM PROM 115

Radius & Ulna 116

Wrist & Hand Bones 117

Forearm Bones 118

Forearm Ligaments 119

Anterior Forearm Muscles 120

Posterior Forearm Muscles 122

Anterior Muscles Detailed 124

Thenar & Hypothenar Muscles 130

Central Hand Muscles 131

Self Quiz 132

Anterior Arm Layers 133

Answers 134

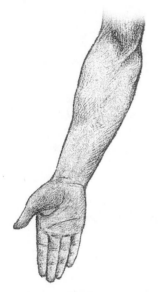 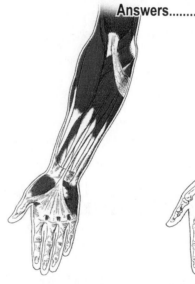 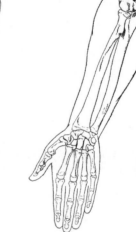

Surface anatomy   Myofascial   Bony Landmarks

Video on proCentral

Palpation Checklist

- ☐ Medial epicondyle
- ☐ Ulnar groove
- ☐ Wrist flexors
- ☐ Pronator teres
- ☐ Lateral epicondyle
- ☐ Wrist extensors
- ☐ Thumb extensors
- ☐ Interossei
- ☐ Thenar/hypothenar pad

- ☐ Carpal tunnel
- ☐ Tunnel of Guyon (ulnar)
- ☐ Anatomic snuff box
- ☐ Metacarpals 1-5
- ☐ Thumb (#1)
- ☐ Finger (#2-5)
- ☐ Scaphoid
- ☐ Lunate, Triquetrum
- ☐ Pisiform

- ☐ Dorsal (Lister's) tubercle
- ☐ Trapezium, Trapezoid
- ☐ Capitate
- ☐ Hamate (hook)
- ☐ Ulnar/radial styloids
- ☐ Triangular fibrocartilage
- ☐ Collateral ligaments
- ☐ . . . .
- ☐ . . . .

Forearm, Wrist & Hand

Joint type: synovial
Pivot (distal radioulnar)
Gliding (intercarpal)
Ellipsoid (radiocarpal & ulnocarpal)
Saddle (trapeziometacarpal)
Condyloid (MCP)
Hinge (PIP, IP, DIP)

AROM
Distal radioulnar
 Supination .... 85°-90°
 Pronation .... 85°-90°

Wrist
 Flexion .... 80°
 Extension .... 70°
 Ulnar Flexion .... 30°
 Radial Flexion .... 20°

Fingers
 Flexion (2-5 MCP) ... 90°
 Extension (MP) .... 40°
 Abduction .... 20°
 Adduction .... 20°

PIP joint
 Flexion .... 100°
 Extension .... 0°

DIP joint
 Flexion .... 80°
 Extension .... 10°

Main muscle actions
Wrist flexion: flexor carpi radialis & flexor carpi ulnaris,
 palmaris longus, flexor digitorum superficialis & profundus
Wrist extension: extensor carpi radialis longus & brevis,
 extensor carpi ulnaris, extensor digitorum
Radial flexion (abduction): extensor carpi radialis longus/
 brevis, flexor carpi radialis
Ulnar flexion (adduction): flexor & extensor carpi ulnaris

Finger flexion: flexor digitorum profundus, superficialis,
 lumbricals
Thumb flexion: flexor pollicis longus & brevis
Finger extension: extensor digitorum
Thumb extension: extensor pollicis longus & brevis
Abduction: dorsal interossei, abductor pollicis longus & brevis
Adduction: palmar interossei, adductor pollicis

Normal joint end feels
Radiocarpal flex/ext: firm ligamentous
Radiocarpal add/abd: firm ligamentous

CMC thumb: elastic
MCP extension: elastic / ligamentous
MCP flexion: firm ligamentous
MCP thumb: firm ligamentous

PIP flexion: firm ligamentous / soft-tissue approximation
PIP extension: firm / ligamentous / elastic
DIP flexion: firm / ligamentous / elastic
DIP extension: firm / ligamentous / elastic

Ligament	Attaches (origin/insertion)	Function
Interosseous membrane	Shafts of radius & ulna	Resists separation of radius & ulna, helps control supination & pronation, attachment point for forearm muscles
Radial Collateral	Radius to scaphoid, trapezium	Supports lateral side of wrist (resists varus forces)
Ulnar Collateral	Ulna to pisiform, triquetrum	Supports medial side of wrist (resists valgus forces, support triangular fibrocartilage)
Dorsal Radiocarpal	Distal radius to scaphoid, lunate, triquetrum	Connects radius to carpals; supports posterior side of wrist
Palmar Intercarpal	Scaphoid to lunate, triquetrum	Holds carpals together
Palmar Plates	Across anterior joint of MP, PIP, DIP	Supports anterior MP, PIP, & DIP joint
Palmar Radiocarpal	Distal radius to scaphoid, lunate, triquetrum	Connects radius to carpals; supports anterior side of wrist
Transverse Carpal	Hamate & pisiform to scaphoid & trapezium	Fibrous sheath which contains carpal tunnel, important part of digital flexor pulley system
Intercarpal	First row of carpals to second row of carpals	Holds carpals together
Collateral	Phalanx to phalanx, sides of MCP, PIP & DIP joints	Supports sides of fingers; resists varus/valgus force

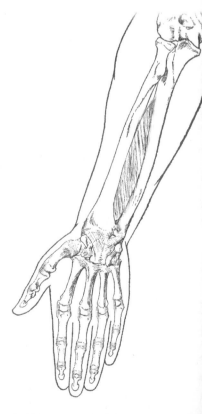

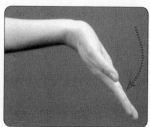

Compare bilaterally, start with unaffected side for PROM & RROM
Prior to assessing ROM the examiner should make an introduction statement:
"Try and move as far as possible, if any of the actions or movements are painful or uncomfortable
please let me know, do not do any action you feel will cause you further injury."

AROM

Flexion

Muscles Activated: flexor carpi radialis & flexor carpi ulnaris, palmaris longus, flexor digitorum superficialis & profundus

Tissue Stretched: extensor carpi radialis longus & brevis, extensor carpi ulnaris, extensor digitorum, anterior carpal ligaments

Tissue Compressed: carpal tunnel & median nerve

Extension

Muscles Activated: extensor carpi radialis longus & brevis, extensor carpi ulnaris, extensor digitorum

Tissue Stretched: flexor carpi radialis & flexor carpi ulnaris, palmaris longus, flexor digitorum superficialis & profundus

Tissue Compressed: posterior carpal ligaments

Abduction (radial flexion)

Muscles Activated: extensor carpi radialis longus/brevis, flexor carpi radialis

Tissue Stretched: flexor & extensor carpi ulnaris, medial carpal ligament, triangular fibrocartilage

Tissue Compressed: lateral carpal ligaments, scaphoid & trapezium

Adduction (ulnar flexion)

Muscles Activated: flexor & extensor carpi ulnaris

Tissue Stretched: extensor carpi radialis longus/brevis, flexor carpi radialis, lateral carpal ligaments

Tissue Compressed: medial carpal ligaments, hamate & triquetrum, TFC

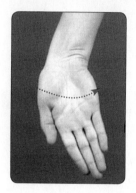

youtube: **Vizniak Wrist**

PROM

Flexion

Tissue Stretched: extensor carpi radialis longus & brevis, extensor carpi ulnaris, extensor digitorum, anterior carpal ligaments

Tissue Compressed: carpal tunnel & median nerve

Extension

Tissue Stretched: flexor carpi radialis & flexor carpi ulnaris, palmaris longus, flexor digitorum superficialis & profundus

Tissue Compressed: posterior carpal ligaments

Abduction (radial flexion)

Tissue Stretched: flexor & extensor carpi ulnaris, medial carpal ligament, triangular fibrocartilage

Tissue Compressed: lateral carpal ligaments, scaphoid & trapezium

Adduction (ulnar flexion)

Tissue Stretched: extensor carpi radialis longus/brevis, flexor carpi radialis, lateral carpal ligaments

Tissue Compressed: medial carpal ligaments, hamate & triquetrum, TFC (triangular fibrocartilage)

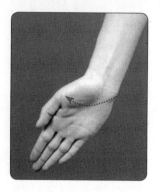
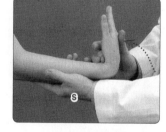

prohealthsys

Name: _____ %

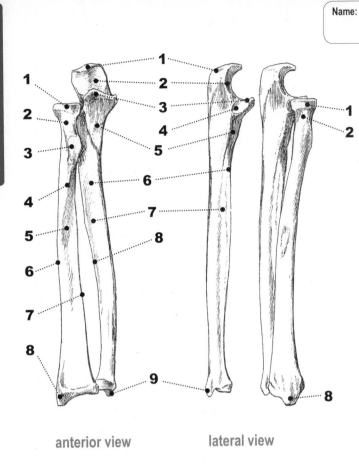

anterior view   lateral view

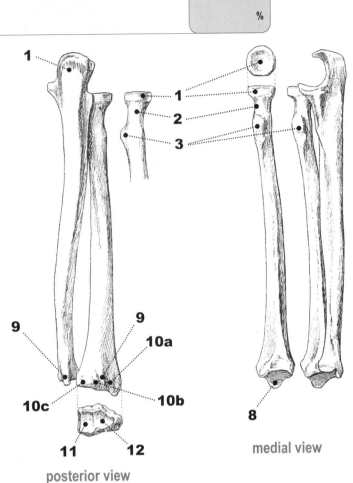

posterior view   medial view

Radius

1. _____

2. _____

3. _____

4. _____

5. _____

6. _____

7. _____

8. _____

9. _____

10. Grooves for tendons

   a. _____

   b. _____

   c. _____

11. _____

12. _____

Ulna

1. _____

2. _____

3. _____

4. _____

5. _____

6. _____

7. _____

8. _____

9. _____

prohealthsys.com   Vizniak & Richer

Name: _____ %

anterior view   lateral view   medial view   posterior view

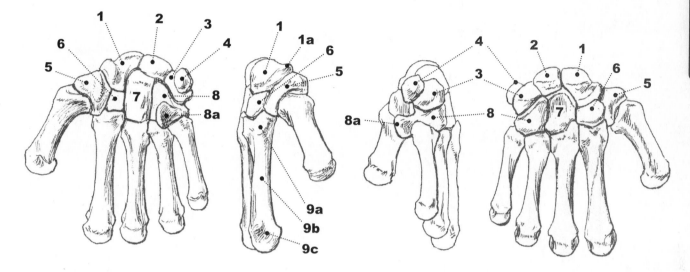

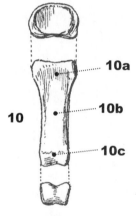

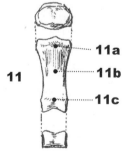

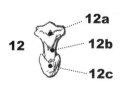

Carpals

1. _____

   a. _____

2. _____

3. _____

4. _____

5. _____

6. _____

7. _____

8. _____

   a. _____

9. 2nd Metacarpal

   a. _____

   b. _____

   c. _____

10. _____

   a. _____

   b. _____

   c. _____

11. _____

   a. _____

   b. _____

   c. _____

12. _____

   a. _____

   b. _____

   c. _____

Name: _____ %

anterior view

posterior view

3
1
4
5
2
6
7
13
8
14
9
12

15

10
18
17
19
11
18
21
16
17
22
20
19
21
23
24
22
24
23
25
26
27
28
29
30

carpal tunnel

17   18

21   19

1st metacarpal
(thumb)

5th metacarpal

Transverse carpal lig.
making carpal tunnel   24

1. _____	11. _____	21. _____
2. _____	12. _____	22. _____
3. _____	13. _____	23. _____
4. _____	14. _____	24. _____
5. _____	15. _____	25. _____
6. _____	16. _____	26. _____
7. _____	17. _____	27. _____
8. _____	18. _____	28. _____
9. _____	19. _____	29. _____
10. _____	20. _____	30. _____

Name:

%

anterior view

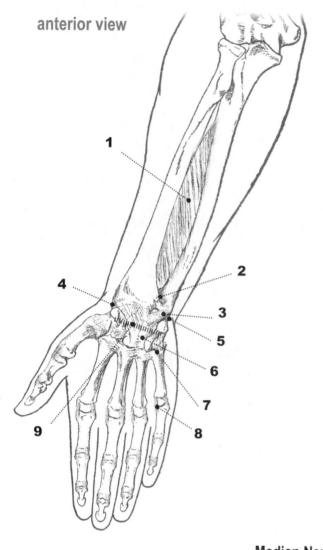

1
4
2
3
5
6
7
9
8

posterior view

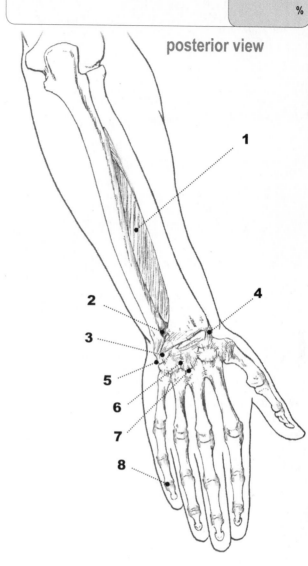

1
2
4
3
5
6
7
8

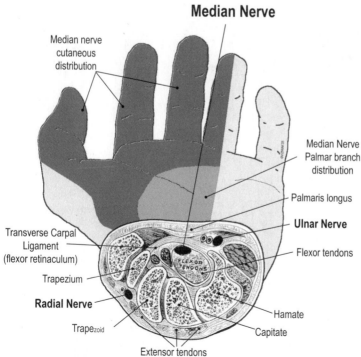

Median Nerve

Median nerve
cutaneous
distribution

Median Nerve
Palmar branch
distribution

Palmaris longus

Transverse Carpal
Ligament
(flexor retinaculum)

Ulnar Nerve

Flexor tendons

Trapezium

Radial Nerve

Hamate

Trapezoid

Capitate

Extensor tendons

1. _____

2. _____

3. _____

4. _____

5. _____

6. _____

7. _____

8. _____

9. _____

Name:

%

1. _____

2. _____

3. _____

4. _____

5. _____

6. _____

7. _____

8. _____

9. _____

10. _____

11. _____

12. _____

13. _____

14. _____

15. _____

16. _____

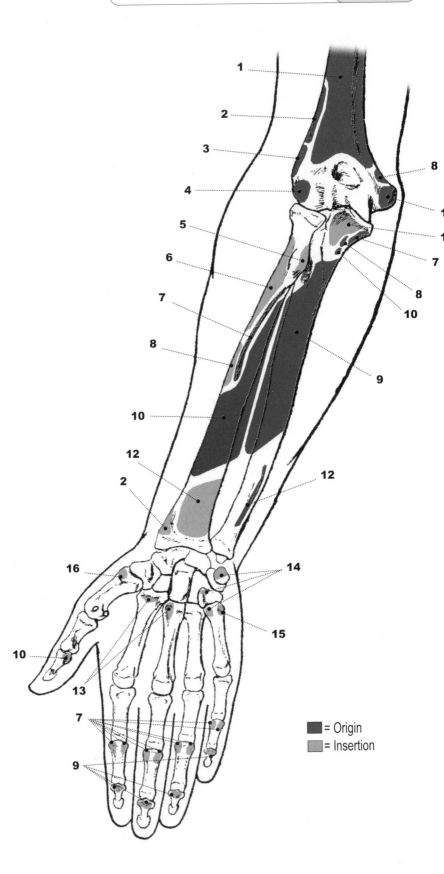

= Origin
= Insertion

prohealthsys

Start with labeling the muscles, then progress to naming
☐ actions, ☐ origins, ☐ insertions, ☐ nerves

Name:

%

1

2

3

4

5

6

6

7

8

10

9

11

Superficial

Deep

1. _____

2. _____

3. _____

4. _____

5. _____

6. _____

7. _____

8. _____

9. _____

10. _____

11. _____

prohealthsys

Name: _____ %

1. _____

2. _____

3. _____

4. _____

5. _____

6. _____

7. _____

8. _____

9. _____

10. _____

11. _____

12. _____

13. _____

14. _____

15. _____

16. _____

17. _____

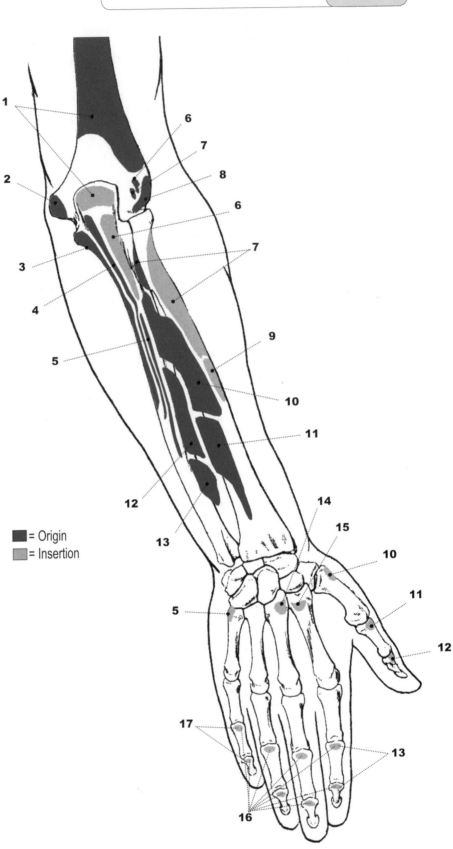

= Origin
= Insertion

Start with labeling the muscles, then progress to naming
□ actions, □ origins, □ insertions, □ nerves

Name:

%

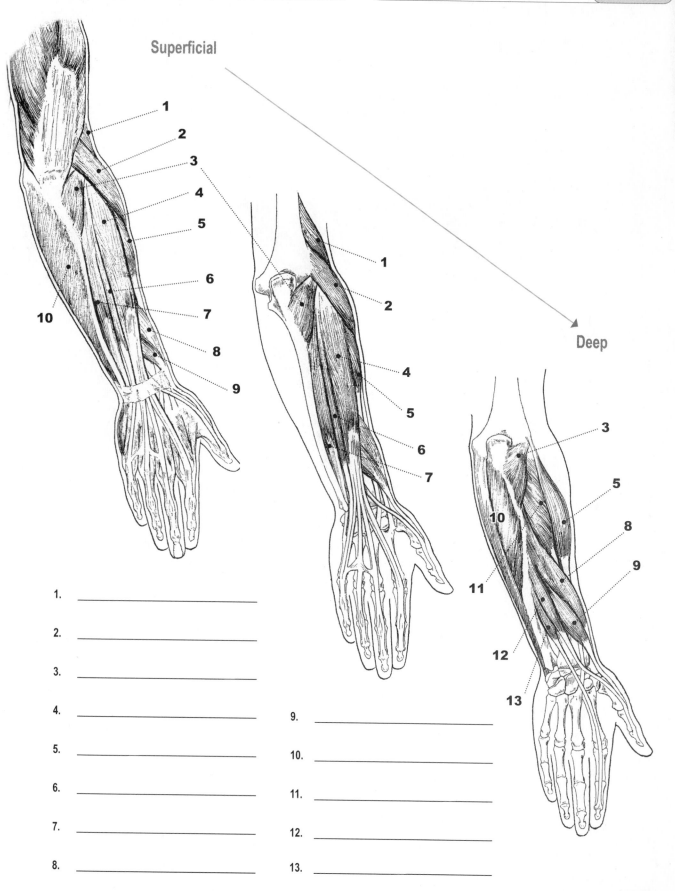

Superficial

Deep

1. _____

2. _____

3. _____

4. _____

5. _____

6. _____

7. _____

8. _____

9. _____

10. _____

11. _____

12. _____

13. _____

Name:

%

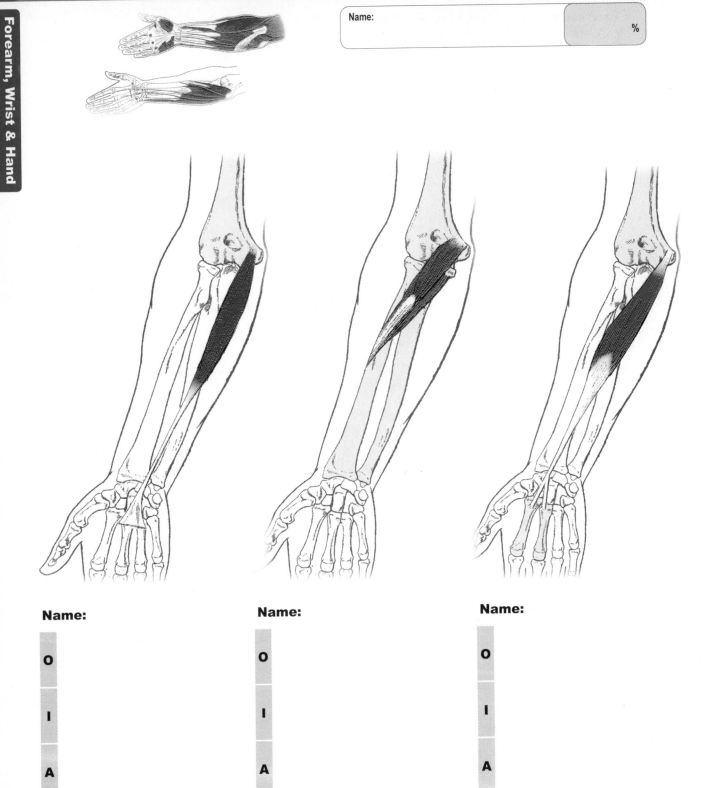

Name:

O

I

A

N

C

Name:

O

I

A

N

C

Name:

O

I

A

N

C

Name:

%

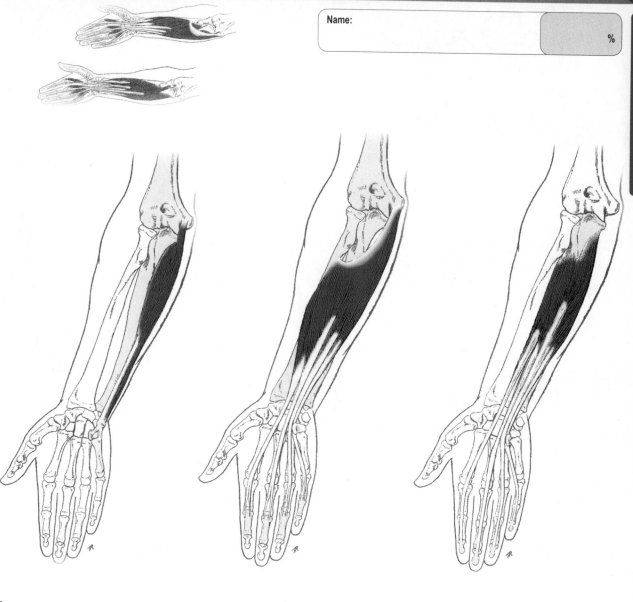

Name:

O

I

A

N

C

Name:

O

I

A

N

C

Name:

O

I

A

N

C

prohealthsys

prohealthsys

Name: _____ %

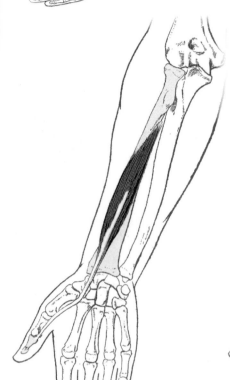

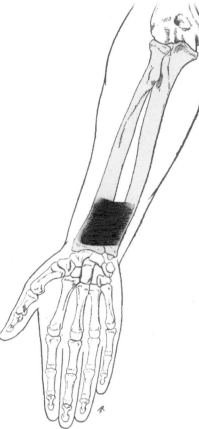

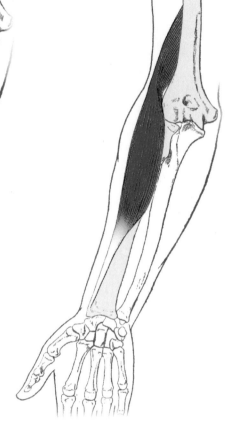

Name:

O

I

A

N

C

Name:

O

I

A

N

C

Name:

O

I

A

N

C

prohealthsys.com   Vizniak & Richer

Name:

%

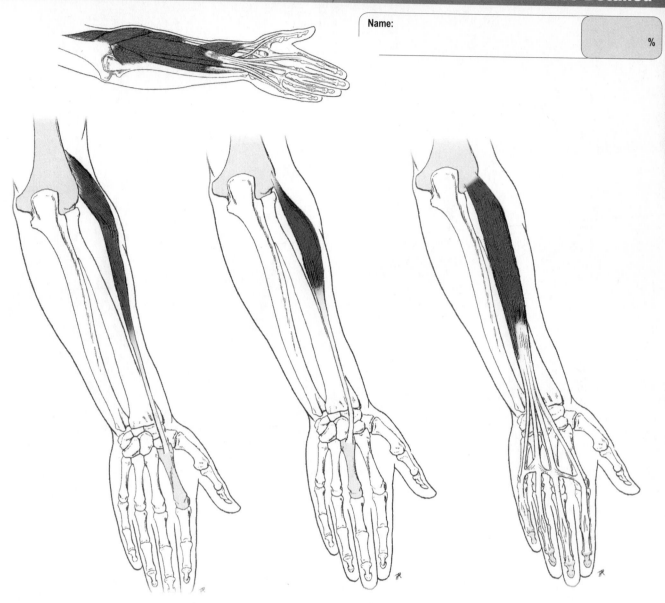

Name:

O

I

I

A

N

C

Name:

O

I

I

A

N

C

Name:

O

I

I

A

N

C

prohealthsys

Name: %

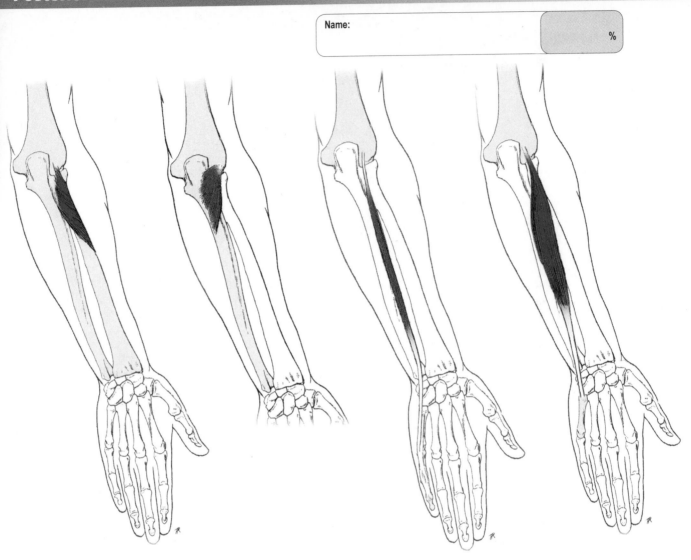

Name:

O

I

A

N

C

Name:

O

I

A

N

C

Name:

O

I

A

N

C

Name:

O

I

A

N

C

prohealthsys

Name: _____ %

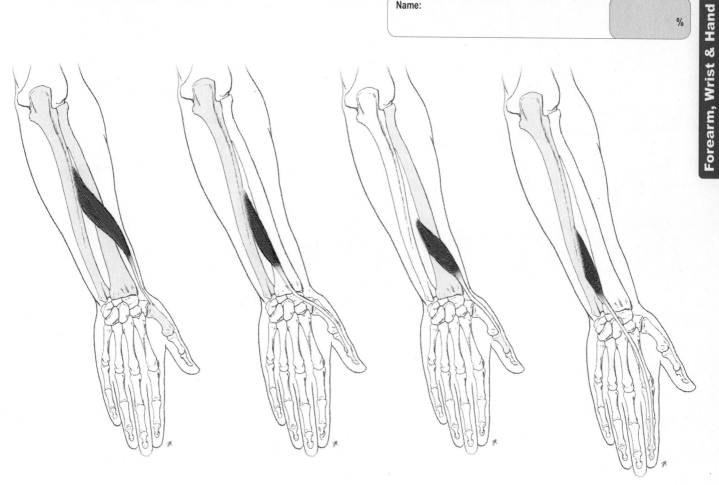

Name:

O
I
A
N
C

Name:

O
I
A
N
C

Name:

O
I
A
N
C

Name:

O
I
A
N
C

Anatomical snuff box

©VIZNIAK

Name: _____ %

Name:

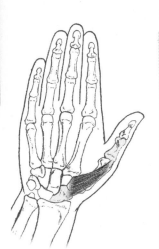

O

I

A

N

C

Name:

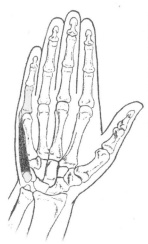

O

I

A

N

C

Name:

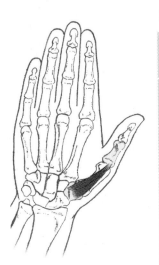

O

I

A

N

C

Name:

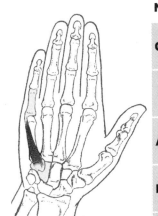

O

I

A

N

C

Name:

O

I

A

N

C

Name:

O

I

A

N

C

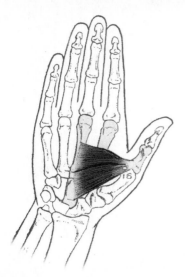

Name:

%

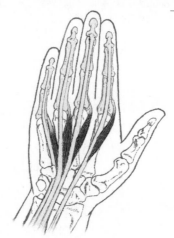

Name:

O
I
A
N
C

Name:

O
I
A
N
C

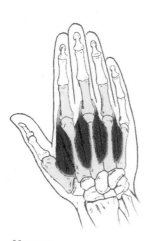

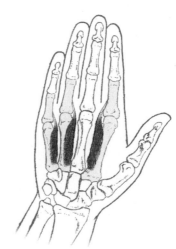

Name:

O
I
A
N
C

Name:

O
I
A
N
C

prohealthsys

Start with labeling the bones, then progress to drawing
☐ muscles, ☐ ligaments, ☐ Os & Is, ☐ nerves, ☐ vessels

Name:

%

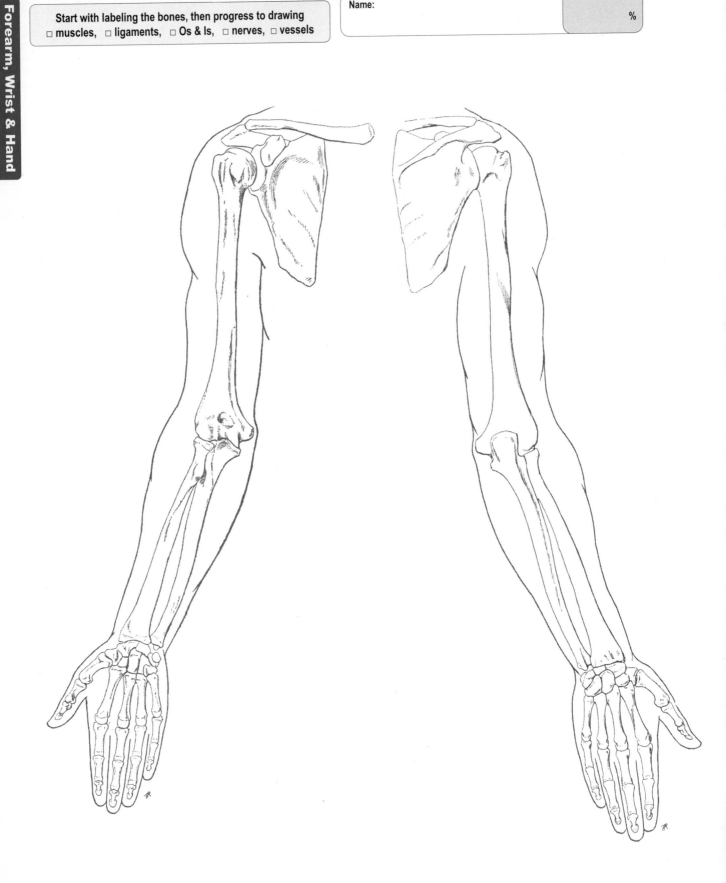

prohealthsys

Start with labeling the structures, then progress to
□ actions, □ ligaments, □ Os & Is, □ nerves, □ vessels

Name:

%

Page 116 Radius & Ulna

Radius
1. Head
2. Neck
3. Radial tuberosity
4. Oblique line
5. Anterior surface
6. Anterior border
7. Interosseous border
8. Styloid process of radius
9. Dorsal (Lister's)tubercle
10. Grooves for tendons
    a. Extensor carpi radialis longus & brevis
    b. Extensor pollicis longus
    c. Extensor digitorum & extensor indicis
11. Articular surface for lunate
12. Articular surface for scaphoid

Ulna
1. Olecranon
2. Trochlear notch
3. Coronoid process
4. Radial notch
5. Ulnar tuberosity
6. Anterior surface
7. Anterior border
8. Interosseous border
9. Styloid process of ulna

Page 117 Wrist & Hand Bones

Carpals
1. Scaphoid
   a. Tubercle of Scaphoid
2. Lunate
3. Triquetrum
4. Pisiform
5. Trapezium
6. Trapezoid
7. Capitate
8. Hamate
   a. Hook of Hamate
9. 2nd Metacarpal
   a. Base
   b. Shaft
   c. Head
10. 2nd proximal phalynx
    a. Base
    b. Shaft
    c. Head
11. 2nd middle phalynx
    a. Base
    b. Shaft
    c. Head
12. 2nd distal phalynx
    a. Base
    b. Shaft
    c. Ungual tuberosity

Page 118 Forearm

Humerus
1. Medial supracondylar ridge
2. Medial epicondyle
3. Lateral supracondylar ridge
4. Lateral epicondyle

Radius
5. Head
6. Neck
7. Radial / bicipital tuberosity
8. Oblique line
9. Interosseous border
10. Styloid process
11. not on drawing

Ulna
12. Olecranon
13. Coronoid process
14. Ulnar tuberosity
15. Posterior border
16. Styloid process

Carpals
17. Scaphoid
18. Lunate
19. Triquetrum
20. Pisiform
21. Trapezium
22. Trapezoid
23. Capitate
24. Hamate

Metacarpals
25. Base
26. Body
27. Head

Phalanges
28. Proximal
29. Middle
30. Distal

Page 119 Forearm Ligaments
1. Interosseous membrane
2. Distal radioulnar ligament
3. Triangular fibrocartilage (TFC)
4. Radial collateral ligament
5. Ulnar collateral ligament
6. Intercarpal ligaments
7. Carpometacarpal ligaments
8. Phalangeal collateral ligaments
9. Transverse carpal ligament (flexor retinaculum)

Page 120, Anterior Forearm Attachments
1. Brachialis
2. Brachioradialis
3. Extensor carpi radialis longus
4. Common extensor tendon*
5. Biceps brachii
6. Supinator
7. Flexor digitorum superficialis
8. Pronator teres
9. Flexor digitorum profundus
10. Flexor pollicis longus
11. Common flexor tendon*
12. Pronator quadratus
13. Flexor carpi radialis
14. Flexor carpi ulnaris
15. Extensor carpi ulnaris
16. Abductor pollicis longus

Page 121 Anterior Forearm Muscles
1. Brachioradialis
2. Pronator teres (superficial head)
3. Flexor carpi radialis
4. Palmaris longus
5. Flexor carpi ulnaris
6. Flexor digitorum superficialis
7. Flexor digitorum profundus
8. Flexor pollicis longus
9. Pronator teres (deep head)
10. Supinator
11. Pronator quadratus

Page 122, Posterior Forearm Attachments
1. Triceps brachii
2. Common flexor tendon*
3. Flexor digitorum profundus
4. Flexor carpi ulnaris (ulnar head)
5. Extensor carpi ulnaris
6. Anconeus
7. Supinator
8. Common extensor tendon*
9. Pronator teres
10. Abductor pollicis longus
11. Extensor pollicis brevis
12. Extensor pollicis longus
13. Extensor indicis
14. Extensor carpi radialis brevis
15. Extensor carpi radialis longus
16. Extensor digitorum
17. Extensor digiti minimi

Page 123, Posterior Forearm Muscles
1. Brachioradialis
2. Extensor carpi radialis longus
3. Anconeus
4. Extensor digitorum
5. Extensor carpi radialis brevis
6. Extensor digiti minimi
7. Extensor carpi ulnaris
8. Abductor pollicis longus
9. Extensor pollicis brevis
10. Flexor carpi ulnaris
11. Supinator
12. Extensor pollicis longus
    Extensor indicis

> For specific muscle information use the Muscle Manual Text, Muscle Tables Chapter or on-line resources

prohealthsys.com   Vizniak & Richer

Learning Objectives

After completing this chapter, students will be able to:

1. Identify and palpate structures of the region (give a list of structures below their palpating hand)

2. Describe the structure, support, and movements of the hip and knee

3. Assess AROM, PROM & RROM of the hip & knee

4. Describe biomechanics & kinesiology of the region, including the screw home mechanism

5. Perform detailed muscle testing and palpation

6. Discuss anatomical variation, ADLs and common injuries of the body region

7. Develop a set of appropriate strength and flexibility exercises for the body region

Hip & Knee Kinematics 136
    AROM.. 137
    PROM.. 138
    RROM.. 139
Femur & Patella 141
Hip & Thigh Bones 142
SI, Hip & Knee Ligaments 143
Hip & Knee Joints 144
Hip Origins & Insertions 145
Gluteal Muscles 146
Posterior Thigh Muscles 147
Medial Thigh Muscles 148
Anterior Thigh Muscles 149
Gluteal Muscles 150
Answers... 158

Hip, Thigh & Knee

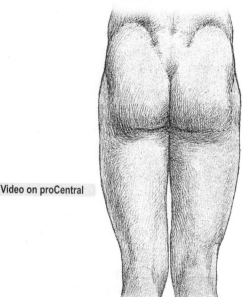
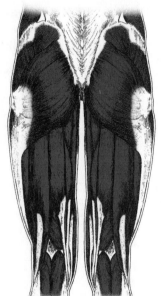
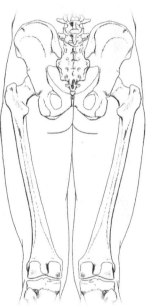

Video on proCentral

Palpation Checklist

- ☐ TFL/ Iliotibial band (ITB)
- ☐ SI joint
- ☐ Sacrotub./spinous lig.
- ☐ Greater trochanter
- ☐ Ischial tuberosity
- ☐ L-spine/sacrum
- ☐ Gluteus max./med.
- ☐ Piriformis
- ☐ Sciatic nerve
- ☐ Hamstrings

- ☐ Popliteal fossa
- ☐ Gastrocnemius heads
- ☐ ASIS/iliac crest
- ☐ Iliopsoas
- ☐ Pubic symphysis
- ☐ Inguinal lig./nodes
- ☐ Femoral triangle & artery
- ☐ Adductor muscles
- ☐ Abdomen
- ☐ Quadriceps

- ☐ Patella (facets, bursa)
- ☐ Patellar ligament
- ☐ Tibial tuberosity
- ☐ Pes anserine
- ☐ Med./lat. knee joint/meniscus
- ☐ Med./lat. femoral condyle
- ☐ Medial & lateral collateral ligs.
- ☐ . . . .
- ☐ . . . .
- ☐ . . . .

Hip Joint type: synovial
- Symphysis (pubic symphysis)
- Ball & socket (acetabulofemoral)

Articular surfaces
- **Acetabulofemoral:** *convex* (head of femur) on *concave* (acetabulum)

Hip active range of motion

Flexion (straight leg)	90°
Flexion (bent knee)	110-120°
Extension	10-15°
Abduction	30-50°
Adduction	30°
Medial (internal) rotation	30-40°
Lateral (external) rotation	40-60°

Main muscle actions
- **Flexion:** iliopsoas, rectus femoris, sartorius
- **Extension:** gluteus maximus, hamstrings
- **Abduction:** gluteus medius & minimus, tensor fasciae latae
- **Adduction:** adductor magnus, gracilis, adductor longus & brevis, pectineus
- **Internal rotation:** tensor fasciae latae, gluteus medius & minimus
- **External rotation:** piriformis, quadratus femoris, superior & inferior gemellus, obturator internus & externus

Resting position
- **Acetabulofemoral:** 30° abduction, 30° flexion & slight external rotation

Close packed position
- **Acetabulofemoral:** full extension, abduction & internal rotation

Hip arthrokinematics
- **Flexion:** mainly pivots (femur may roll superior & glides inferior on acetabulum)
- **Extension:** mainly pivots (femur may roll inferior & glides superior on acetabulum)
- **Abduction:** femur rolls lateral/superior & glides inferior on acetabulum
- **Adduction:** femur rolls medial/inferior & glides superior on acetabulum
- **Internal rotation:** femur rolls medial & glides lateral on acetabulum
- **External rotation:** femur rolls lateral & glides medial on acetabulum

Hip joint forces
- **Standing:** 0.3x body weight
- **Standing one leg:** 2.5x body weight
- **Walking:** 3x body weight
- **Running:** > 4.5x body weight

"Q" angle

- A line drawn from the anterior superior iliac spine through the center of the patella & a line drawn through the center of the patella to the center of the tibial tuberosity

- The term 'Q' is used to represent the main pull of the quadriceps muscle group

- The "Q" angle is greater in women as the hips are set wider apart

- **Women:** should be less than 22° with the knee extended and less than 9° with the knee in 90° of flexion

- **Men:** should be less than 18° with the knee extended and less than 8° with the knee in 90° of flexion

- A large "Q" angle may predispose to osteoarthrosis of the knee, patellar dislocation & may contribute to over pronation

Q-angle

Knee Joint type: synovial
- Bicondylar modified hinge (tibiofemoral) - largest & most complex single joint in body; biaxial
- Gliding (patellofemoral)

Articular surfaces
- **Tibiofemoral:** *flat* (tibial plateau) *on convex* (femoral condyles); menisci create concavity

Active range of motion

Flexion	135°
Extension	0-15°
Medial rotation*	20-30°
Lateral rotation*	30-40° - * knee must be flexed 90° to allow rotation

Main muscle actions
- **Flexion:** semitendinosus, semimembranosus, biceps femoris (hamstrings), sartorius
- **Extension:** vastus medialis, vastus lateralis, vastus intermedius, rectus femoris (quadriceps)
- **Internal rotation** (tibia): popliteus with pes anserine muscles
- **External rotation** (tibia): biceps femoris

Resting position
- **Tibiofemoral:** 25° flexion
- **Patellofemoral:** full extension (straight leg)

Close packed position
- **Tibiofemoral:** full extension & external tibial rotation
- **Patellofemoral:** full flexion

Open kinetic chain
- **Tibiofemoral:**
  Flexion: tibia rolls & glides posterior on femur
  Extension: tibia rolls & glides anterior on femur
- **Patellofemoral:**
  Flexion: inferior patellar glide on femur
  Extension: superior patellar glide on femur

Closed kinetic chain
- **Tibiofemoral:**
  Flexion: femur rolls posterior & glides anterior on tibia (squatting)
  Extension: femur rolls anterior & glides posterior on tibia (moving from seated to standing)

Osteokinematics
- Patellar surface of femur condyles begin to contact patella at 20° flexion; then progress superior to 90° & medial/lateral at 135° of flexion
- Medial meniscus is attached to medial collateral ligament & semimembranosus muscle
- Lateral meniscus is attached to posterior cruciate ligament & popliteus muscle (more mobile)

Genu valgum & varum

- **Genu valgum:** Q > 22° (women), 18° (men)

  - Also known as "knocked knees"

- **Genu varum:** Q angle < 0° (distal tibia points medially) - also known as "bow legs"

- **Genu recurvatum:** hyperextension of knee > -5°

Genu valgum   Genu varum

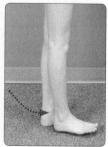
Compare bilaterally; prior to ROM examiner should make an introduction statement:
"Try and move as far as possible, if any of the actions or movements are painful or uncomfortable please let me know, do not do any action you feel will cause you further injury."

Flexion

Muscles Activated: iliopsoas, rectus femoris, sartorius

Tissue Stretched: gluteus maximus, hamstrings , sciatic nerve

Tissue Compressed: anterior hip muscles, anterior joint capsule, inguinal ligament, femoral artery, femoral nerve

Extension

Muscles Activated: gluteus maximus, hamstrings

Tissue Stretched: iliopsoas, rectus femoris, sartorius, anterior iliofemoral ligament & joint capsule, femoral nerve

Tissue Compressed: posterior hip muscles, posterior joint capsule

Abduction

Muscles Activated: gluteus medius & minimus, tensor fasciae latae

Tissue Stretched: adductor magnus, gracilis, adductor longus & brevis, medial hip joint capsule

Tissue Compressed: lateral hip structures (joint capsule, lateral acetabular labrum)

Adduction

Muscles Activated: adductor magnus, gracilis, adductor l. & b.

Tissue Stretched: gluteus medius & minimus, tensor fasciae latae, iliotibial band

Tissue Compressed: medial hip structures

Lateral Rotation

Muscles Activated: piriformis, quadratus femoris, superior & inferior gemellus, obturator internus & externus

Tissue Stretched: tensor fasciae latae, gluteus medius & minimus, anterior joint capsule

Tissue Compressed: posterior hip structures

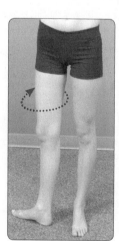

Medial Rotation

Muscles Activated: tensor fasciae latae, gluteus medius & minimus

Tissue Stretched: piriformis, quadratus femoris, superior & inferior gemellus, obturator internus & externus, posterior joint capsule

Tissue Compressed: anterior joint capsule

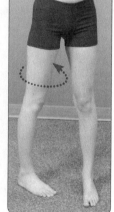

Knee Flexion

Muscles Activated: semitendinosus, semimembranosus, biceps femoris (hamstrings), popliteus, sartorius

Tissue Stretched: quadriceps, femoral nerve

Tissue Compressed: popliteal fossa structure (popliteal artery, tibial nerve). patella compressed into femoral condyles

Knee AROM

knee must be flexed 90° to allow rotation (~5° per side)

Knee Extension

Muscles Activated: vastus medialis, vastus lateralis, vastus intermedius rectus femoris (quadriceps)

Tissue Stretched: semitendinosus, semimembranosus, biceps femoris (hamstrings), popliteus, gastrocnemius, sciatic nerve

Tissue Compressed: anterior knee structures

Hip, Thigh & Knee

Compare bilaterally; if possible palpate joint during PROM & use the shortest lever possible; apply over pressure at end ROM; introduction statement:
"If any of the actions or movements are painful or uncomfortable please let me know."

Flexion

Tissue Stretched: gluteus maximus, hamstrings , sciatic nerve

Tissue Compressed: anterior hip muscles, anterior joint capsule, inguinal ligament, femoral artery, femoral nerve

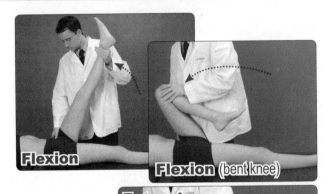

Flexion

Flexion (bent knee)

Extension

Tissue Stretched: iliopsoas, rectus femoris, sartorius, anterior iliofemoral ligament & joint capsule, femoral nerve

Tissue Compressed: posterior hip muscles, posterior joint capsule

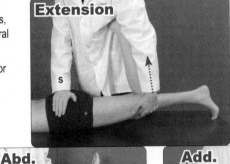

Extension

Abduction

Tissue Stretched: adductor magnus, gracilis, adductor longus & brevis, medial hip joint capsule

Tissue Compressed: lateral hip structures (joint capsule, lateral acetabular labrum)

Adduction

Tissue Stretched: gluteus medius & minimus, tensor fasciae latae, iliotibial band

Tissue Compressed: medial hip structures

Abd.

Add.

Medial Rotation

Tissue Stretched: piriformis, quadratus femoris, superior & inferior gemellus, obturator internus & externus, posterior joint capsule

Tissue Compressed: anterior capsule

Lateral Rotation

Tissue Stretched: tensor fasciae latae, gluteus medius & minimus, anterior joint capsule

Med. Rotation

Lat. Rotation

Flexion

Tissue Stretched: quadriceps, femoral nerve (if done with hip straight)

Tissue Compressed: popliteal fossa structure (popliteal artery, tibial nerve). patella compressed into femoral condyles

Knee PROM

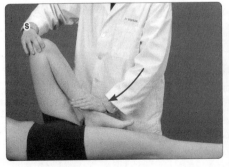
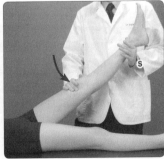

Extension

Tissue Stretched: semitendinosus, semimembranosus, biceps femoris (hamstrings), popliteus, gastrocnemius, sciatic nerve

Tissue Compressed: anterior knee structures

Compare bilaterally; patient instructions for assessing general muscle strength:
"I am going to try and move you in _____ direction, don't let me do it" or "resist my force"

Resisted Flexion
Muscles Activated: iliopsoas, rectus femoris, sartorius, pectineus

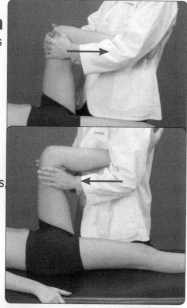

youtube: **Vizniak Hip**

Extension
Muscles Activated: gluteus maximus, hamstrings

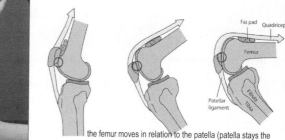

the femur moves in relation to the patella (patella stays the same distance from the tibia due to the patellar ligament)

Abduction
Muscles Activated: gluteus medius & minimus, tensor fasciae latae

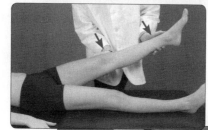

Adduction
Muscles Activated: adductor magnus, gracilis, adductor longus & brevis

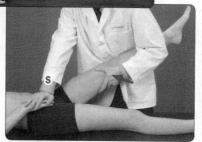

Adduction

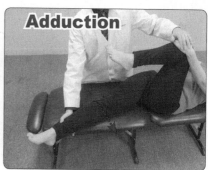

Lateral Rotation
Muscles Activated: piriformis, quadratus femoris, superior & inferior gemellus, obturator internus & externus

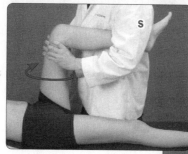

Medial Rotation
Muscles Activated: tensor fasciae latae, gluteus medius & minimus

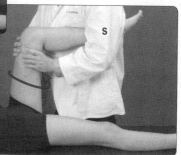

Hip, Thigh & Knee

Name: _____ %

1. _____
2. _____
3. _____
4. _____
5. _____
6. _____
7. _____
8. _____
9. _____
10. _____
11. _____
12. _____
13. _____
14. _____
15. _____
16. _____
17. _____
18. _____
19. _____
20. _____
21. _____
22. _____
23. _____

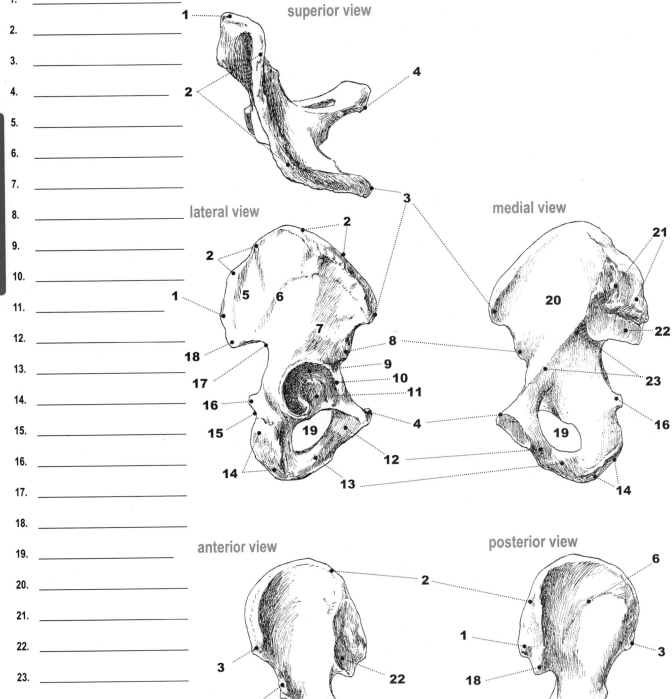

superior view

lateral view

medial view

anterior view

posterior view

Name: _____ %

anterior view

2
3
1
4
5
6
7
8

posterior view

19
18
17
16
15
14a
14b
13
12
10
9
11
6
7

lateral view

3
6
7

medial view

19
16
12
10
9

1. _____
2. _____
3. _____
4. _____
5. _____
6. _____
7. _____
8. _____

9. _____
10. _____
11. _____
12. _____
13. _____
14. _____
   a. _____
   b. _____

15. _____
16. _____
17. _____
18. _____
19. _____

Patella

lateral view

anterior view

medial view

posterior view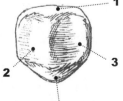

1
2
3
4

1. _____
2. _____
3. _____
4. _____

Name: _____ %

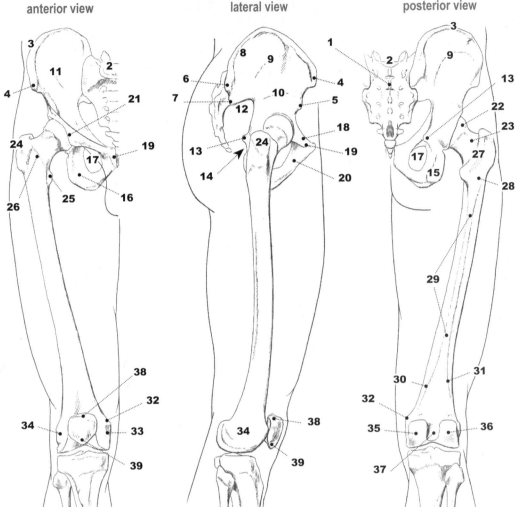

anterior view   lateral view   posterior view

Sacrum

1. _____

2. _____

Os Coxae (ilium, ischium & pubis)

3. _____

4. _____

5. _____

6. _____

7. _____

8. _____

9. _____

10. _____

11. _____

12. _____

13. _____

14. _____

15. _____

16. _____

17. _____

18. _____

19. _____

20. _____

21. _____

Femur

22. _____

23. _____

24. _____

25. _____

26. _____

27. _____

28. _____

29. _____

30. _____

31. _____

32. _____

33. _____

34. _____

35. _____

36. _____

37. _____

Patella

38. _____

39. _____

Hip, Thigh & Knee

Name: _____ %

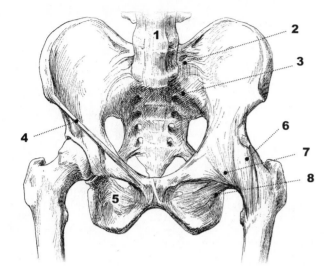

anterior view

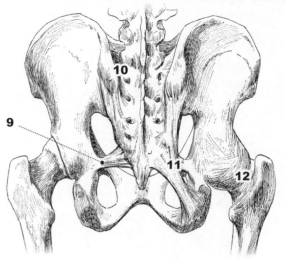

Pelvis & Hip

1. _____

2. _____

3. _____

4. _____

5. _____

6. _____

7. _____

8. _____

9. _____

10. _____

11. _____

12. _____

13. _____

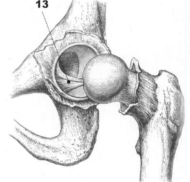

Knee

anterior view   posterior view

1. _____

2. _____

3. _____

4. _____

5. _____

6. _____

7. _____

8. _____

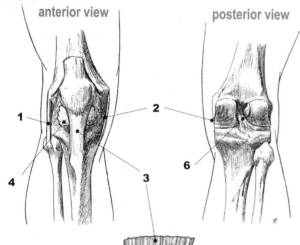

superior view

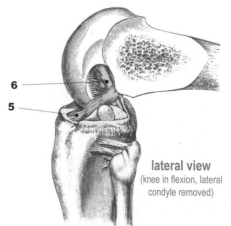

lateral view
(knee in flexion, lateral condyle removed)

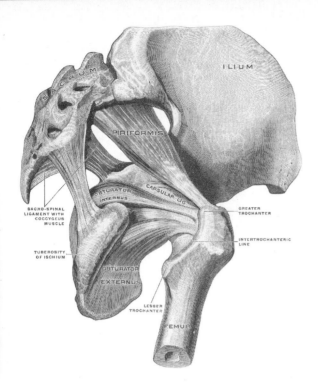

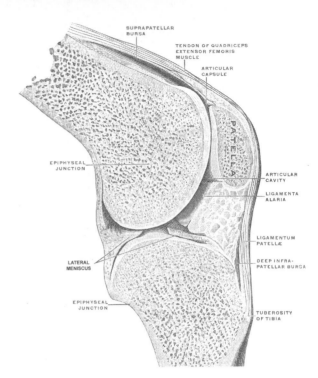

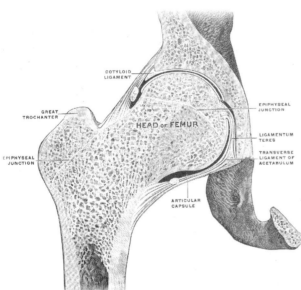

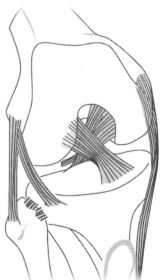

Ligament	Attaches (origin/insertion)	Function
Iliofemoral	AIIS to intertrochanteric line of femur	Supports anterior hip; resists in movements of extension, internal rotation, external rotation
Ischiofemoral	Posterior acetabulum to iliofemoral ligament	Resists adduction & internal rotation
Pubofemoral	Pubic part of acetabulum, superior rami to intertrochanteric line	Resists in movements of abduction & external rotation
Ligament teres	Acetabular notch & transverse ligament to pit on head of femur	Transmits vessels to head of femur; may resist distraction forces of joint
Obturator Membrane	Covers obturator foramen	Attachment point of obturator internus & externus

Ligament	Attaches (origin/insertion)	Function
Patellar (infrapatellar tend.)	Interior patella to tibial tuberosity	Transmits force from quadriceps to tibia
Anterior Cruciate	Anterior intercondylar area of tibia to medial surface of lateral femoral condyle	Resists anterior tibial translation & extension, internal rotation, flexion (tight in full extension)
Posterior cruciate	Posterior tibial spine to inner lateral femoral condyle	Resists posterior tibial movement, movements flexion & rotation (tight in full extension)
Medial (tibial) collateral	Medial epicondyle of femur to medial condyle of tibia & medial meniscus	Resists valgus forces (tight in extension) & internal/external rotation (direct attachment medial meniscus)
Lateral (fibular) collateral	Lateral epicondyle of femur to head of fibula	Resists varus forces (tight in extension)
Anterolateral lig (ALL)[1]	Lateral femur epicondyle to proximal tibia (attaches to lateral meniscus)	Supports anterolateral stability of the knee (m influence meniscus mobility)
Proximal Tib-Fib	Tibia to fibular head	Holds fibula against tibia, resists superior, ant and posterior fibular translation (heel strike

1.   Steven Claes, Evie Vereecke, Michael Maes, Jan Victor, Peter Verdonk, Johan Bellemans. Anatomy of the anterolateral ligament of the knee. Journal of Anatomy, 2013; 223 (4): 321 DOI: 10.1111/jo

Coronary ligaments hold the meniscus to the tibia and **transverse ligaments** connect the menisci anteriorly

Name: _____ %

anterior view

posterior view

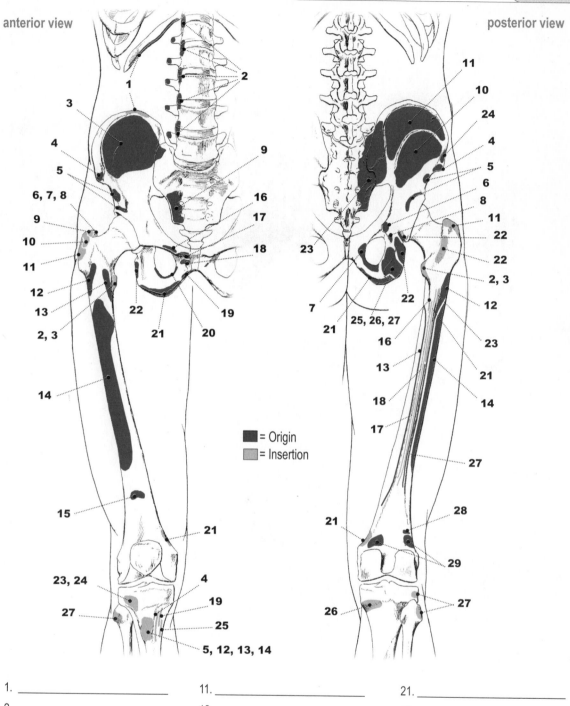

= Origin
= Insertion

1. _____
2. _____
3. _____
4. _____
5. _____
6. _____
7. _____
8. _____
9. _____
10. _____

11. _____
12. _____
13. _____
14. _____
15. _____
16. _____
17. _____
18. _____
19. _____
20. _____

21. _____
22. _____
23. _____
24. _____
25. _____
26. _____
27. _____
28. _____
29. _____

Start with labeling the muscles, then progress to naming
☐ actions, ☐ origins, ☐ insertions, ☐ nerves

Name:

%

Hip, Thigh & Knee

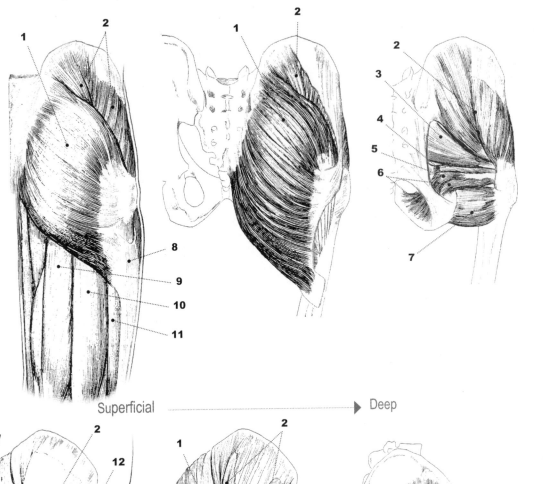

Superficial ----------► Deep

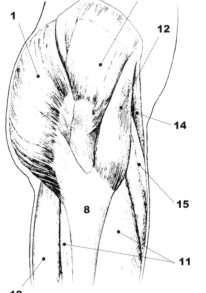

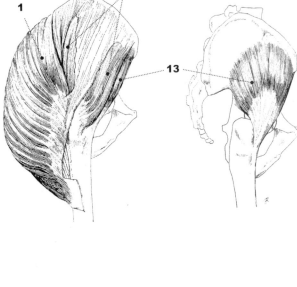

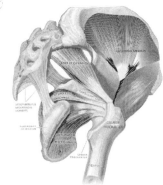

1. _____
2. _____
3. _____
4. _____
5. _____

6. _____
7. _____
8. _____
9. _____
10. _____

11. _____
12. _____
13. _____
14. _____
15. _____

prohealthsys

Start with labeling the muscles, then progress to naming
□ actions, □ origins, □ insertions, □ nerves

Name:

%

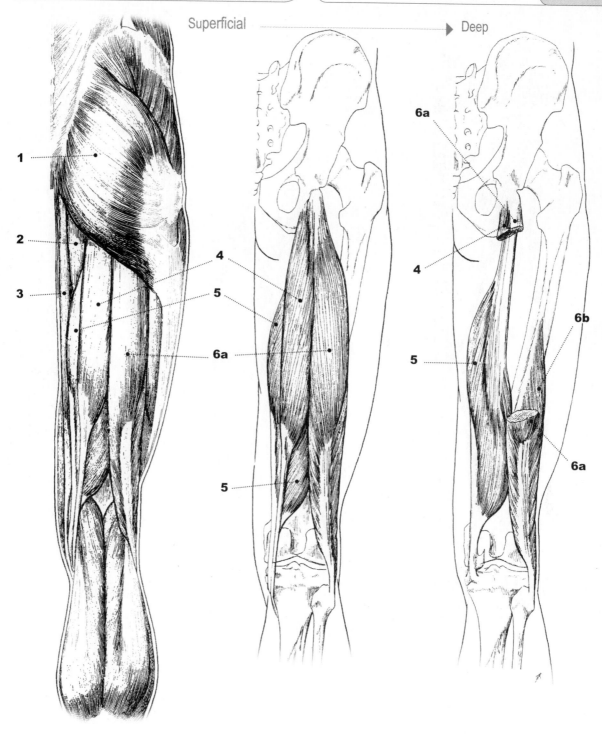

Superficial

Deep

1

2

3

4

5

6a

6a

4

5

5

6a

5

6b

6a

1. _____

2. _____

3. _____

4. _____

5. _____

6. _____

  a. _____

  b. _____

prohealthsys

Start with labeling the muscles, then progress to naming
☐ actions, ☐ origins, ☐ insertions, ☐ nerves

Name: _____ %

Hip, Thigh & Knee

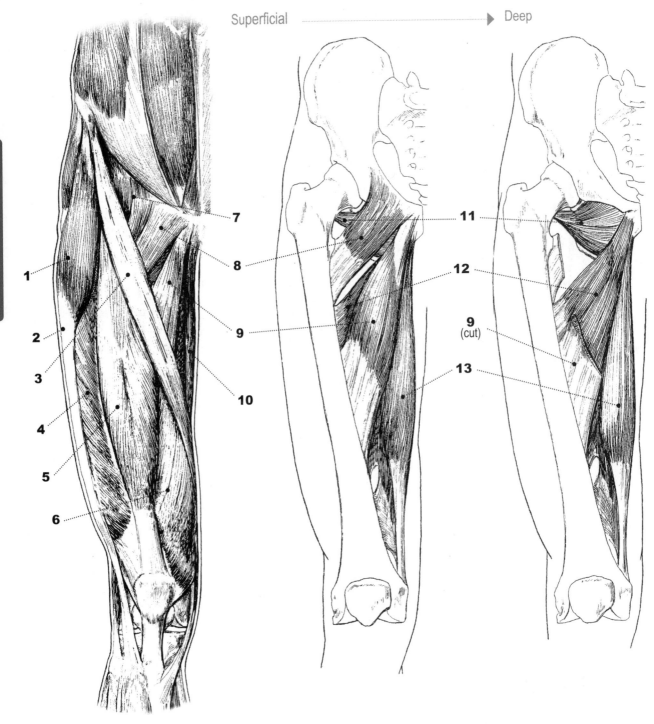

Superficial ➔ Deep

1.
2.
3.
4.
5.
6.
7.
8.
9.
10.
11.
12
9 (cut)
13

1. _____
2. _____
3. _____
4. _____
5. _____

6. _____
7. _____
8. _____
9. _____
10. _____

11. _____
12. _____
13. _____

Start with labeling the muscles, then progress to naming
☐ actions, ☐ origins, ☐ insertions, ☐ nerves

Name:

%

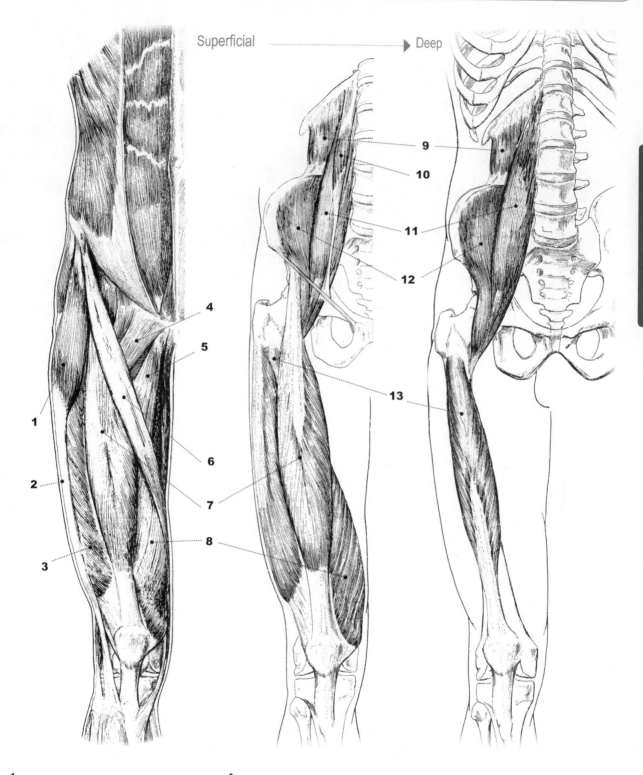

Superficial → Deep

1. _____
2. _____
3. _____
4. _____
5. _____

6. _____
7. _____
8. _____
9. _____
10. _____

11. _____
12. _____
13. _____

prohealthsys

Name: _____ %

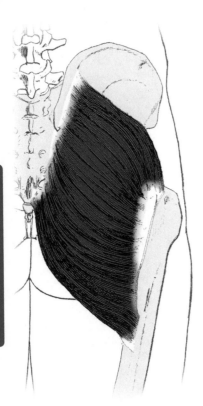
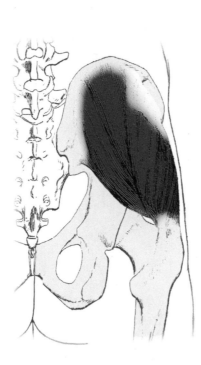
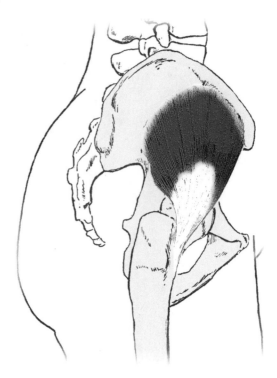

Name:

O

I

A

C

Name:

O

I

A

C

Name:

O

I

A

C

prohealthsys

Name:

%

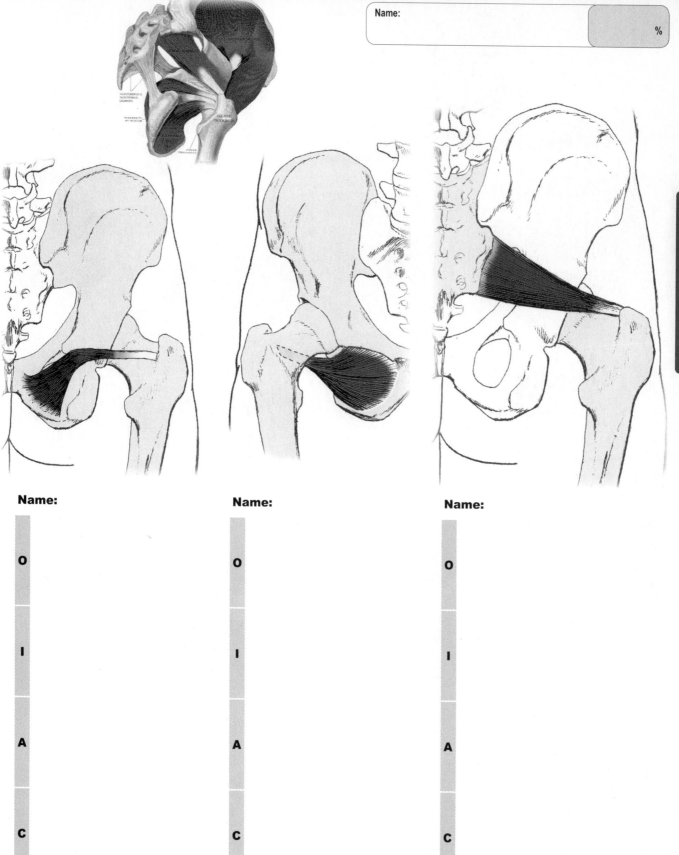

Hip, Thigh & Knee

Name:

O

I

A

C

Name:

O

I

A

C

Name:

O

I

A

C

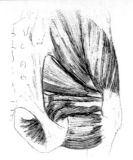

Name: _____ %

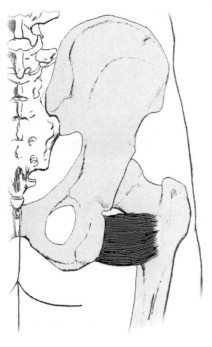

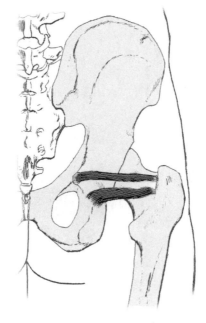

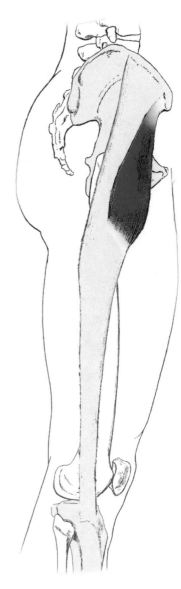

Name:

O

I

A

C

Name:

O

I

A

C

Name:

O

I

A

C

prohealthsys.com   Vizniak & Richer

Name: _____ %

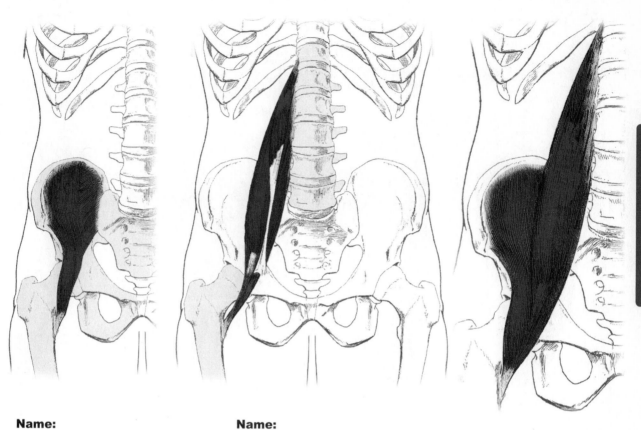

Hip, Thigh & Knee

Name: _____

O

I

A

C

Name: _____

O

I

A

C

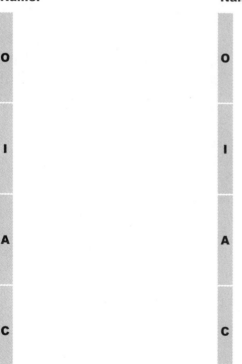

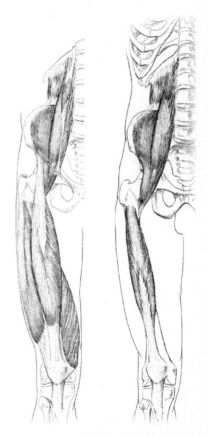

Name: _____ %

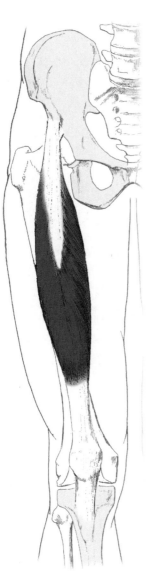
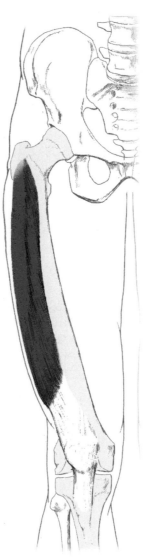
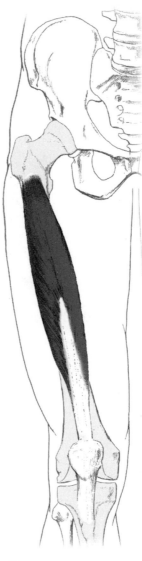

Name:

O

I

A

C

Name:

O

I

A

C

Name:

O

I

A

C

Name:

O

I

A

C

Name:

_____ %

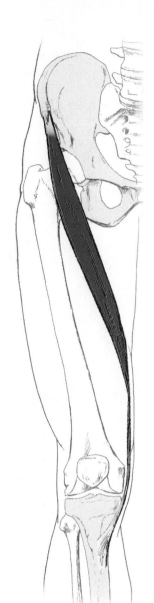
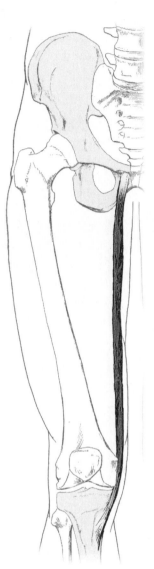
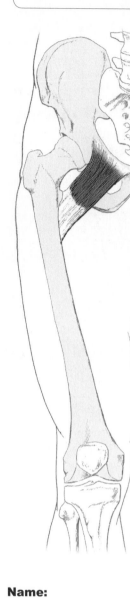
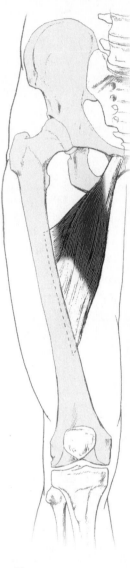

Name:

O

I

A

C

Name:

O

I

A

C

Name:

O

I

A

C

Name:

O

I

A

C

Name: _____ %

Hip, Thigh & Knee

Name:

O	
I	
A	
C	

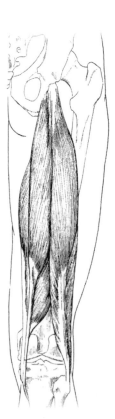
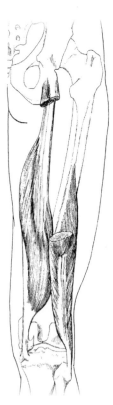

Hamstring Strain

Name:

%

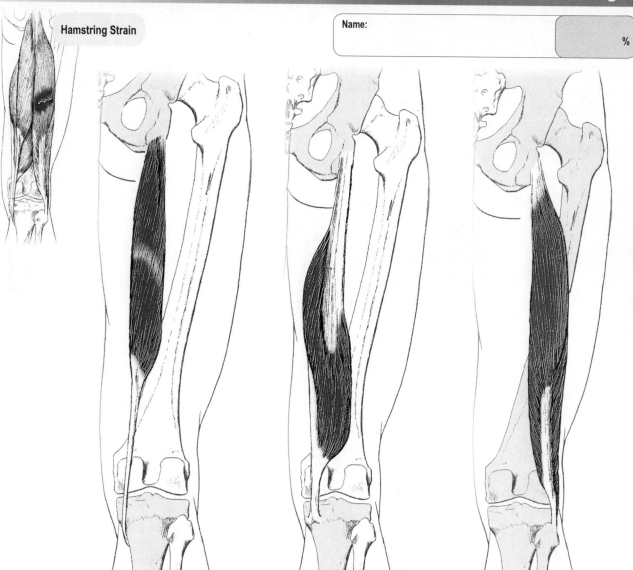

Hip, Thigh & Knee

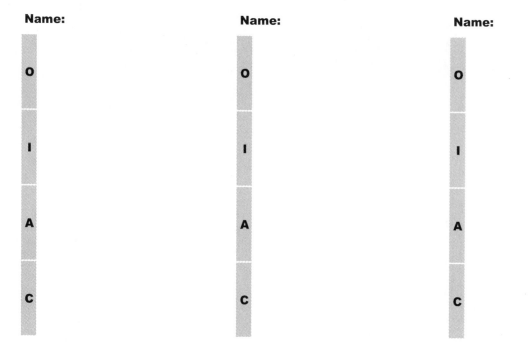

Name:

O

I

A

C

Name:

O

I

A

C

Name:

O

I

A

C

Hip, Thigh & Knee

Page 140 Hip Bone Ilium (Os Coxae)
1. Posterior superior iliac spine (PSIS)
2. Iliac crest
3. Anterior superior iliac spine (ASIS)
4. Pubic turbercle
5. Posterior gluteal line
6. Anterior gluteal line
7. Inferior gluteal line
8. Anterior inferior iliac spine
9. Acetabulum
10. Margin of acetabulum
11. Acetabular notch
12. Inferior pubic ramus
13. Ramus of ischium
14. Ischial tuberosity
15. Lesser sciatic notch
16. Ischial spine
17. Greater sciatic notch
18. Posterior inferior iliac spine (PIIS)
19. Obturator foramen
20. Iliac fossa
21. Iliac tuberosity
22. Auricular surface (for sacrum)
23. Arcuate line

Page 141 Femur & Patella
Femur
1. Head
2. Neck
3. Greater trochanter
4. Intertrochanteric line
5. Shaft (body)
6. Lateral epicondyle
7. Lateral condyle
8. Patellar surface
9. Medial condyle
10. Medial epicondyle
11. Intercondylar fossa
12. Adductor tubercle
13. Popliteal surface
14. Linea aspera
    a. Medial lip
    b. Lateral lip
15. Gluteal tuberosity
16. Lesser trochanter
17. Intertrochanteric crest
18. Trochanteric fossa
19. Fovea for ligament of head of femur

Patella
1. Base
2. Medial articular facet
3. Lateral Articular Facet
4. Apex

Page 142 Hip, femur & knee
Sacrum
1. S2 tubercle
2. Sacral base
Os Coxae (ilium, ischium & pubis)
3. Iliac crest
4. Anterior superior iliac spine
5. Anterior inferior iliac spine
6. Posterior superior iliac spine
7. Posterior inferior iliac spine
8. Posterior gluteal line
9. Anterior gluteal line
10. Inferior gluteal line
11. Iliac fossa
12. Greater sciatic notch
13. Ischial spine

For specific muscle
information use the Muscle
Manual Text, Muscle Tables
Chapter or on-line resources

14. Lesser sciatic notch
15. Ischial tuberosity
16. Ramus of ischium
17. Obturator foramen
18. Superior pubic ramus
19. Pubic tubercle
20. Inferior pubic ramus
21. Acetabulum

Femur
22. Head
23. Neck
24. Greater trochanter
25. Lesser trochanter
26. Intertrochanteric line
27. Intertrochanteric crest
28. Gluteal tuberosity
29. Linea aspera
30. Medial supracondylar ridge
31. Lateral supracondylar ridge
32. Adductor tubercle
33. Medial epicondyle
34. Lateral epicondyle
35. Medial condyle
36. Lateral condyle
37. Intercondylar fossa

Patella
38. Base
39. Apex

Page 143 SI, Hip & Knee Joint
Pelvis & Hip
1. Anterior longitudinal ligament
2. Iliolumbar ligaments
3. Anterior sacroiliac ligaments
4. Inguinal ligament
5. Obturator membrane
6. Iliofemoral ligament
7. Pubofemoral ligament
8. Ischiofemoral ligament
9. Sacrospinous ligament
10. Posterior sacroiliac ligament
11. Sacrotuberus ligament
12. Acetabulofemoral joint capsule
13. Ligamentum teres (to head of femur)

Knee
1. Lateral (fibular) collateral ligament
2. Medial (tibial) collateral ligament
3. Patellar ligament (infrapatellar tendon)
4. Infrapatellar fat pad
5. Anterior cruciate ligament
6. Posterior cruciate ligament
7. Medial meniscus
8. Lateral meniscus

Page 145, Hip Origins & Insertions
1. Quadratus lumborum
2. Psoas major
3. Iliacus
4. Sartorius
5. Rectus femoris
6. Superior gemellus
7. Obturator internus
8. Inferior gemellus
9. Piriformis
10. Gluteus minimus
11. Gluteus medius
12. Vastus lateralis
13. Vastus medialis
14. Vastus intermedius
15. Articularis genu
16. Pectineus
17. Adductor longus
18. Adductor brevis
19. Gracilis
20. Obturator externus
21. Adductor magnus
22. Quadratus femoris
23. Gluteus maximus
24. Tensor fasciae latae

25. Semitendinosus
26. Semimembranosus
27. Biceps femoris
28. Plantaris
29. Gastrocnemius

Page 146 Gluteal Muscles
1. Gluteus maximus
2. Gluteus medius
3. Piriformis
4. Superior gemellus
5. Obturator internus
6. Inferior gemellus
7. Quadratus femoris
8. Iliotibial band
9. Semitendinosus
10. Biceps femoris (long head)
11. Vastus lateralis
12. Tensor fasciae latae
13. Gluteus minimus
14. Sartorius
15. Rectus femoris

Page 147 Posterior Thigh Muscles
1. Gluteus maximus
2. Adductor magnus
3. Gracillis
4. Semitendinosus
5. Semimembranosus
6. Biceps femoris
    a. Long head
    b. Short head

Page 148 Medial Thigh Muscles
1. Tensor fasciae latae
2. Iliotibial band
3. Sartorius
4. Vastus lateralis
5. Rectus femoris
6. Vastus medialis
7. Iliopsoas
8. Pectineus
9. Adductor longus
10. Gracilis
11. Obturator externus
12. Adductor brevis
13. Adductor magnus

Page 149 Anterior Thigh Muscles
1. Tensor fasciae latae
2. Iliotibial band
3. Vastus lateralis
4. Pectineus
5. Adductor longus
6. Sartorius
7. Rectus femoris
8. Vastus medialis
9. Quadratus lumborum
10. Psoas minor
11. Psoas major
12. Iliacus
13. Vastus intermedius

Where are the lungs located?

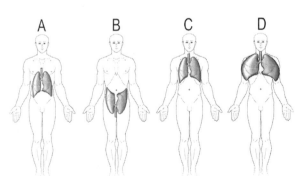

A   B   C   D

Learning Objectives

After completing this chapter, students will be able to:

1. Identify and palpate structures of the region (give a list of structures below their palpating hand)

2. Describe the structure, support, and movements of the leg ankle and foot

3. Assess AROM, PROM & RROM of the region

4. Describe biomechanics & kinesiology of the region, including arches of the foot & pronation

5. Perform detailed muscle testing and palpation

6. Discuss anatomical variation, ADLs and common injuries of the body region

7. Develop a set of strength and flexibility exercises for the body region

Ankle & Foot Kinematics	160
Ankle AROM & PROM	161
Fibula & Tibia	162
Tibia & Fibula	163
Bones of Foot	164
Ankle & Foot Ligaments	165
Ankle Ligaments & Fascia	166
Ankle & Foot Articulations	167
Anterior Leg Muscles	168
Lateral Leg Muscles	169
Posterior Leg Superficial	170
Posterior Leg Deep	171
Anterior Leg Muscles	172
Lateral Leg Muscles	173
Posterior Leg Muscles	174
Dorsal Foot Muscles	176
Intrinsic Foot Muscles	177
Foot Muscles Layer 1	178
Foot Muscles Layer 2	179
Foot Muscles Layer 3	180
Foot Muscles Layer 4	181
Answers	182

Leg, Foot & Ankle

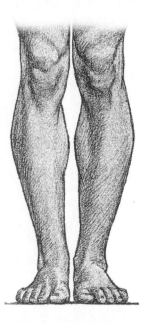
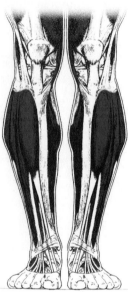
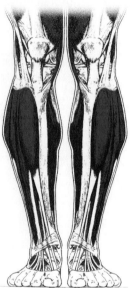

Palpation Checklist

- ☐ Tibial tuberosity & fibular head
- ☐ Tibial crest & knee joint line
- ☐ Lat./Med. malleolus
- ☐ Navicular (tuberosity)
- ☐ Cuboid & cuneiforms
- ☐ Talus (head, neck, trochlea)
- ☐ Calcaneus
- ☐ Sustentaculum tali
- ☐ Metatarsals
- ☐ Phalanges (MP / PIP / DIP joints)

- ☐ Sinus tarsi
- ☐ Ant. talofibular lig.
- ☐ Calcaneofibular lig.
- ☐ Post. talofibular lig.
- ☐ Spring ligament
- ☐ Deltoid ligament
- ☐ Subtalar joint
- ☐ Midtarsal joint
- ☐ Tarsometatarsal joints
- ☐ Gastrocnemius/soleus

Video on **proCentral**

- ☐ Achilles tendon
- ☐ TDH muscles (Tib post, flex Digi & Hal)
- ☐ Tarsal tunnel (tibial nerve)
- ☐ Fibularis L., B. & tertius muscles
- ☐ Tib. ant., EHL, EDL muscles
- ☐ Plantar fascia & muscles
- ☐ Tibial & dorsal pedal pulse
- ☐ . . . .
- ☐ . . . .
- ☐ . . . .

Joint type: synovial

Hinge (talocrural, metatarsophalangeal & interphalangeal)

Gliding (subtalar, midtarsal, intertarsal joints)

AROM

Talocrural (tibiotalar)
Plantar flexion ...... 40°
Dorsiflexion .... 20°

Subtalar & Mid tarsal
Inversion .... 30°
Eversion .... 15°

Metatarsophalangeal
Flexion .... 75°
Extension .... 35°

Interphalangeal
Flexion .... ~60°
Extension .... ~20°

Normal joint end feels

Talocrural: firm ligamentous
Subtalar: firm ligamentous
TMT: elastic firm
MTP extension: elastic / ligamentous
MTP flexion: firm / ligamentous / elastic
MTP big toe: firm / ligamentous / elastic
PIP flexion: firm / ligamentous / elastic
PIP extension: firm / ligamentous / elastic
DIP flexion: firm / ligamentous / elastic
DIP extension: firm / ligamentous / elastic

Main muscle actions

Plantar flexion: mainly soleus, gastrocnemius; assisted by tibialis posterior, flexor digitorum longus, flexor hallucis longus

Dorsiflexion: mainly tibialis anterior; assisted by extensor digitorum longus, ext. hallucis longus

Inversion: tibialis anterior, tibialis posterior

Eversion: fibularis longus, brevis & tertius

1st toe flexion: flexor hallucis longus & brevis

Toe 2-5 flexion: flexor digitorum longus & brevis, lumbricals

1st toe extension: ext. hallucis longus & brevis

Toe extension: extensor digitorum longus & brevis

Abduction: dorsal interossei

Adduction: palmar interossei

- Numbering of digits 1→5, medial → lateral
- The term 'hallux' means 'big toe'
- The term 'ray' may be used to describe toe/digit

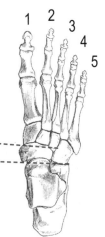

Joints of the foot

- Midtarsal joint - - - - - - -
- Subtalar joint - - - - - - - -

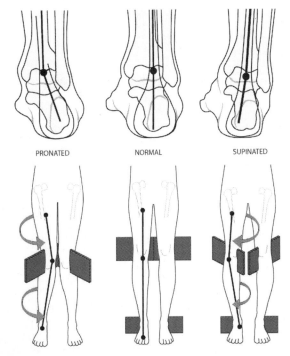

PRONATED   NORMAL   SUPINATED

Sole

Foot (bottom view)

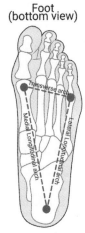

Compare bilaterally, start with unaffected side for PROM & Muscle Testing
Prior to assessing ROM the examiner should make an introduction statement:
"Try and move as far as possible, if any of the actions or movements are painful or uncomfortable please let me know, do not do any action you feel will cause you further injury."

AROM

Plantar Flexion

Muscles Activated: soleus, gastrocnemius, tibialis posterior, flexor digitorum longus, flexor hallicus longus, plantaris

Tissue Stretched: tibialis anterior, extensor digitorum longus, anterior ankle joint capsule & ligaments

Tissue Compressed: posterior ankle structures

Dorsiflexion

Muscles Activated: tibialis anterior, extensor digitorum longus

Tissue Stretched: soleus, gastrocnemius, tibialis posterior, flexor digitorum longus, flexor hallicus longus, Achilles tendon

Tissue Compressed: anterior ankle structure (joint capsule)

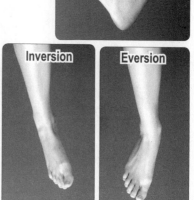
Plantar flexion

Inversion (adduction)

Muscles Activated: tibialis anterior, tibialis posterior

Tissue Stretched: fibularis longus, brevis & tertius, lateral ankle ligaments (anterior talofibular, calcaneofibular & posterior talofibular)

Tissue Compressed: medial ankle structures

Eversion (abduction)

Muscles Activated: fibularis longus, brevis & tertius

Tissue Stretched: tibialis anterior, tibialis posterior, medial collateral (deltoid) ligament of ankle

Tissue Compressed: lateral ankle structures

Inversion   Eversion

youtube: **Vizniak Ankle**

PROM

Plantar Flexion

Tissue Stretched: tibialis anterior, extensor digitorum longus, anterior ankle joint capsule & ligaments

Dorsiflexion

Tissue Stretched: soleus, gastrocnemius, tibialis posterior, flexor digitorum longus, flexor hallicus longus, Achilles tendon

Eversion (abduction)

Tissue Stretched: tibialis anterior, tibialis posterior, medial collateral (deltoid) ligament of ankle

Inversion (adduction)

Tissue Stretched: fibularis longus, brevis & tertius, lateral ankle ligaments (anterior talofibular, calcaneofibular & posterior talofibular)

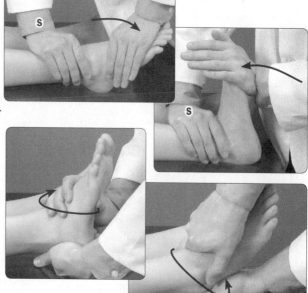

Leg, Foot & Ankle

anterior view

lateral view

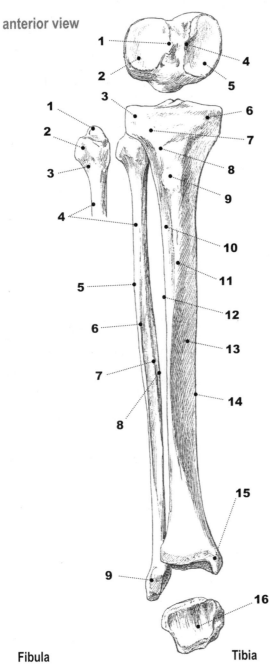

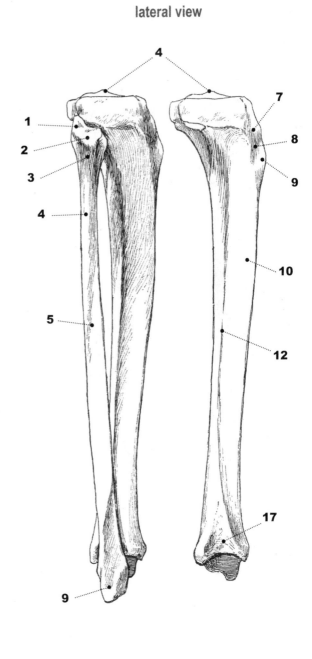

Fibula

1. _____
2. _____
3. _____
4. _____
5. _____
6. _____
7. _____
8. _____
9. _____

Tibia

1. _____
2. _____
3. _____
4. _____
5. _____
6. _____
7. _____
8. _____
9. _____

10. _____
11. _____
12. _____
13. _____
14. _____
15. _____
16. _____
17. _____

prohealthsys

Start with labeling the bones, then progress to drawing
□ muscles, □ ligaments, □ Os & Is, □ nerves, □ vessels

Name:

%

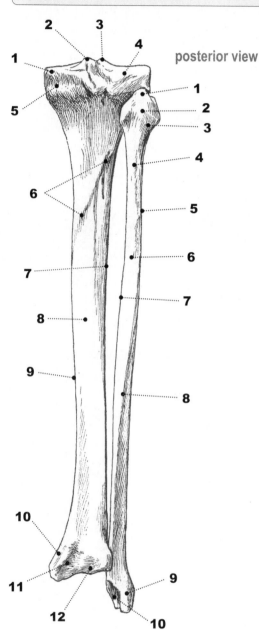

posterior view

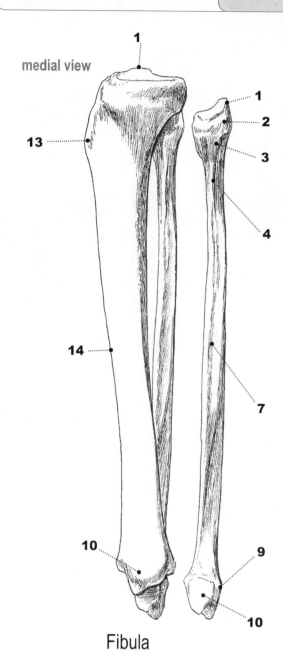

medial view

Tibia

1. _____
2. _____
3. _____
4. _____
5. _____
6. _____
7. _____

8. _____
9. _____
10. _____
11. _____
12. _____
13. _____
14. _____

Fibula

1. _____
2. _____
3. _____
4. _____
5. _____
6. _____
7. _____
8. _____
9. _____
10. _____

Start with labeling the bones, then progress to drawing
□ muscles, □ ligaments, □ Os & Is, □ nerves, □ vessels

Name: _____ %

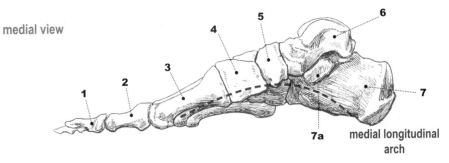

medial view

medial longitudinal
arch

lateral view

lateral longitudinal
arch

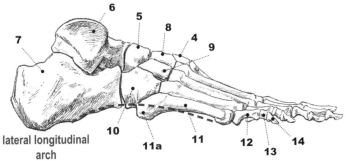

superior view

inferior view

Transverse arch

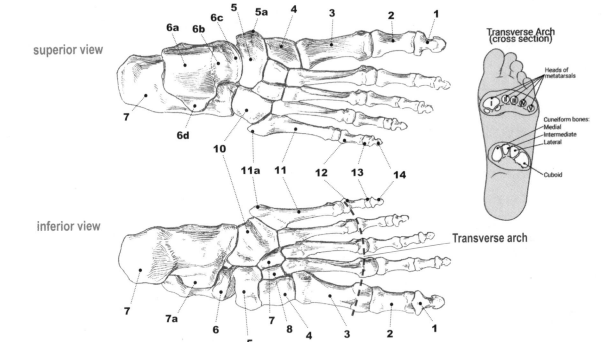

Transverse Arch
(cross section)

Heads of
metatarsals

Cuneiform bones:
Medial
Intermediate
Lateral

Cuboid

1. _____
2. _____
3. _____
4. _____
5. _____
   a. _____

6. _____
   a. _____
   b. _____
   c. _____
   d. _____
7. _____
   a. _____
8. _____

9. _____
10. _____
11. _____
    a. _____
12. _____
13. _____
14. _____

Leg, Foot & Ankle

Name: _____ _____ %

lateral view

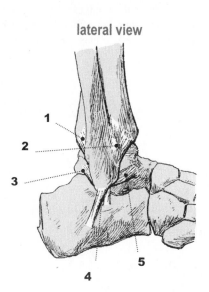

1
2
3
4
5

medial view

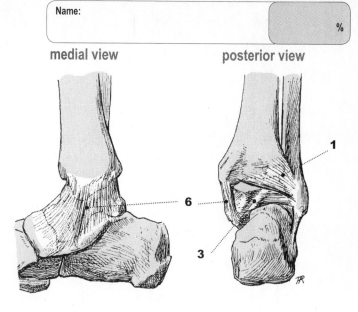

posterior view

6
1
3

Leg, Foot & Ankle

superior view

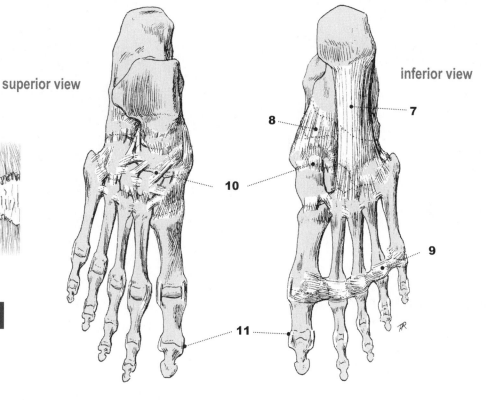

inferior view

7
8
10
9
11

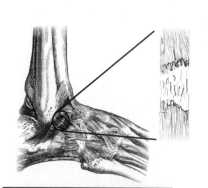

Clinical Note

During an **inversion ankle sprain** any or all of the 5 lateral ligaments may be damaged

Lateral ankle

1. _____
2. _____
3. _____
4. _____
5. _____

Medial ankle

6. _____

Sole of foot

7. _____
8. _____
9. _____

10. _____
11. _____

Clinical Note

The plantar fascia is somewhat continuous over the calcaneus connecting to the Achilles tendon - stretching the gastrosoleus can help reduce symptoms of plantar fascitis

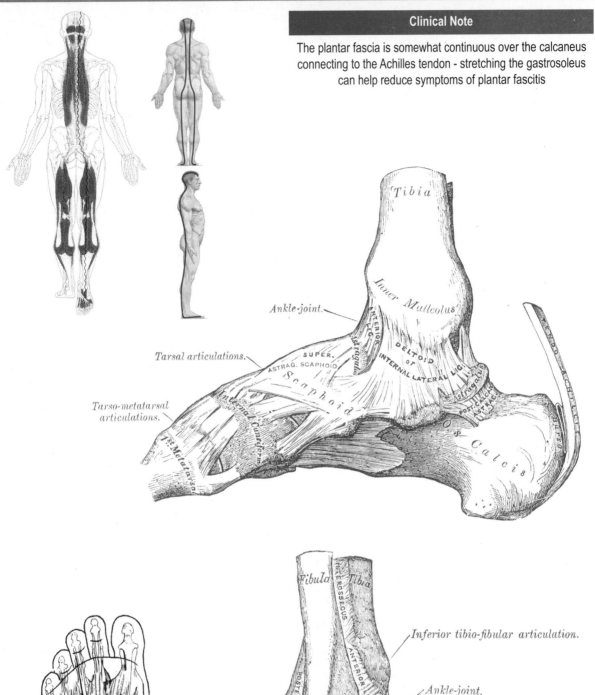

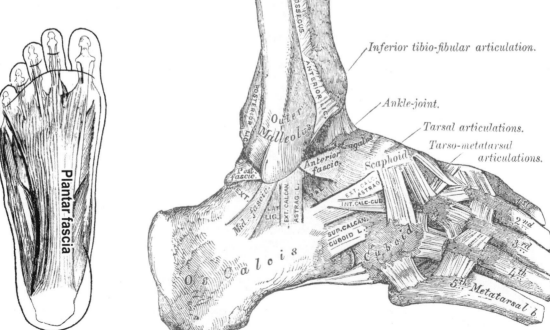

Name: [   ] %

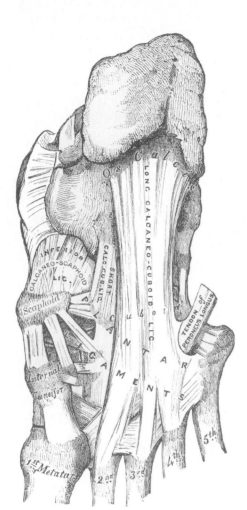

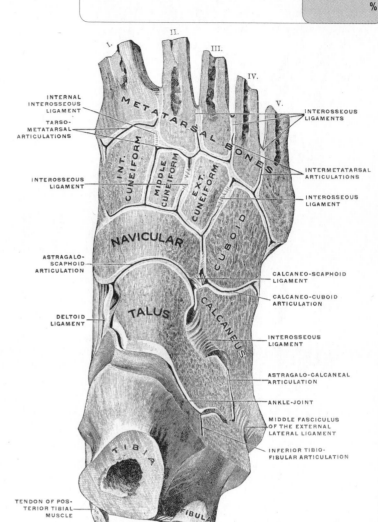

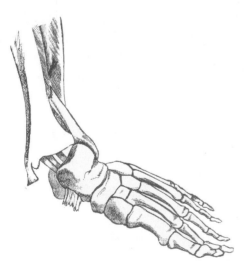

- Pott's fracture secondary to forced eversion of the ankle

Ligament	Attaches (origin/insertion)	Function
Interosseous	Shaft of fibula to tibia	Resists separation of tibia & fibula, muscle attachment point
Tibiofibular (anterior/posterior)	Distal fibula to tibia	Resists separation of tibia & fibula
Anterior talofibular	Lateral malleolus to neck of talus	Resists anterior displacement of foot/talar tilt; resists plantar flexion & inversion
Calcaneofibular	Lateral malleolus to tubercle on outer calcaneus	Resists inversion & backward translation of foot
Posterior talofibular	Inner, back, lateral malleolus to posterior surface of talus	Resists plantar flexion, dorsiflexion, inversion
Deltoid	Medial malleolus to talus, navicular, calcaneus	Resists valgus forces to ankle; plantar flexion, dorsiflexion, eversion, & abduction of foot
Spring or Plantar calcaneonavicular	Anterior margin of calcaneus to inferior navicular	Supports arch (lengthens during gait cycle)
Long plantar	Inferior calcaneus to cuboid & metatarsals	Supports arch (lengthens during gait cycle)
Transverse metatarsal	Tarsals to metatarsals	Supports arch; maintains relationship between tarsals & metatarsals
Intertarsal	Tarsal to tarsal	Maintain articular relationship & arch
Collateral	Phalanx to phalanx, sides of MTP, PIP & DIP joints	Supports sides of toes; resists varus/valgus force

prohealthsys

Start with labeling the muscles, then progress to naming
☐ actions, ☐ origins, ☐ insertions, ☐ nerves

Name:

%

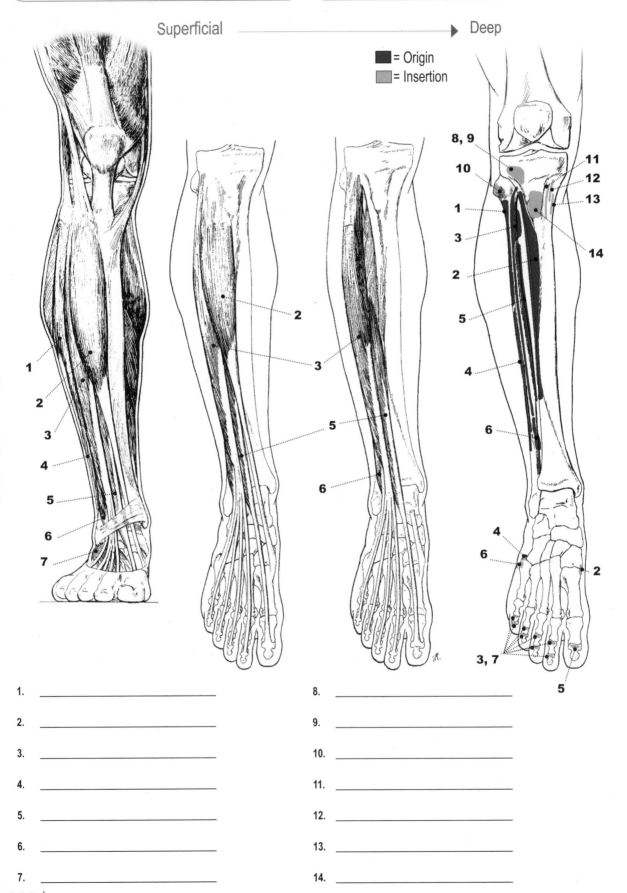

Superficial ➤ Deep

■ = Origin
■ = Insertion

Leg, Foot & Ankle

1. _____

2. _____

3. _____

4. _____

5. _____

6. _____

7. _____

8. _____

9. _____

10. _____

11. _____

12. _____

13. _____

14. _____

Start with labeling the muscles, then progress to naming
□ actions, □ origins, □ insertions, □ nerves

Name:

%

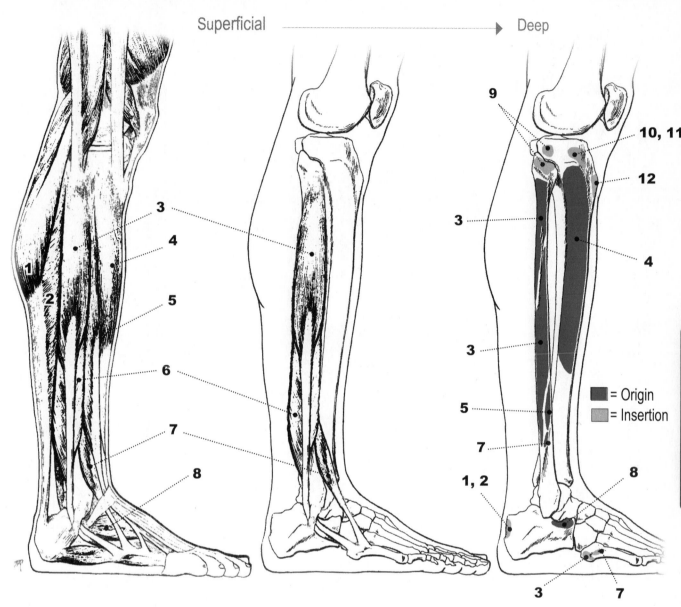

Superficial →→→→→ Deep

= Origin
= Insertion

Leg, Foot & Ankle

1. _____

2. _____

3. _____

4. _____

5. _____

6. _____

7. _____

8. _____

9. _____

10. _____

11. _____

12. _____

prohealthsys

Start with labeling the muscles, then progress to naming
☐ actions, ☐ origins, ☐ insertions, ☐ nerves

Name: _____ %

Leg, Foot & Ankle

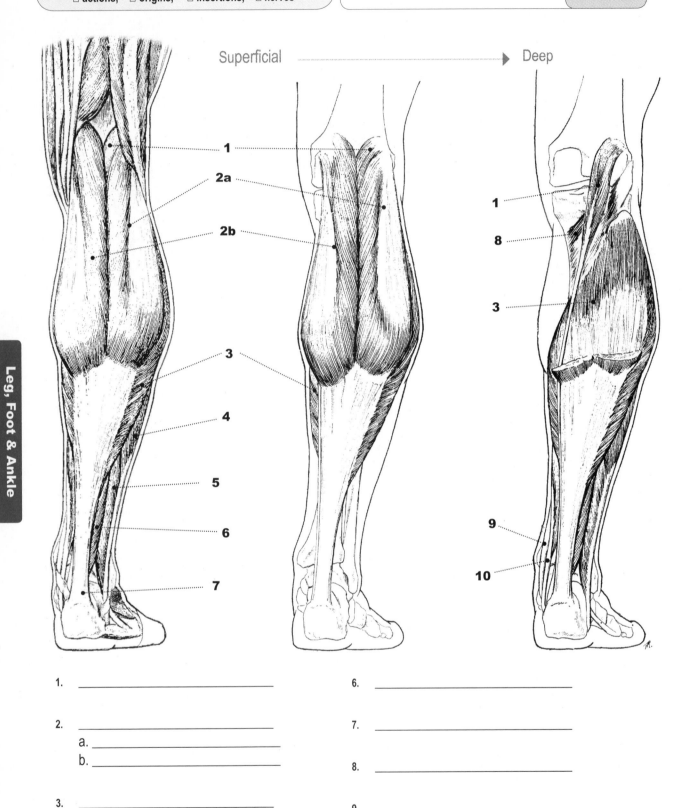

Superficial ————————▶ Deep

1. _____   6. _____

2. _____   7. _____
    a. _____
    b. _____   8. _____

3. _____   9. _____

4. _____   10. _____

5. _____

prohealthsys.com   Vizniak & Richer

prohealthsys

Start with labeling the muscles, then progress to naming
□ actions,   □ origins,   □ insertions,   □ nerves

Name:

%

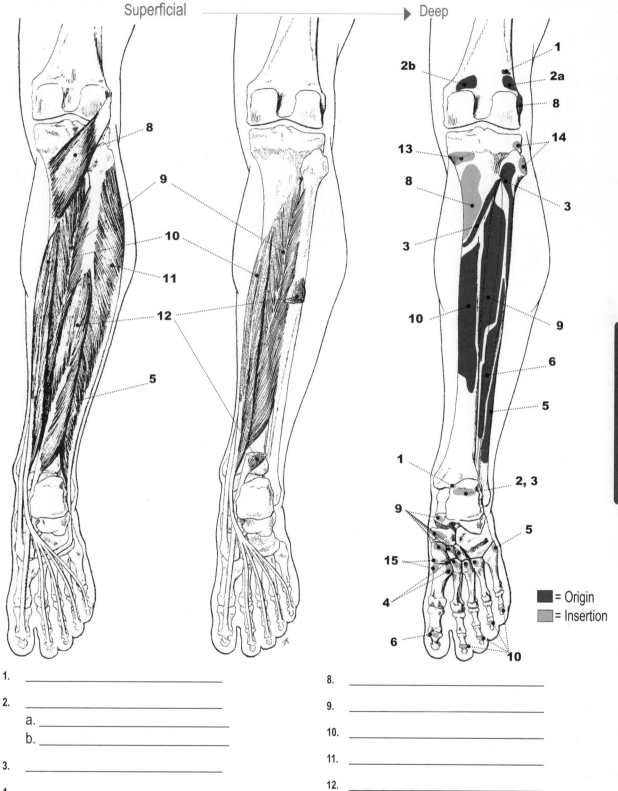

Superficial

Deep

= Origin

= Insertion

Leg, Foot & Ankle

1. _____

2. _____

a. _____

b. _____

3. _____

4. _____

5. _____

6. _____

7. Achilles tendon (not visible)

8. _____

9. _____

10. _____

11. _____

12. _____

13. _____

14. _____

Name: _____ %

Leg, Foot & Ankle

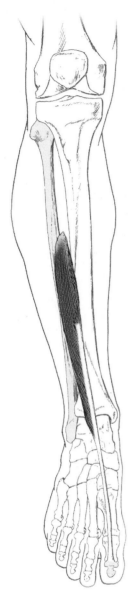

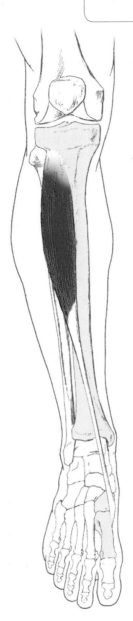

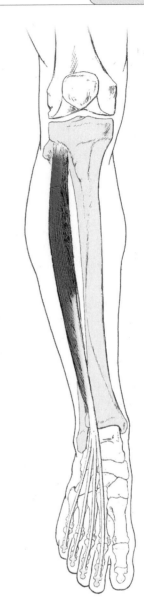

Name:

O

I

A

C

Name:

O

I

A

C

Name:

O

I

A

C

prohealthsys

The Leg has 4 fascial bound compartments - increased blood pressure can result in a compartment syndrome

1. **Anterior:** tibialis anterior, extensor dig. longus, extensor hallucis longus & fibularis tertius, anterior tibial artery, deep peroneal nerve

2. **Lateral:** fibularis longus & brevis, common & superficial fibular nerve, fibular artery

3. **Superficial posterior:** contains gastrocnemius, soleus & plantaris, lesser saphenous v.

4. **Deep posterior:** contains flexor digitorum longus, flexor hallucis longus, popliteus, & tib. posterior, posterior tibial artery & vein & tibial nerve

Name: _____ %

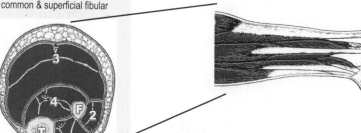

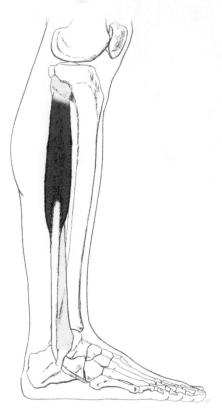

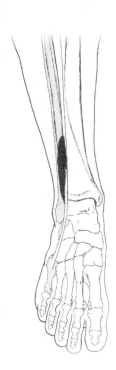

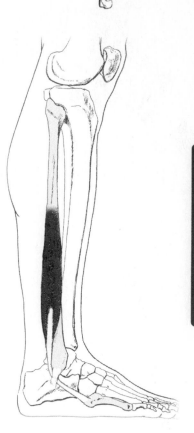

Leg, Foot & Ankle

Name: _____

O

I

A

C

Name: _____

O

I

A

C

Name: _____

O

I

A

C

prohealthsys

Name:

%

Leg, Foot & Ankle

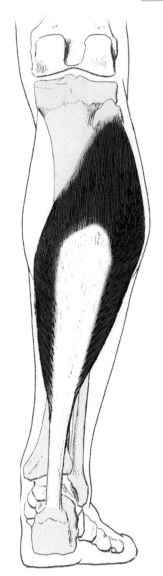
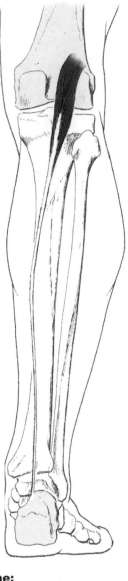

Name:

O

I

A

C

Name:

O

I

A

C

Name:

O

I

A

C

Name:

O

I

A

C

prohealthsys.com   Vizniak & Richer

Name: [   ] %

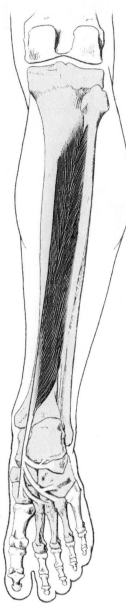

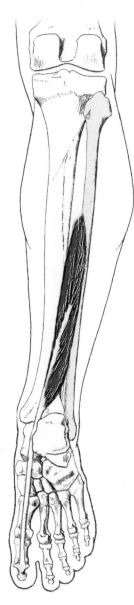

Name:

O
I
A
C

Name:

O
I
A
C

Name:

O
I
A
C

Name: _____ %

Leg, Foot & Ankle

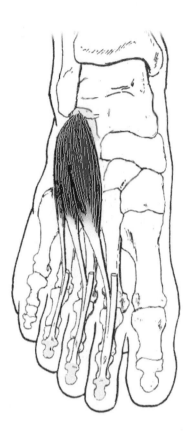

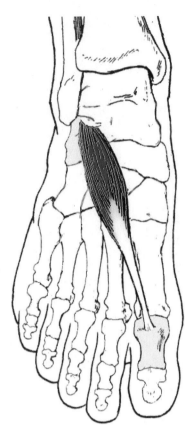

Name:

O

I

A

C

Name:

O

I

A

C

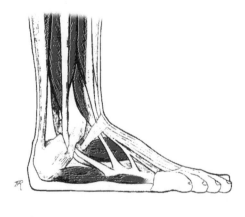

Name:

_____ %

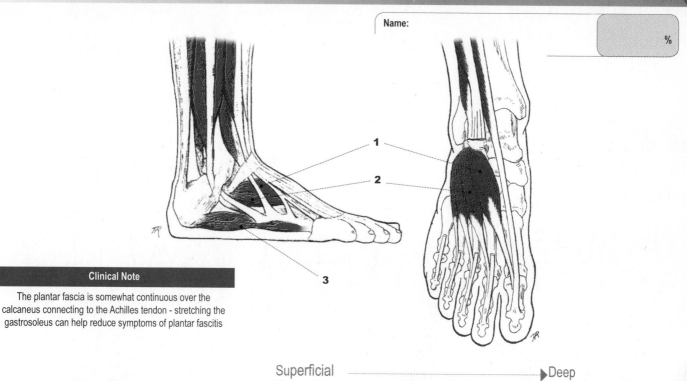

Clinical Note

The plantar fascia is somewhat continuous over the calcaneus connecting to the Achilles tendon - stretching the gastrosoleus can help reduce symptoms of plantar fascitis

Superficial ····· ▶Deep

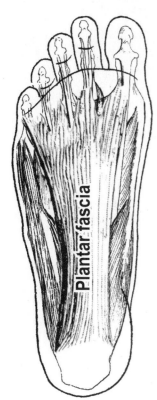

Plantar fascia

Layer 1

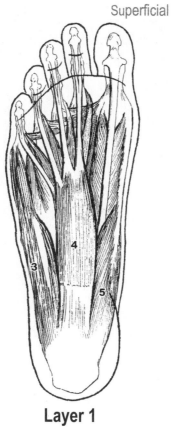

Layer 2

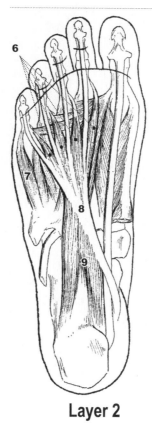

Layer 3

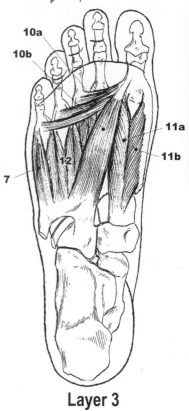

Leg, Foot & Ankle

1. _____	7. _____	11. _____
2. _____	8. _____	a. _____
3. _____	9. _____	b. _____
4. _____	10. _____	12. _____
5. _____	a. _____	
6. _____	b. _____	

Name: _____ %

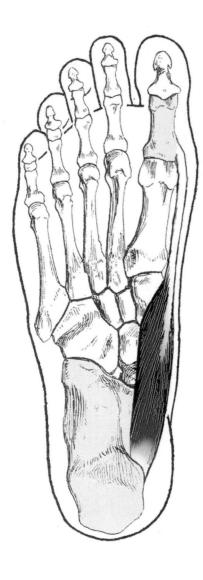

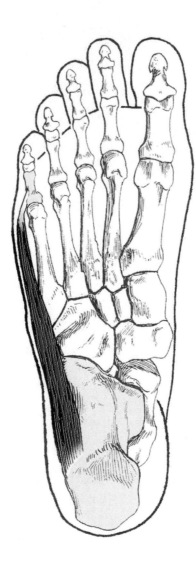

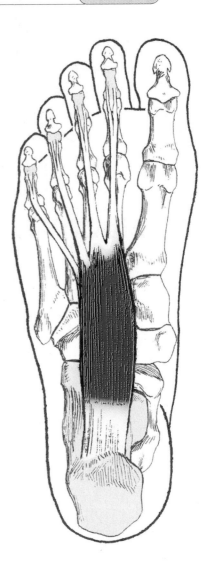

Name:

O

I

A

C

Name:

O

I

A

C

Name:

O

I

A

C

prohealthsys

Name:

%

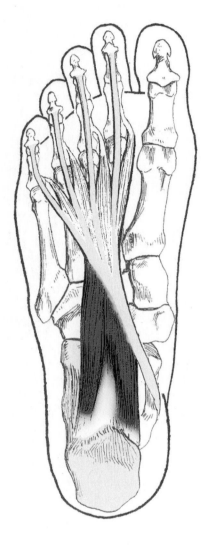

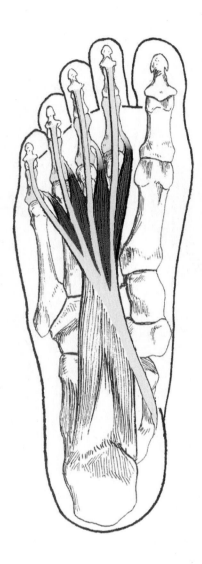

Name:

O

I

A

C

Name:

O

I

A

C

prohealthsys

Name: _____ %

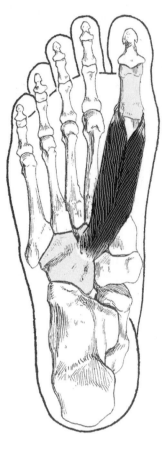

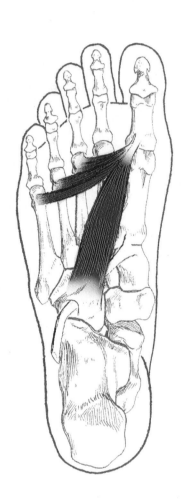

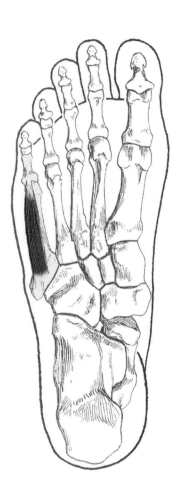

Name:

O

I

A

C

Name:

O

I

A

C

Name:

O

I

A

C

prohealthsys

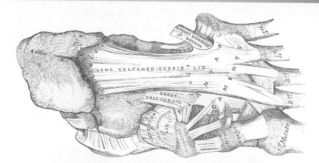

Ligaments of Foot Arches

Weakness or laxity of the foot muscles & ligaments can
lead to overpronation, fallen arches & flat feet

Name: _____ %

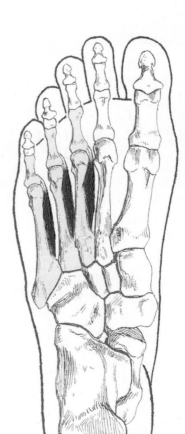

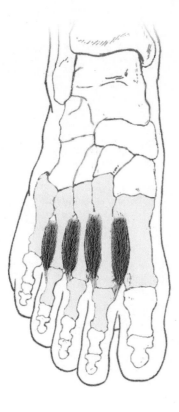

Name:

| O |
| I |
| A |
| C |

Name:

| O |
| I |
| A |
| C |

Page 162 Fibula & Tibia
Fibula
1. Apex (styloid process)
2. Head
3. Neck
4. Shaft (body)
5. Lateral surface
6. Anterior border
7. Interosseous border
8. Medial surface
9. Lateral malleolus

Tibia
1. Lateral intercondylar tubercle
2. Lateral articular facet
3. Lateral condyle
4. Medial intercondylar tubercle
5. Medial articular facet
6. Medial condyle
7. Gerdy's tubercle
8. Oblique line
9. Tibial tuberosity
10. Lateral surface
11. Anterior border/crest
12. Interosseous border
13. Medial surface
14. Medial border
15. Medial malleolus
16. Inferior articular surface for talus
17. Fibular notch

Page 163 Tibia & Fibula
Tibia
1. Medial condyle
2. Medial intercondylar tubercle
3. Lateral intercondylar tubercle
4. Lateral condyle
5. Fossa for semimembranosus insertion
6. Soleal line
7. Interosseous border
8. Posterior surface
9. Medial border
10. Medial malleolus
11. Groove for tibialis posterior
12. Posterior malleolus
13. Tibial tuberosity
14. Anterior border

Fibula
1. Apex (styloid process)
2. Head
3. Neck
4. Shaft (body)
5. Lateral surface
6. Posterior surface
7. Interosseous border/medial crest
8. Posterior border
9. Lateral malleolus
10. Articular surface

Page 164 Foot bones
1. 1st Distal phalynx
2. 1st Proximal phalynx
3. 1st Metatarsal

4. Medial cuneiform
5. Navicular
   a. Navicular tuberosity
6. Talus
   a. Trochlea of talus
   b. Neck of talus
   c. Head of talus
   d. Lateral process
7. Calcaneus
   a. Sustentaculum tali
8. Intermedial cuneiform
9. Lateral cuneiform
10. Cuboid
11. 5th Metatarsal
    a. Styloid process
12. 5th proximal phalynx
13. 5th intermediate phalynx
14. 5th distal phalynx

Page 165 Foot/Ankle ligaments
Lateral ankle
1. Posterior tibiofibular ligament
2. Anterior tibiofibular ligament
3. Posterior talofibular ligament
4. Calcaneofibular ligament
5. Anterior talofibular ligament
   Medial ankle
6. Deltoid (medial collateral) ligament
   Sole of foot
7. Long plantar ligament
8. Spring (plantar calcaneonavicular) ligament
9. Transverse metatarsal ligament
10. Intertarsal ligaments
11. Interphalangeal collateral ligaments

Page 168 Anterior Leg Muscles
1. Fibularis (peroneus) longus
2. Tibialis anterior
3. Extensor digitorum longus
4. Fibularis (peroneus) brevis
5. Extensor hallucis longus
6. Fibularis (peroneus) tertius
7. Extensor digitorum brevis
8. Gluteus maximus (ITB)
9. Tensor fasciae latae (ITB)
10. Biceps femoris
11. Sartorius
12. Gracilis
13. Semitendinosus
14. Quadriceps femoris tendon

Page 169 Lateral Leg Muscles
1. Gastrocnemius
2. Soleus
3. Fibularis (peroneus) longus
4. Tibialis anterior
5. Extensor digitorum longus
6. Fibularis (peroneus) brevis
7. Fibularis (peroneus) tertius
8. Extensor digitorum brevis
9. Biceps femoris
10. Gluteus maximus
11. Tensor fasciae latae
12. Quadriceps femoris tendon

Page 170 Superficial Post. Leg
1. Plantaris
2. Gastrocnemius
   a. Lateral head
   b. Medial head
3. Soleus
4. Fibularis (peroneus) longus
5. Fibularis (peroneus) brevis
6. Flexor hallucis longus
7. Achilles tendon (not shown)
8. Popliteus
9. Tibialis posterior
10. Flexor digitorum longus
11. Fibularis (peroneus) longus
12. Semimembranosus
13. Biceps femoris
14. Tibialis anterior

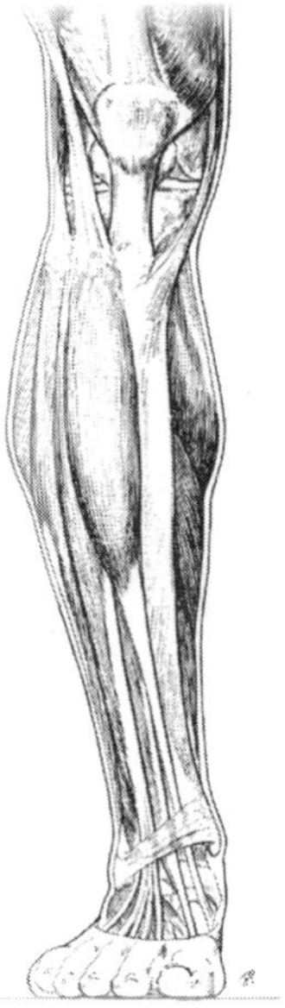

Page 171 Foot Muscles
1. Extensor hallucis brevis
2. Extensor digitorum brevis
3. Abductor digiti minimi
4. Flexor digitorum brevis
5. Abductor hallucis
6. Lumbricals
7. Flexor digiti minimi
8. Flexor digitorum longus tendon
9. Quadratus plantae
10. Adductor hallucis
    a. Transverse head
    b. Oblique head
11. Flexor hallucis brevis
    a. Lateral head
    b. Medila head
12. Interossei muscles

Leg, Foot & Ankle *(vertical side tab)*

▶ **Video on proCentral**

For specific muscle
information use the
Muscle Manual Text,
Muscle Tables Chapter
or on-line resources

Learning Objectives
After completing this chapter, the student will be able to:

1. Identify and outline peripheral nerve pathways
2. Describe regional motor and cutaneous innervation
3. Explain potential sites of peripheral nerve compression and resulting symptoms
4. Describe dermatomes, myotomes and peripheral nerve distribution
5. Identify and outline regional artery and vein pathways

▶ **Youtube: Vizniak Nerve**

Motor Nerves Upper Body 184
Brachial Plexus 185
Motor Nerves Lower Body 186
Lumbosacral Plexus.................................. 187
Brachial Plexus 188
Lumbosacral Plexus.................................. 189
Upper Limb Nerves................................... 190
Cutaneous Innervation............................. 194
Spinal Nerves and Reflexes..................... 196

Blood Vessels & Heart 197
Veins of the Body 198
Arteries of the Body 199
Veins of the Head & Neck 200
Arteries of the Head & Neck 201
Veins of Upper & Lower Extremity............ 202
Arteries of Upper & Lower Extremity........ 203

Answers.. 204

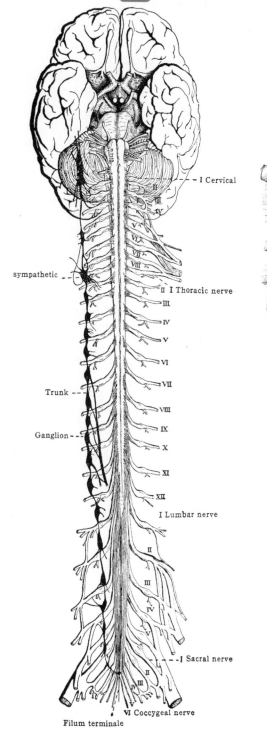

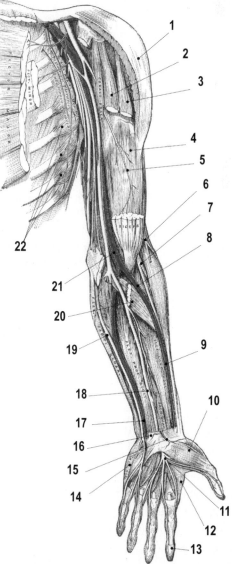

prohealthsys

Name the muscles supplied by each nerve

Name: _____ %

Suprascapular nerve
1. _____
2. _____

Long thoracic nerve
3. _____

Dorsal scapular nerve
4. _____
5. _____

Axillary nerve
6. _____
7. _____

Musculocutaneous nerve
8. _____
9. _____
10. _____

Median nerve
Forearm
11. _____
12. _____
13. _____
14. _____
15. _____
16. _____
17. _____
Hand
18. _____
19. _____
20. _____

Radial nerve
Arm
21. _____
22. _____
23. _____
24. _____

Forearm
25. _____
26. _____
27. _____
28. _____
29. _____
30. _____
31. _____
32. _____
33. _____

Ulnar nerve
Forearm
34. _____
35. _____

Hand
36. _____
37. _____
38. _____
39. _____
40. _____

Fill out the spinal levels associated with each muscle or action = Myotome

Muscle/Action	C3	C4	C5	C6	C7	C8	T1
Levator scapulae							
Rhomboids							
Deltoid							
Pectoralis major							
Latissimus dorsi							
Elbow flexion							
Elbow extension							
Supination							
Pronation							
Wrist extension							
Wrist flexion							
Finger extension							
Finger flexion							
Finger adduction & abduction							
Intrinsic hand muscles							

Neurovascular

prohealthsys

Name the branches of the Brachial Plexus? Name what the branches supply? Motor? Sensory?

Name: _____ %

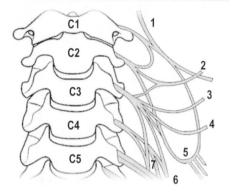

Cervical plexus (C1-C4)

1. _____
2. _____
3. _____
4. _____
5. _____
6. _____
7. _____

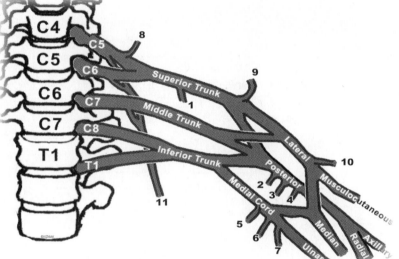

Brachial plexus (C5-T1)

1. _____
2. _____
3. _____
4. _____
5. _____
6. _____
7. _____
8. _____
9. _____
10. _____
11. _____

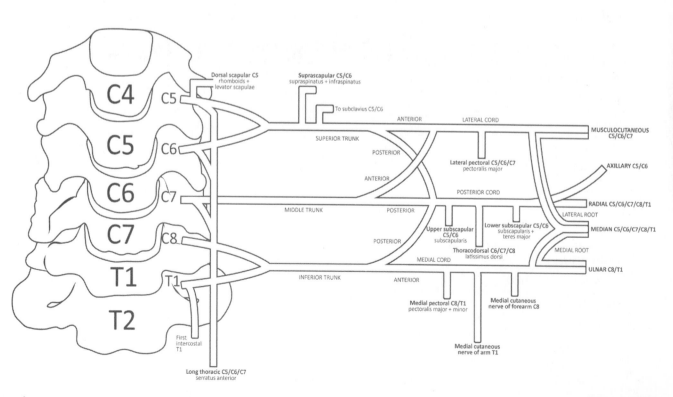

Dorsal scapular C5
rhomboids +
levator scapulae

Suprascapular C5/C6
supraspinatus + infraspinatus

To subclavius C5/C6

ANTERIOR   LATERAL CORD   MUSCULOCUTANEOUS
                                                  C5/C6/C7
SUPERIOR TRUNK
POSTERIOR
                         Lateral pectoral C5/C6/C7
ANTERIOR   pectoralis major   AXILLARY C5/C6

                         POSTERIOR CORD

MIDDLE TRUNK   POSTERIOR   RADIAL C5/C6/C7/C8/T1
                                                   LATERAL ROOT
                 Upper subscapular   Lower subscapular C5/C6
                 C5/C6   subscapularis +   MEDIAN C5/C6/C7/C8/T1
                 subscapularis   teres major
                 POSTERIOR   Thoracodorsal C6/C7/C8   MEDIAL ROOT
                 MEDIAL CORD   latissimus dorsi

INFERIOR TRUNK   ANTERIOR   ULNAR C8/T1

                 Medial pectoral C8/T1   Medial cutaneous
                 pectoralis major + minor nerve of forearm C8

First
intercostal
T1
                         Medial cutaneous
                         nerve of arm T1

Long thoracic C5/C6/C7
serratus anterior

prohealthsys

Name: _____ %

Name the muscles supplied by each nerve

Superior gluteal nerve
1. _____
2. _____
3. _____

Inferior gluteal nerve
4. _____

Femoral nerve
Thigh
5. _____
6. _____

Quadriceps:
7. _____
8. _____
9. _____
10. _____

Obturator nerve
11. _____
12. _____
13. _____
14. _____
15. _____

Sciatic nerve (tibial division)
16. _____
17. _____
18. _____
19. _____
Leg
20. _____
21. _____
22. _____
23. _____
24. _____
Foot
25. _____
26. _____

Sciatic nerve (fibular/peroneal division)
27. _____
Leg (deep fibular nerve)
28. _____
29. _____
30. _____
31. _____
Foot (superficial fibular nerve)
32. _____
33. _____
34. _____

Fill out the spinal levels associated with each action = Myotome

Muscle group/Action	L1	L2	L3	L4	L5	S1	S2
Hip extension & external rotation							
Hip external rotation							
Hip abduction & internal rotation							
Hip abduction							
Hip extension							
Hip flexion							
Knee flexion							
Knee extension							
Extensor hallicus							
Toe extension							
Plantarflexion							
Dorsiflexors							
Ankle inversion							
Ankle eversion							

Neurovascular

Name: _____ %

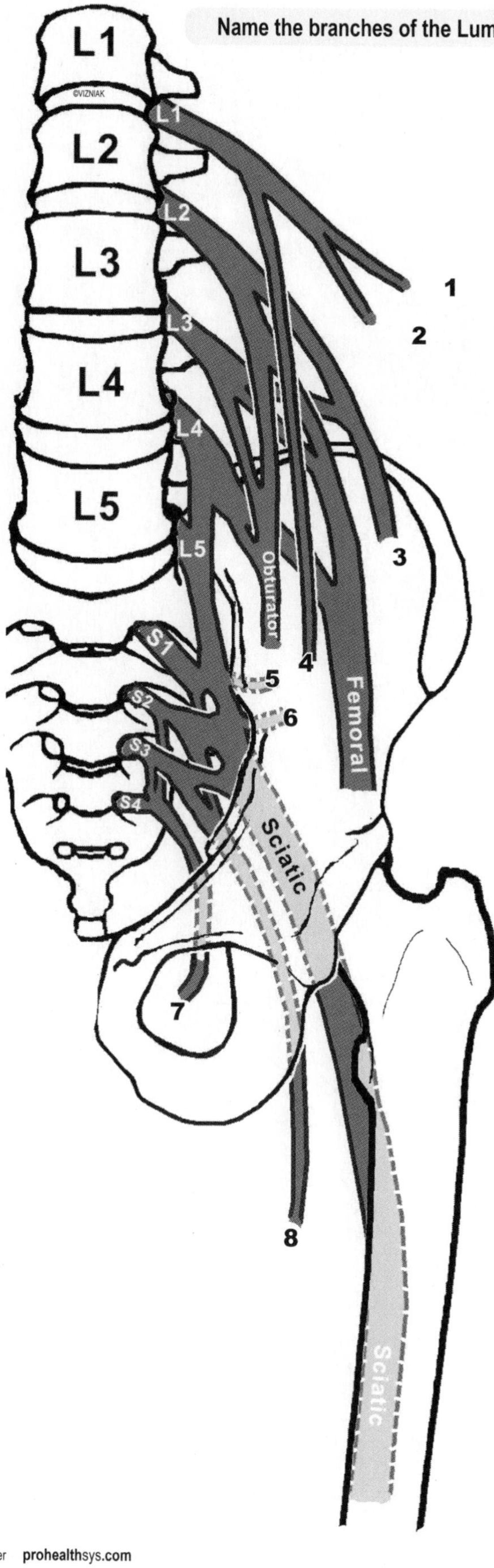

Name the branches of the Lumbosacral Plexus? What do they supply?

L1
L2
L3
L4
L5

L1
L2
L3
L4
L5

S1
S2
S3
S4

©VIZNIAK

Obturator

Femoral

Sciatic

Sciatic

1
2
3
4
5
6
7
8

1. _____

2. _____

3. _____

4. _____

5. _____

6. _____

7. _____

8. _____

prohealthsys

Neurovascular

prohealthsys

Color this page

Name:

%

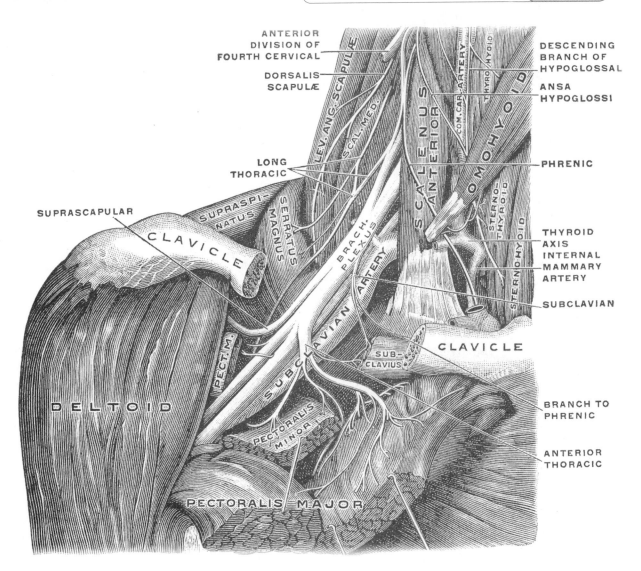

ANTERIOR
DIVISION OF
FOURTH CERVICAL

DORSALIS
SCAPULÆ

LONG
THORACIC

SUPRASCAPULAR

CLAVICLE

SUPRASPI-
NATUS

SERRATUS
MAGNUS

LEV. ANG. SCAPULÆ

SCAL. MED.

SCALENUS ANTERIOR

BRACH. PLEXUS

OMOHYOID

THYRO-HYOID

COM. CAR. ARTERY

DESCENDING
BRANCH OF
HYPOGLOSSAL

ANSA
HYPOGLOSSI

PHRENIC

STERNO-THYROID

STERNO-HYOID

THYROID
AXIS
INTERNAL
MAMMARY
ARTERY

SUBCLAVIAN

SUBCLAVIAN ARTERY

PECT. M.

DELTOID

PECTORALIS
MINOR

SUB-
CLAVIUS

CLAVICLE

BRANCH TO
PHRENIC

ANTERIOR
THORACIC

PECTORALIS MAJOR

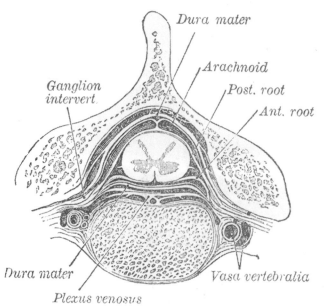

Dura mater

Arachnoid

Post. root

Ant. root

Ganglion
intervert.

Dura mater

Plexus venosus

Vasa vertebralia

prohealthsys

Color this page

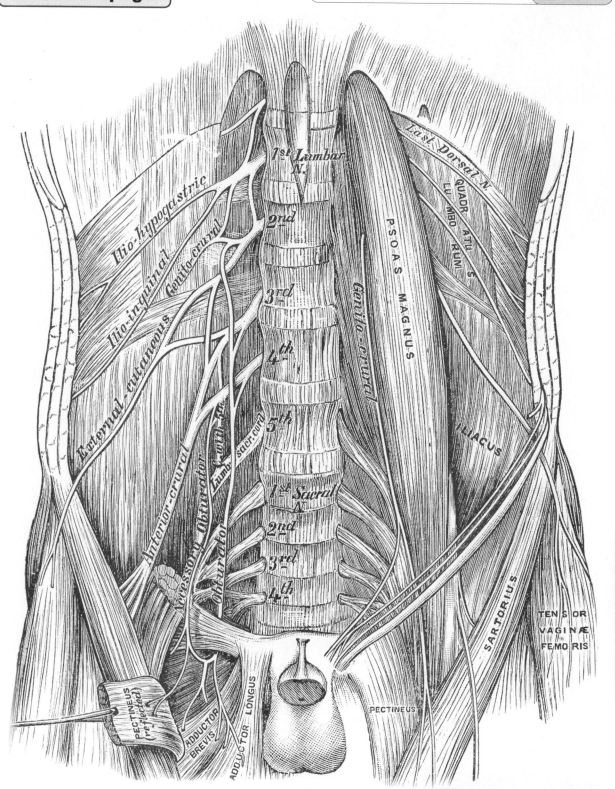

Neurovascular

Anatomical Naming Note

Psoas Magnus = Psoas Major

Tensor Vaginae* Femoris = TFL

* Vagina is latin for 'covering' - tensor vaginae femoris tenses the covering (fascia lata) of the femoral muscles

Name: _____ %

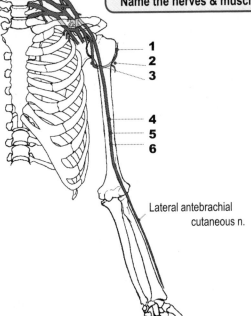

1
1a
1b
1c
2
3
4
5
6
7
8
9
10
11
12
13

Name the nerve & muscles it supplies

Nerve: _____

1. _____
   a. _____
   b. _____
   c. _____
2. _____
3. _____
4. _____
5. _____
6. _____
7. _____
8. _____
9. _____
10. _____
11. _____
12. _____
13. _____

Name the nerves & muscles they supplies

1
2
3
4
5
6

Lateral antebrachial cutaneous n.

Nerve: _____

1. _____
2. _____
3. _____

Nerve: _____

4. _____
5. _____
6. _____

Neurovascular

Name: _____ %

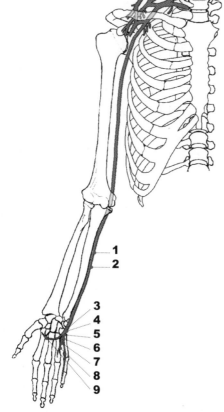

Name the nerve & muscles it supplies

Nerve: _____

1. _____
2. _____
3. _____
4. _____
5. _____
6. _____
7. _____
8. _____
9. _____
10. _____
11. _____

Name the nerve & muscles it supplies

Nerve: _____

1. _____
2. _____
3. _____
4. _____
5. _____
6. _____
7. _____
8. _____
9. _____

Neurovascular

 Youtube: Vizniak Nerve

Name the nerves & muscles they supply

Name: _____ %

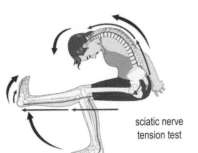

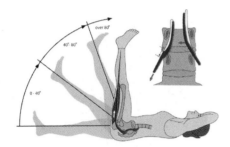

sciatic nerve
tension test

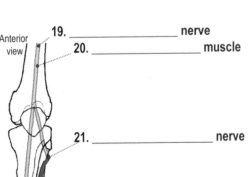

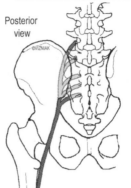

Posterior
view

1. _____ **nerve** (tibial division)

2. _____ muscle
3. _____ muscle
4. _____ muscle

5. _____ muscle

6. _____ nerve

7. _____ nerve
8. _____ muscle
9. _____ muscle
10. _____ muscle
11. _____ muscle
12. _____ muscle
13. _____ muscle

19. _____ nerve
20. _____ muscle

Anterior
view

14. _____ nerve
15. _____ muscle
16. _____ muscle
17. _____ muscle
18. _____ muscle

21. _____ nerve

22. _____ nerve
23. _____ muscle
24. _____ muscle
25. _____ muscle
26. _____ muscle

27. _____ nerve
28. _____ muscle
29. _____ muscle
30. _____ muscle

Youtube: Vizniak Nerve

prohealthsys

Name the nerve & muscles it supplies

Name: _____ %

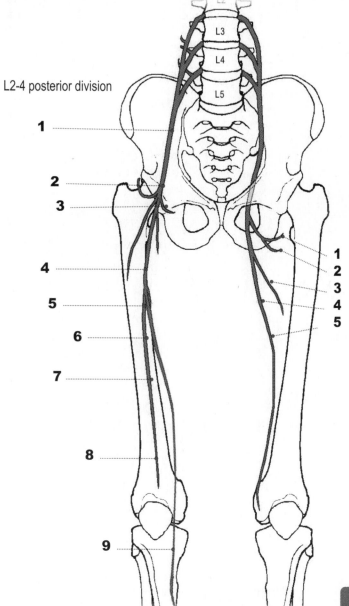

L2-4 posterior division

L2-4 anterior division

Youtube: Vizniak Nerve

Neurovascular

Nerve: _____

1. _____
2. _____
3. _____
4. _____
5. _____
6. _____
7. _____
8. _____
9. _____

Nerve: _____

1. _____
2. _____
3. _____
4. _____
5. _____

Name: _____ %

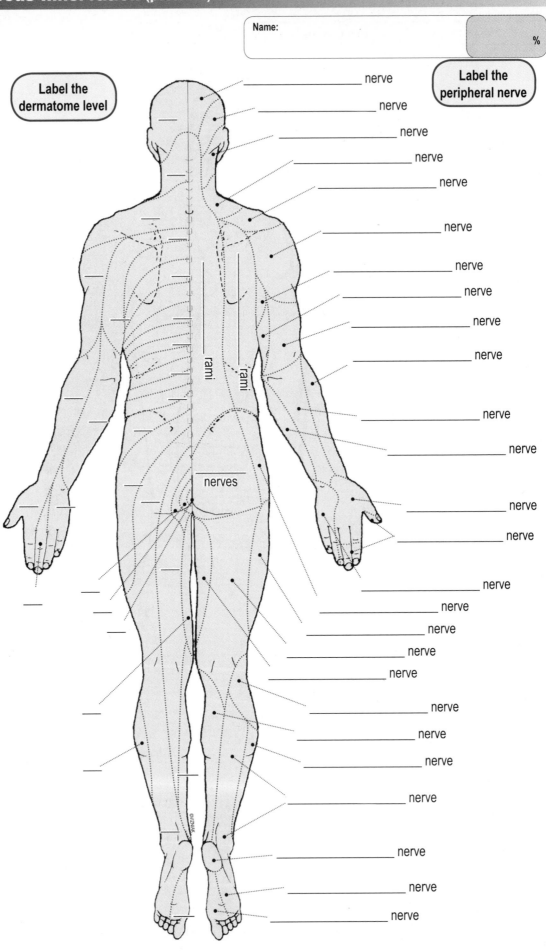

Label the
dermatome level

Label the
peripheral nerve

_____ nerve

_____ nerve

_____ nerve

_____ nerve

_____ nerve

_____ nerve

_____ nerve

_____ nerve

_____ nerve

_____ nerve

_____ nerve

_____ nerve

_____ nerve

_____ nerve

_____ nerve

_____ nerve

_____ nerve

_____ nerve

_____ nerve

_____ nerve

_____ nerve

_____ nerve

_____ nerve

_____ nerve

rami

rami

nerves

Neurovascular

prohealthsys

Name:

%

Label the
peripheral nerve

Label the
dermatome level

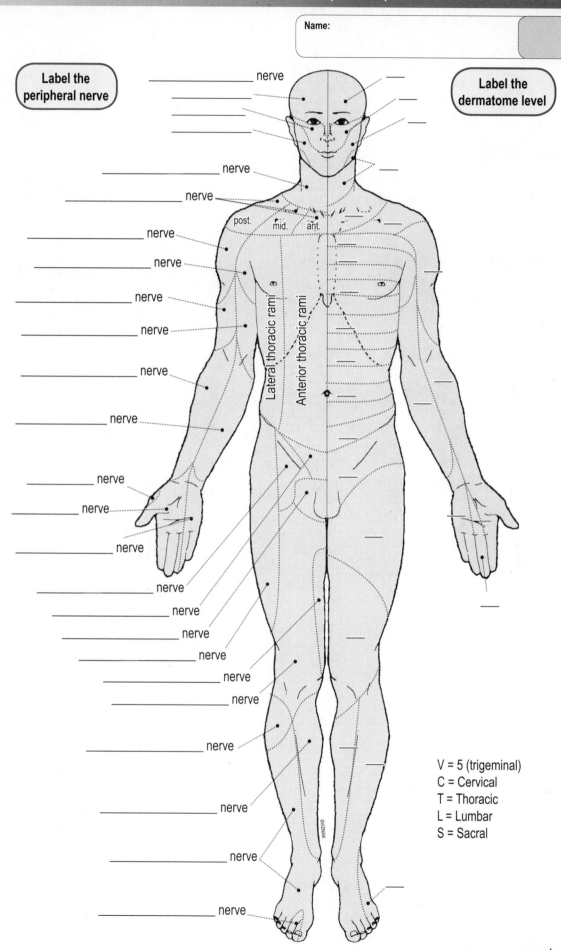

_____ nerve

_____

_____

_____

_____ nerve

_____ nerve

post.   mid.   ant.

_____ nerve

_____ nerve

_____ nerve

_____ nerve

_____ nerve

Lateral thoracic rami

Anterior thoracic rami

_____ nerve

_____ nerve

_____ nerve

_____ nerve

_____ nerve

_____ nerve

_____ nerve

_____ nerve

_____ nerve

_____ nerve

V = 5 (trigeminal)
C = Cervical
T = Thoracic
L = Lumbar
S = Sacral

_____ nerve

_____ nerve

_____ nerve

@VIZNIAK

Neurovascular

Neurovascular

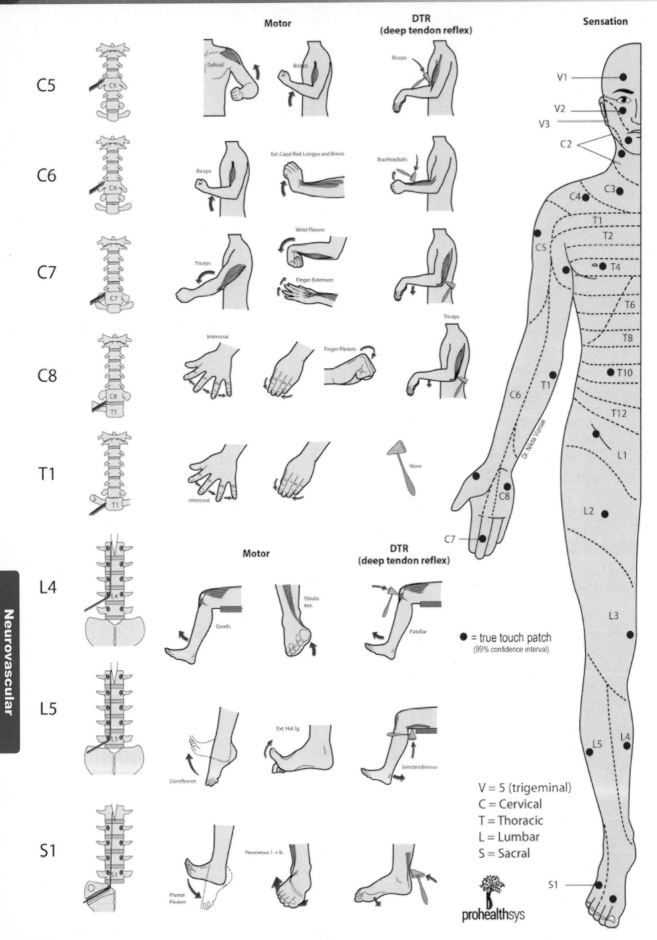

Motor   DTR (deep tendon reflex)   Sensation

C5 — Deltoid, Biceps / Biceps / V1, V2, V3, C2

C6 — Biceps, Ext. Carpi Rad. Longus and Brevis / Brachioradialis / C3, C4, C5

C7 — Triceps, Wrist Flexors, Finger Extensors / Triceps / T1, T2, T4, T6, T8

C8 — Interossei, Finger Flexors / T10, T12

T1 — Interossei / None / L1, L2

L4 — Quads, Tibialis Ant. / Patellar / L3

L5 — Dorsiflexion, Ext. Hal. lg. / Semitendinosus / L4, L5

S1 — Plantar Flexion, Peroneous l. + b. / S1

Dr. Nikita Vizniak

C6, C7, C8, T1

● = true touch patch
(99% confidence interval)

V = 5 (trigeminal)
C = Cervical
T = Thoracic
L = Lumbar
S = Sacral

prohealthsys

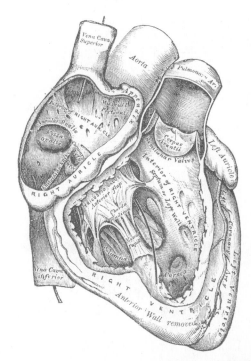

Brain blood supply -
Circle of Willis

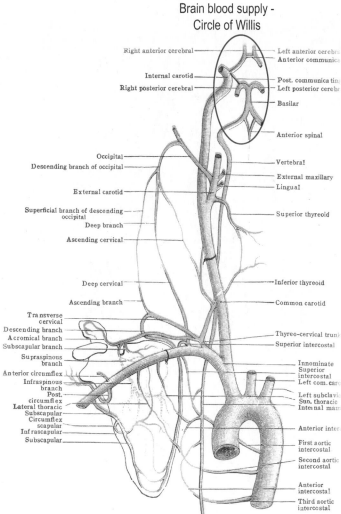

Right anterior cerebral — — Left anterior cerebra
Anterior communica
Internal carotid — — Post. communica tin
Right posterior cerebral — — Left posterior cerebr
— Basilar
— Anterior spinal
Occipital — — Vertebral
Descending branch of occipital — — External maxillary
External carotid — — Lingual
Superficial branch of descending occipital — — Superior thyreoid
Deep branch
Ascending cervical
Deep cervical — — Inferior thyreoid
Ascending branch — — Common carotid
Transverse cervical
Descending branch — — Thyreo-cervical trunk
Acromical branch — — Superior intercostal
Subscapular branch
Supraspinous branch — — Innominate
Anterior circumflex — — Superior intercostal
Infraspinous branch — — Left com. carc
Post. circumflex — — Left subclavia
Lateral thoracic — — Sup. thoracic
Subscapular — — Internal mamm
Circumflex scapular
Infrascapular — — Anterior inter
Subscapular — — First aortic intercostal
— Second aortic intercostal
— Anterior intercostal
— Third aortic intercostal

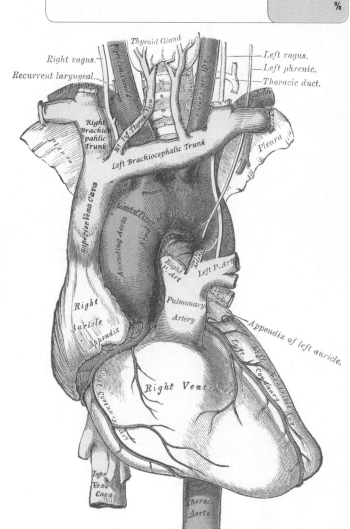

Name: _____ %

1. _____

2. _____

3. _____

4. _____

5. _____

6. _____

7. _____

8. _____

9. _____

10. _____

11. _____

12. _____

13. _____

14. _____

15. _____

16. _____

17. _____

18. _____

19. _____

20. _____

21. _____

22. _____

23. _____

24. _____

25. _____

Neurovascular

Vein Variation

Veins of the body show an increase in anatomical variation as the diameter of the vessels get smaller

Name:

%

1. _____
2. _____
3. _____
4. _____
5. _____
6. _____
7. _____
8. _____
9. _____
10. _____
11. _____
12. _____
13. _____
14. _____
15. _____
16. _____
17. _____
18. _____
19. _____
20. _____
21. _____
22. _____
23. _____
24. _____
25. _____
26. _____
27. _____
28. _____
29. _____
30. _____
31. _____
32. _____
33. _____

Youtube: Vizniak Arteries

©VIZNIAK

Neurovascular

prohealthsys

Name: _____ %

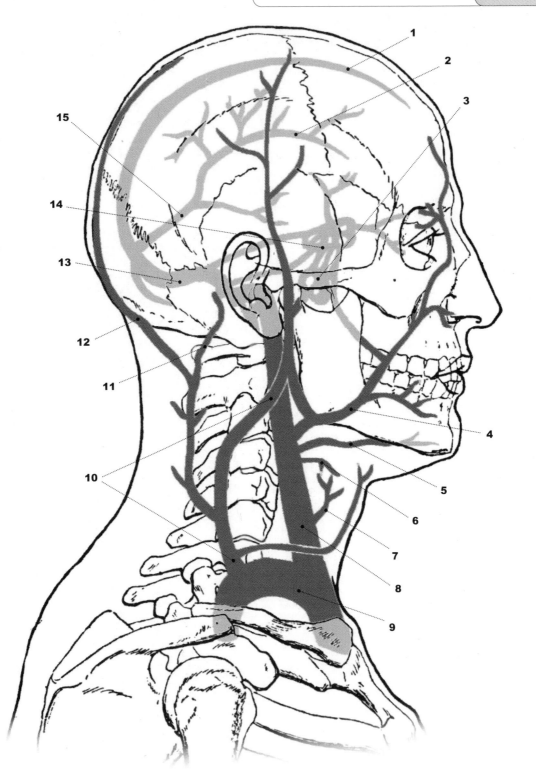

15
14
13
12
11
10

1
2
3

4
5
6
7
8
9

1. _____
2. _____
3. _____
4. _____
5. _____

6. _____
7. _____
8. _____
9. _____
10. _____

11. _____
12. _____
13. _____
14. _____
15. _____

Neurovascular

prohealthsys

Vertebral Arteries & Basilar Artery
(right lateral view)

Basilar Artery

Rectus capitis posterior minor

C3 Spinous Process

Vertebral Artery

C3 Spinal Nerve

Thyrocervical Trunk

Name:

%

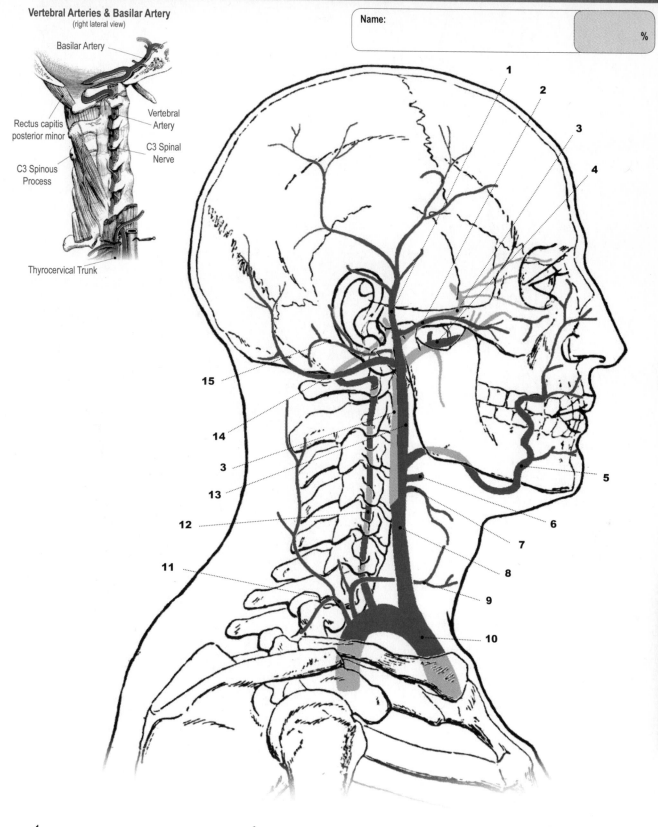

1. _____
2. _____
3. _____
4. _____
5. _____

6. _____
7. _____
8. _____
9. _____
10. _____

11. _____
12. _____
13. _____
14. _____
15. _____

Name: _____ %

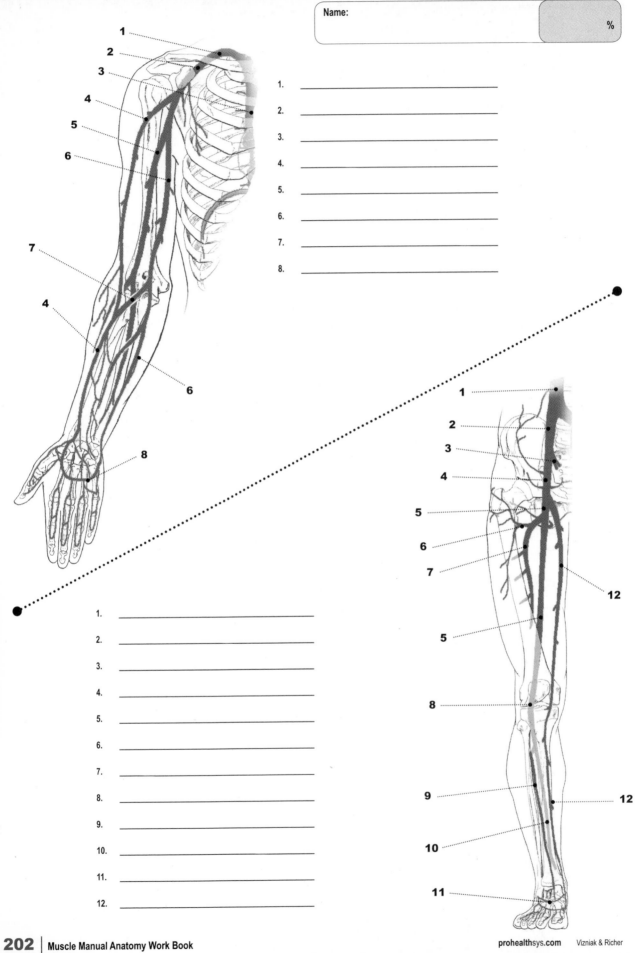

1. _____
2. _____
3. _____
4. _____
5. _____
6. _____
7. _____
8. _____

1. _____
2. _____
3. _____
4. _____
5. _____
6. _____
7. _____
8. _____
9. _____
10. _____
11. _____
12. _____

Neurovascular

Name: _____ %

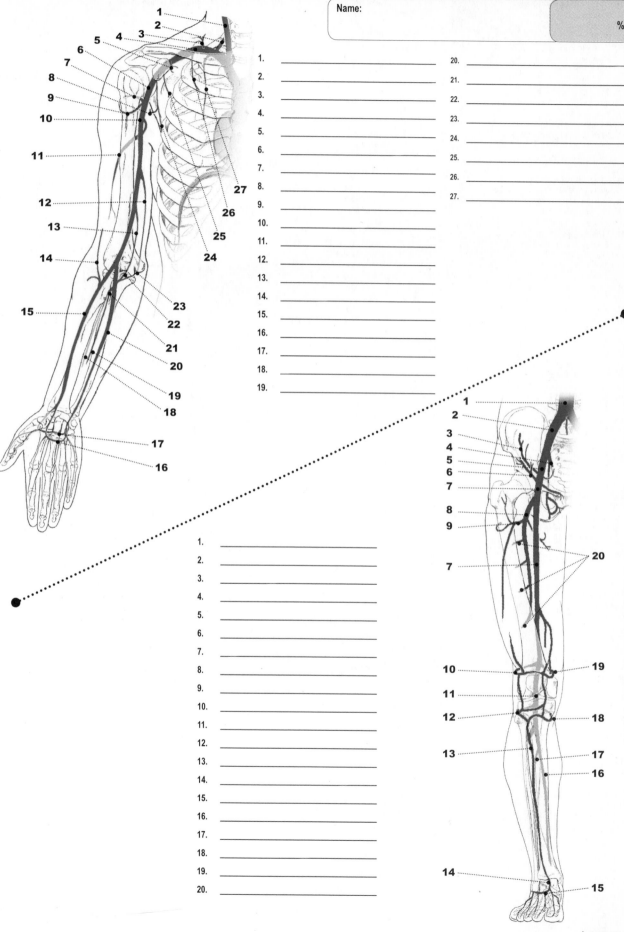

1. _____
2. _____
3. _____
4. _____
5. _____
6. _____
7. _____
8. _____
9. _____
10. _____
11. _____
12. _____
13. _____
14. _____
15. _____
16. _____
17. _____
18. _____
19. _____

20. _____
21. _____
22. _____
23. _____
24. _____
25. _____
26. _____
27. _____

1. _____
2. _____
3. _____
4. _____
5. _____
6. _____
7. _____
8. _____
9. _____
10. _____
11. _____
12. _____
13. _____
14. _____
15. _____
16. _____
17. _____
18. _____
19. _____
20. _____

Neurovascular

Page 184 Motor Upper Extremity

1. Supraspinatus (C4, C5)
2. Infraspinatus (C5, C6)
3. Serratus anterior (C5-C7)
4. Levator scapulae
5. Rhomboid major & minor
6. Deltoid (C5, C6)
7. Teres minor (C5, C6)
8. Biceps brachii (C5, C6)
9. Brachialis (C5, C6)
10. Coracobrachialis (C5, C6, C7)
11. Pronator teres (C6, C7)
12. Flexor carpi radialis (C6, C7)
13. Palmaris longus (C7, C8)
14. Flexor digitorum superficialis (C7, C8, T1)
15. Flexor digitorum profundus (lateral ½)
16. Flexor pollicis longus (C8, T1)
17. Pronator quadratus (C8, T1)
18. Abductor pollicis brevis
19. Opponens pollicis & flexor pollicis brevis
20. Lumbricals I & II
21. Brachioradialis (C5, C6, C7)
22. Extensor carpi radialis (C6-C7)
23. Anconeus (C7, C8, T1)
24. Triceps (long/lateral/medial head) (C6-C8)
25. Supinator (C5, C6)
26. Extensor carpi radialis brev. (C7, C8)
27. Extensor digitorum (C7, C8)
28. Extensor digiti minimi (C7, C8)
29. Extensor carpi ulnaris (C7, C8)
30. Abductor pollicis longus (C7, C8)
31. Extensor pollicis longus (C7, C8)
32. Extensor pollicis brevis (C7, C8)
33. Extensor indicis (C7, C8)
34. Flexor carpi ulnaris (C7, C8)
35. Flexor digitorum profundus (medial 1/2)
36. Flexor & abductor digiti minimi brevis
37. Opponens digiti minimi
38. Lumbricals III & IV, interossei
39. Adductor pollicis
40. Flexor pollicis brevis (ulnar portion)

Levator scapulae (C3-C5)
Rhomboids (C4-C5)
Deltoid (C5-C6)
Pectoralis major (C6-T1)
Latissimus dorsi (C6-C8)
Elbow flexion (C5-C6)
Elbow extension (C7-C8)
Supination (C5-C6)
Pronation (C6-T1)
Wrist extension (C6-C8)
Wrist flexion (C7-C8)
Finger extension (C6-C8)
Finger flexion (C7-T1)
Finger adduction & abduction (C8-T1)
Intrinsic hand muscles (C8-T1)

Page 185
Cervical Plexus (C1-C4)

41. **Hypoglossal n** (CN XII)
42. **Lesser Occipital** n.
43. **Greater Auricular** n.
44. Transverse Cervical n.
45. **Ansa cervicalis** (branches to infrahyoid muscles)
46. Supraclavicular branches
47. **Phrenic n.** (C3-4-5 keep the diaphragm alive)

Brachial Plexus

1. Nerve to subclavius
2. Upper subscapular nerve
3. Thoracodorsal (middle subscapular) nerve
4. Lower subscapular nerve
5. Median pectoral nerve
6. Medial brachial cutaneous (sensory)
7. Medial antebrachial cutaneous (sensory)
8. Dorsal scapular nerve
9. Suprascapular nerve
10. Lateral pectoral nerve
11. Long thoracic nerve

Page 186 Motor Lower Extremity

1. Tensor fasciae latae (L4, L5)
2. Gluteus medius (L5, S1)
3. Gluteus minimus (L5, S1)
4. Gluteus maximus (L5, S1, S2)
5. Pectineus (L2, L3)
6. Sartorius (L2, L3)
7. Rectus femoris (L2, L3, L4)
8. Vastus lateralis (L2, L3, L4)
9. Vastus intermedius (L2, L3, L4)
10. Vastus medialis (L2, L3, L4)
11. Gracilis (L2, L3)
12. Adductor longus (L2, L3, L4)
13. Adductor brevis (L2, L3, L4)
14. Adductor magnus (L2, L3, L4)
15. Obturator externus (L3, L4)
16. Popliteus (L4, L5, S1)
17. Semitendinosus (L5, S1, S2)
18. Semimembranosus (L5, S1, S2)
19. Biceps femoris (long head) (L5, S1, S2)
20. Tibialis posterior (L4, L5)
21. Gastrocnemius (S1, S2)
22. Plantaris & Soleus (S1, S2)
23. Flexor digitorum longus (S2, S3)
24. Flexor hallucis longus (S2, S3)
25. Abductor hallucis & abductor digiti minimi
26. Dorsal interossei
27. Biceps femoris (short head) (L5, S1, S2)
28. Tibialis anterior (L4, L5)
29. Extensor hallucis longus (L5, S1)
30. Extensor digitorum longus (L5, S1)
31. Fibularis tertius (L5, S1)
32. Extensor digitorum brevis
33. Fibularis longus (L5, S1, S2)
34. Fibularis brevis (L5, S1, S2)

Hip extension & external rotation (L5-S2)
Hip external rotation (L4-S2)
Hip abduction & internal rotation (L2-L4)
Hip abduction (L4-S1)
Hip extension (L5-S2)
Hip flexion (L1-L4)
Knee flexion (L4-S2)
Knee extension (L2-L4)
Extensor hallucis (L4-S1)
Toe extension (L4-S1)
Plantarflexion (L4-S2)
Dorsiflexors (L4-S1)
Ankle inversion (L4-S1)
Ankle eversion (L4-S1)

Page 187 Lumbosacral Plexus

1. Iliohypogastric nerve
2. Ilioinguinal nerve
3. Lateral femoral cutaneous nerve
4. Genitofemoral nerve
5. Superior gluteal nerve
6. Inferior gluteal nerve
7. Pudendal nerve
8. Posterior femoral cutaneous nerve

Page 190
Radial Nerve

1. Triceps brachii (C6, C7, C8)
   a. Long head
   b. Medial (deep) head
   c. Lateral head
2. Brachioradialis (C5, C6, C7)
3. Extensor carpi radialis (C6, C7)
4. Anconeus (C7, C8, T1)
5. Supinator (C7, C8)
6. Extensor carpi radialis brevis (C7, C8)
7. Extensor digitorum (C7, C8)
8. Extensor digiti minimi (C7, C8)
9. Extensor carpi ulnaris (C7, C8)
10. Abductor pollicis longus (C7, C8)
11. Extensor pollicis longus (C7, C8)
12. Extensor pollicis brevis (C7, C8)
13. Extensor indicis (C7, C8)

Axillary Nerve

1. Deltoid (C5, C6)
2. Teres minor (C5, C6)
3. Triceps Long Head (C5, C6)

Musculocutaneous Nerve

4. Biceps brachii (C5, C6)
5. Brachialis (C5, C6)
6. Coracobrachialis (C5, C6, C7)

Page 191 Median Nerve

1. Pronator teres (C6, C7)
2. Flexor carpi radialis (C6, C7)
3. Palmaris longus (C7, C8)
4. Flexor digitorum superficialis (C7, C8, T1)
5. Flexor digitorum profundus (lateral ½)
6. Flexor pollicis longus (C8, T1)
7. Pronator quadratus (C8, T1)
8. Abductor pollicis brevis (C8, T1)
9. Opponens pollicis (C8, T1)
10. Flexor pollicis brevis (C8, T1)
11. Lumbricals I & II (C8, T1)

Page 191 Ulnar Nerve

1. Flexor carpi ulnaris (C7, C8)
2. Flexor digitorum profundus (medial 1/2)
3. Palmaris brevis (C8, T1)
4. Flexor digiti minimi (C8, T1)
5. Abductor digiti minimi brevis (C8, T1)
6. Opponens digiti minimi (C8-T1)
7. Lumbricals III & IV (C8, T1)
8. Dorsal & palmar interossei (C8, T1)
9. Adductor pollicis (C8, T1)

Page 192 Sciatic Nerve

1. Sciatic nerve (tibial division)
2. Semitendinosus (L5, S1, S2)
3. Semimembranosus (L5, S1, S2)
4. Biceps femoris (L5, S1, S2) (long head)
5. Popliteus (L4, L5, S1)
6. Common fibular nerve
7. Tibial nerve
8. Gastrocnemius (S1, S2)
9. Soleus (S1, S2)
10. Plantaris (S1, S2)
11. Tibialis posterior (L4, L5)
12. Flexor digitorum longus (S2, S3)
13. Flexor hallucis longus (S2, S3)
14. Medial plantar nerve
15. Abductor hallucis (S2, S3)
16. Abductor digiti minimi (S2, S3)
17. Flexor hallucis brevis (S2, S3)
18. Dorsal interossei (S2, S3)
19. Sciatic nerve (fibular/peroneal division)
20. Biceps femoris (L5, S1, S2) (short head)
21. Common fibular (peroneal) nerve
22. Deep fibular nerve
23. Tibialis anterior (L4, L5)
24. Extensor hallucis longus (L5, S1)
25. Extensor digitorum longus (L5, S1)
26. Fibularis tertius (L5, S1)
27. Superficial fibular nerve
28. Fibularis longus (L5, S1, S2)
29. Fibularis brevis (L5, S1, S2)
30. Extensor digitorum brevis (S1, S2)

Page 193 Femoral & Obturator Nerves
Femoral nerve (L2-4 posterior division)

1. Iliacus (L2, L3)
2. Sartorius (L2, L3)
3. Pectineus (L2, L3)
4. Rectus femoris (L2, L3, L4)
5. Vastus lateralis (L2, L3, L4)
6. Vastus intermedius (L2, L3, L4)
7. Vastus medialis (L2, L3, L4)
8. Articularis genu (L3, L4)
9. Saphenous Nerve (sensory only L4)

Obturator nerve (L2-4 anterior division)

1. Obturator externus (L3, L4)
2. Adductor brevis (L2, L3, L4)
3. Adductor longus (L2, L3, L4)
4. Gracilis (L2, L3)
5. Adductor magnus (L2, L3, L4)

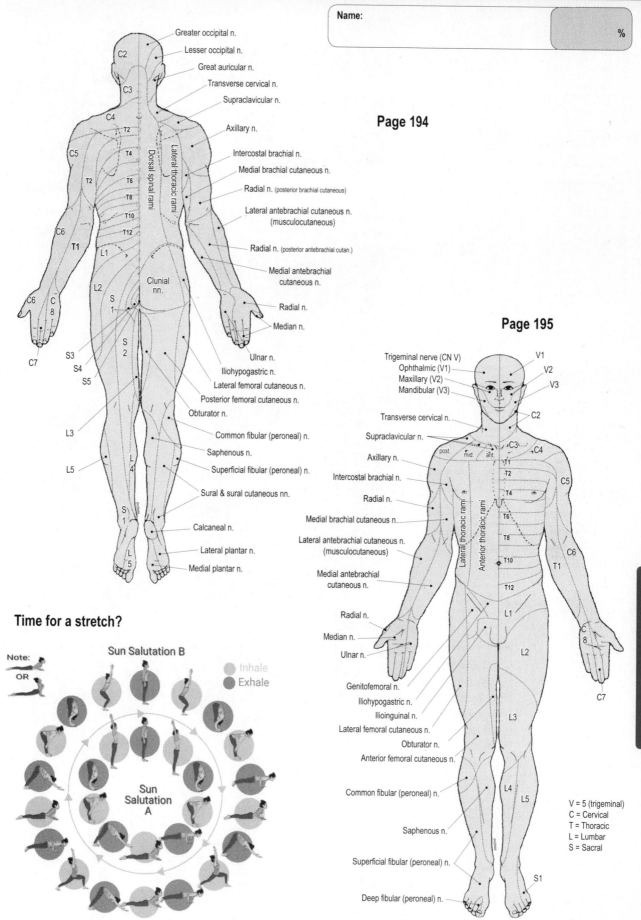

Name: _____ %

Page 194

Greater occipital n.
Lesser occipital n.
Great auricular n.
Transverse cervical n.
Supraclavicular n.
Axillary n.
Intercostal brachial n.
Medial brachial cutaneous n.
Radial n. (posterior brachial cutaneous)
Lateral antebrachial cutaneous n.
(musculocutaneous)
Radial n. (posterior antebrachial cutan.)
Medial antebrachial cutaneous n.
Radial n.
Median n.
Ulnar n.
Iliohypogastric n.
Lateral femoral cutaneous n.
Posterior femoral cutaneous n.
Obturator n.
Common fibular (peroneal) n.
Saphenous n.
Superficial fibular (peroneal) n.
Sural & sural cutaneous nn.
Calcaneal n.
Lateral plantar n.
Medial plantar n.

C2, C3, C4, C5, C6, T1, C6, C8, C7
T2, T4, T2, T6, T8, T10, T12, L1, L2, L3, L5
Dorsal spinal rami
Lateral thoracic rami
Clunial nn.
S1, S2, S3, S4, S5, L4, S1, L5

Page 195

Trigeminal nerve (CN V)
Ophthalmic (V1)
Maxillary (V2)
Mandibular (V3)
Transverse cervical n.
Supraclavicular n.
Axillary n.
Intercostal brachial n.
Radial n.
Medial brachial cutaneous n.
Lateral antebrachial cutaneous n.
(musculocutaneous)
Medial antebrachial cutaneous n.
Radial n.
Median n.
Ulnar n.
Genitofemoral n.
Iliohypogastric n.
Ilioinguinal n.
Lateral femoral cutaneous n.
Obturator n.
Anterior femoral cutaneous n.
Common fibular (peroneal) n.
Saphenous n.
Superficial fibular (peroneal) n.
Deep fibular (peroneal) n.

V1, V2, V3
C2, C3, C4, C5, C6, T1, C8, C7
post. mid. ant.
T1, T2, T4, T6, T8, T10, T12, L1, L2, L3, L4, L5, S1
Lateral thoracic rami
Anterior thoracic rami

V = 5 (trigeminal)
C = Cervical
T = Thoracic
L = Lumbar
S = Sacral

Time for a stretch?

Note:
OR

Sun Salutation B

● Inhale
● Exhale

Sun Salutation A

Neurovascular

Page 198 Veins of Body
1. Superior sagittal sinus
2. External jugular vein
3. Internal jugular vein
4. Subclavian vein
5. Axillary vein
6. Superior vena cava
7. Cephalic vein
8. Basilic vein
9. Median cubital vein
10. Median antecubital vein
11. Palmar venous arch
12. Inferior vena cava
13. Common iliac vein
14. Internal iliac vein
15. External iliac vein
16. Femoral vein
17. Profunda femoris vein
18. Great saphenous vein
19. Popliteal vein
20. Small saphenous vein
21. Dorsal venous arch
22. Renal vein
23. Hepatic veins
24. Segmental veins
25. Brachiocephalic

Page 199 Arteries of Body
1. Superficial temporal artery
2. Circle of Willis
3. Internal carotid artery
4. Basilar artery
5. External carotid artery
6. Vertebral artery
7. Common carotid artery
8. Brachiocephalic trunk
9. Subclavian artery
10. Axillary artery
11. Humeral circumflex artery
12. Brachial artery
13. Radial artery
14. Ulnar artery
15. Deep palmar arch
16. Superficial palmar arch
17. Common iliac artery
18. Internal iliac artery
19. External iliac artery
20. Deep femoral artery
21. Femoral artery
22. Popliteal artery
23. Genicular artery
24. Anterior tibial artery
25. Posterior tibial artery
26. Fibular artery
27. Dorsal pedis artery
28. Abdominal aorta
29. Inferior mesenteric artery
30. Renal artery
31. Superior mesenteric artery
32. Celiac trunk
33. Thyrocervical trunk

Page 200 Veins of Head & Neck
1. Superior sagittal sinus
2. Inferior sagittal sinus
3. Hypophyseal portal system
4. Facial vein
5. Lingual vein
6. Superior thyroid vein
7. Inferior thyroid vein
8. Internal jugular vein
9. Subclavian vein
10. External jugular vein
11. Posterior auricular vein
12. Occipital vein
13. Transverse sinus
14. Cavernous sinus
15. Straight sinus

Page 201 Arteries Head & Neck
1. Superficial temporal artery
2. Transverse facial artery
3. Internal carotid artery
4. Maxillary artery
5. Facial artery
6. Lingual artery
7. Superior thyroid artery
8. Common carotid artery
9. Inferior thyroid artery
10. Brachiocephalic trunk
11. Costocervical trunk
12. Vertebral artery
13. External carotid artery
14. Occipital artery
15. Posterior auricular artery

Page 202 Veins of the upper & lower extremity
1. Subclavian vein
2. Axillary vein
3. Superior vena cava

4. Cephalic vein
5. Deep brachial vein
6. Basilic vein
7. Median cubital vein
8. Palmar venous arch

1. Inferior vena cava
2. Common iliac vein
3. Internal iliac vein
4. External iliac vein
5. Femoral vein
6. Lateral femoral circumflex vein
7. Deep (profundus) femoral vein
8. Popliteal vein
9. Anterior tibial vein
10. Small (short) saphenous vein
11. Dorsal venous arch
12. Great (long) saphenous vein

Page 203 Arteries upper & lower extremity
1. **Common carotid artery**
2. **Vertebral artery**
3. Thyrocervical trunk
4. **Subclavian artery**
5. Thoracoacromial artery
6. **Axillary artery**
7. Post. humeral circumflex a.
8. Scapular circumflex artery
9. Anterior humeral circumflex a.
10. **Brachial artery**
11. Deep brachial artery
12. Superior ulnar collateral a.
13. Inferior ulnar collateral artery
14. Radial recurrent artery
15. **Radial artery**
16. Superficial palmar arch
17. Deep palmar arch
18. Posterior interosseous artery
19. Anterior interosseous artery
20. **Ulnar artery**
21. Common interosseous artery
22. Anterior ulnar recurrent artery
23. Posterior ulnar recurrent a.
24. Thoracodorsal artery
25. Long thoracic artery
26. Superior thoracic artery
27. Internal thoracic artery

1. **Aorta(abdominal)**
2. **Common iliac artery**
3. Deep iliac circumflex artery
4. **Internal iliac artery**
5. **External iliac artery**
6. Superficial iliac circumflex artery
7. **Femoral artery**
8. **Deep (profundus) femoral artery**
9. Lateral femoral circumflex artery
10. Superior lateral genicular artery
11. **Popliteal artery**
12. Inferior lateral genicular artery
13. **Anterior tibial artery**
14. **Dorsal pedis artery**
15. Arcuate artery
16. **Posterior tibial artery**
17. Fibular artery
18. Inferior medial genicular artery
19. Superior medial genicular artery
20. **Perforating arteries** (through adductor magnus muscle)

> For specific information use the Muscle Manual Text, Flashcards, Muscle Tables Chapter or on-line resources

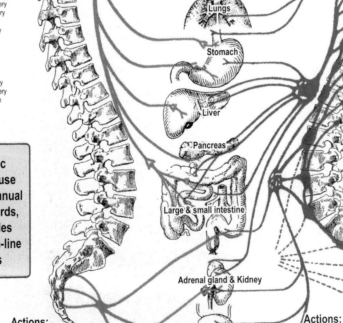

Homunculus

Somatosensory

Motor

Parasympathetic (rest & digest)
CN III, VII, IX, X
S2-3-4

Sympathetic (fight or flight)
Sympathetic chain
T1-L2

Eye (pupil)
Lacrimal
Respiratory passage
Salivary glands
Heart
Lungs
Stomach
Liver
Pancreas
Large & small intestine
Adrenal gland & Kidney
Bladder
Reproductive organs

Actions:
↓ skeletal muscle blood flow
↓ heart & respiration rate
↑ digestion; constricts pupils

Actions:
↑ skeletal muscle blood flow
↑ heart & respiration rate
↓ digestion; dilate pupils

prohealthsys

prohealthsys

Muscles of Facial Expression 208

Muscles of Mastication & Eye Move 209

Neck Muscles 210

Back Muscles 212

Shoulder Muscles................................214

Arm Muscles 215

Forearm Muscles................................216

Hand Muscles 218

Abdominal Wall Muscles.......................219

Gluteal Region Muscles 220

Thigh Muscles.....................................221

Leg Muscles 222

Foot Muscles.......................................223

Exercise Rehab. ------------------------

   Foam Roller Exercises 224

   Body Weight Exercises 225

   Gym Ball Exercises 226

   Yoga Poses 227

   Self stretches 228

Muscles 229

Bones Ligaments Skeleton 230

Final Exam Written 232

Final Exam Practical.............................233

▶ Video on website

FUN, on-line jeopardy style quizzes available **on prohealthsys**

Explore Our Library of VIDEO Resources for Students and Practitioners
˅

C-Spine & Head	T-Spine & Torso	L-Spine, Pelvis & SI	Shoulder & Arm
✚ Anatomy	✚ Anatomy	✚ Anatomy	✚ Anatomy
✚ Palpation	✚ Palpation	✚ Palpation	✚ Palpation
✚ ROM	✚ ROM	✚ ROM	✚ ROM
✚ Muscle Testing	✚ Muscle Testing	✚ Muscle Testing	✚ Muscle Testing
✚ Special Tests	✚ Special Tests	✚ Special Tests	✚ Special Tests
✚ Conditions	✚ Conditions	✚ Conditions	✚ Conditions

Muscle Tables

Name: _____ %

Muscle	Origin	Insertion	Action	Nerve
Buccinator	maxilla & mandible (posterior alveolar process of both bones) pterygomandibular raphe	modiolus (just lateral to the angle of the mouth	compresses cheek(s)	facial nerve (CN VII)
Corrugator supercilii	frontal bone lateral to glabella	skin of medial portion of eyebrows	draws eyebrows downward & medially ("thinker's brow")	facial nerve (CN VII)
Depressor anguli oris	along oblique line of mandible lateral aspect of mental tubercle of mandible	modiolus (near angle of mouth)	depresses angle(s) of mouth (frown)	facial nerve (CN VII)
Depressor labii inferioris	mandible (between symphysis & mental foramen)	skin & fascia of lower lip	draws lower lip downward & laterally everts lower lip	facial nerve (CN VII)
Depressor septi nasi	incisive fossa of maxilla	septum & alar cartilage of nose	constricts notrils	facial nerve (CN VII)
Frontalis	galea aponeurotica	skin & fascia above nose & eyes	draws scalp posteriorly to raise eyebrows & wrinkle brow (surprise)	facial nerve (CN VII)
Levator anguli oris	below infraorbital foramen of maxilla	modiolus (near angle of mouth)	elevates angle(s) of mouth (smiling)	facial nerve (CN VII)
Levator labii superioris	medial inferior orbital margin of maxilla	upper lip muscles	elevates upper lip everts upper lip	facial nerve (CN VII)
Levator labii superioris alaeque nasi	frontal process of maxilla	lateral slip: upper lip muscles medial slip: alar cartilage (nose)	elevates & everts upper lip flares nostrils	facial nerve (CN VII)
Mentalis	incisive fossa of mandible	skin & fascia of chin	elevation of lower lip; everts lower lip; wrinkles skin of chin	facial nerve (CN VII)
Nasalis	transverse part: maxilla (lateral to nose) alar part: maxilla, superior to canine alveolar process	transverse part: opposite side nasalis over upper cartilage of nose alar part: alar cartilage of nose	flares nostrils (particularly in forced respiration)	facial nerve (CN VII)
Occipitalis	lateral 2/3 of superior nuchal line & external occipital protuberance	galea aponeurotica	draws back scalp to raise eyebrows & wrinkle brow (surprise)	facial nerve (CN VII)
Orbicularis oculi	orbital portion: nasal process of frontal bone palpebral portion: palpebral ligament; lacrimal portion: lacrimal crest of lacrimal bone	circumferentially around orbit meeting at the origin	closes eye tightly, squinting of the eye; depresses upper eye lid elevates lower eyelid (palpebral part)	facial nerve (CN VII)
Orbicularis oris	modiolus (lateral to angle of mouth)	circumferentially around mouth; blends with other muscles	closes mouth; protrudes lips (puckering of lips)	facial nerve (CN VII)
Platysma	subcutaneous fascia (over deltoid-pectoral region)	mandible & subcutaneous fascia of lower face	tenses skin over lower neck (creates ridge in skin) depress mandible & lower lip	facial nerve (CN VII)
Procerus	nasal bone & cartilages	skin & fascia between eyebrows	draws medial eyebrow downward (menacing expression); wrinkles skin of superior nose	facial nerve (CN VII)
Risorius	parotid fascia (superficial to masseter)	modiolus (near angle of mouth)	draws angle of mouth laterally (false smile)	facial nerve (CN VII)
Zygomaticus major	zygomatic bone (anterior to zygomatic-temporal suture)	modiolus (near angle of mouth)	elevates angle of mouth (smiling) pulls angle of mouth laterally	facial nerve (CN VII)
Zygomaticus minor	zygomatic bone (posterior to zygomatic-maxillary suture)	skin, fascia & muscles of upper lip	elevates upper lip (smile); everts upper lip	facial nerve (CN VII)

Muscle Tables

prohealthsys

Name:

%

Muscles of Mastication

Muscle	Origin	Insertion	Action	Nerve
Lateral pterygoid	superior head: greater wing of sphenoid inferior head: lateral surface of lateral pterygoid plate	superior head: capsule & articular disc of TMJ inferior head: neck of mandibular condyle	protraction of the mandible (open mouth) lateral deviation of mandible to side opposite of contraction (during chewing)	trigeminal nerve (CN V)
Masseter	superficial part: zygomatic process of maxilla; inferior border of zygomatic arch deep part: posterior aspect of inferior border of zygomatic arch	superficial part: angle & ramus of mandible deep part: superior ramus & coronoid process of mandible	elevation of mandible (clenches teeth) protraction of mandible (anterior fibers) retraction of mandible (posterior fibers)	trigeminal nerve (CN V)
Medial pterygoid	medial surface of lateral pterygoid plate of sphenoid palatine bone & pterygoid fossa	inner surface of mandibular ramus & angle of mandible	elevation of mandible (clenches teeth) protraction of mandible lateral deviation of mandible	trigeminal nerve (CN V)
Temporalis	temporal fossa	coronoid process & upper ramus of mandible	elevation of mandible retraction of mandible (posterior fibers)	trigeminal nerve (CN V)

Lateral pterygoid is the only muscle of mastication to help open the mouth

Muscles of Eye Movement

Muscle	Origin	Insertion	Action	Nerve
Inferior rectus	common tendinous ring (off body & lesser wing of sphenoid); margins of optic canal	sclera just behind cornea	depression of eye (look down)	occulomotor nerve (CN III)
Lateral rectus	common tendinous ring (off body & lesser wing of sphenoid); margins of optic canal	sclera just behind cornea	abduction of eye	abducens nerve (CN VI)
Medial rectus	common tendinous ring (off body & lesser wing of sphenoid); margins of optic canal	sclera just behind cornea	adduction of eye	occulomotor nerve (CN III)
Superior rectus	common tendinous ring (off body & lesser wing of sphenoid); margins of optic canal	sclera just behind cornea	elevation of eye (look up)	trochlear nerve (CN IV)
Superior oblique	body of sphenoid (above optic canal)	upper lateral quadrant of posterior half of sclera (via trochlea, as a pulley)	rotation of eye downward & medially depression of adducted eye	occulomotor nerve (CN III)
Inferior oblique	orbital surface of maxilla	lower lateral quadrant of posterior half of sclera (via suspensory ligament, as a pulley)	rotation of eye upward & laterally; elevation of adducted eye	occulomotor nerve (CN III)
Levator palpebrae superioris	lesser wing of sphenoid bone (anterior surface)	upper eyelid (fascia & skin)	elevates upper eyelid	occulomotor nerve (CN III)

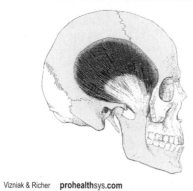
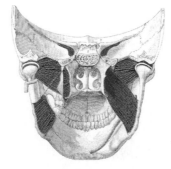
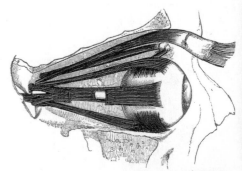

Muscle Tables

Cover table with a piece of table and fill in the boxes - no peaking ☺
On-line Table quizzes available at: prohealthsys.com

Name: _____ %

Muscle	Origin	Insertion	Action	Nerve
Superficial Anterior Neck				
Platysma	Superficial fascia over upper part of deltoid & pectoralis major	mandible; skin & muscles over mandible & angle of mouth	depresses lower jaw & lip & angle of mouth wrinkles skin of neck	facial nerve (CN VII)
Sternoclei-domastoid (SCM)	sternal head: manubrium of sternum clavicular head: medial 1/3 of clavicle	mastoid process of temporal bone lateral 1/2 of superior nuchal line	rotates to side opposite of contraction laterally flexes to contracted side bilaterally flexes neck	motor: spinal accessory (CN XI) sensory: ventral rami of C2, C3
Suprahyoid Muscles				
Digastric	anterior belly from digastric fossa of mandible posterior belly from mastoid notch	intermediate tendon attached to body of hyoid	elevates hyoid & tongue; depresses mandible	anterior belly: mylohyoid nerve or trigeminal nerve posterior belly: facial nerve (CN VII)
Mylohyoid	mylohyoid line of mandible	median raphe & body of hyoid bone	elevates hyoid & tongue; depresses mandible	mylohyoid nerve or trigeminal nerve (CN V)
Stylohyoid	styloid process	body of hyoid	elevates hyoid	facial nerve (CN VII)
Geniohyoid	genial tubercle of mandible	body of hyoid	elevates hyoid & tongue	C1 via hypoglossal nerve
Infrahyoid Muscles				
Sternohyoid	manubrium of sternum & medial end of clavicle	body of hyoid	depresses hyoid & larynx	ansa cervicalis
Sternothyroid	manubrium of sternum 1st costal cartilage	oblique line of thyroid cartilage	depresses thyroid cartilage & larynx	ansa cervicalis
Thyrohyoid	oblique line of thyroid cartilage	body & greater horn of hyoid	depresses & retracts hyoid & larynx	C1 via hypoglossal nerve
Omohyoid	inferior belly: medial lip of suprascapular notch & suprascapular ligament superior belly: intermediate tendon	inferior belly: intermediate tendon superior belly: body of hyoid	depresses & retracts hyoid & larynx	ansa cervicalis
Deep Anterior Cervical Muscles (prevertebrals)				
Longus cervicis (coli)	lower anterior vertebral bodies & TP of C3-T3	anterior vertebral bodies & TP C1-C6	flexion & lateral flexion of neck; rotation of neck	cervical spinal nerves (ventral rami C2-C6)
Longus capitis	TP of C3-C5 (anterior tubercles)	occipital bone (basilar portion)	flexion of head & neck; lateral flexion of head & neck	cervical spinal nerves (ventral rami C1-C3)
Rectus capitis anterior	atlas (C1) (anterior base of TP)	occipital bone (basilar part anterior to foramen magnum)	flexion of head	cervical spinal nerves (ventral rami C1-C2)
Rectus capitis lateralis	atlas (C1) (superior surface of TP)	occipital bone (jugular process)	lateral flexion of head	cervical spinal nerves (ventral rami C1-C2)
Scalenes (paravertebrals)				
Anterior scalene	TP of C3-C6 (anterior tubercles)	1st rib (scalene tubercle)	elevation of 1st rib (if neck is stabilized) flexion & lateral flexion of neck rotation of neck (weakly)	cervical spinal nerves (ventral rami C3-C6)
Middle scalene	TP C2-C7 (posterior tubercle)	1st rib (behind anterior scalene)	flexion & lateral flexion of neck elevation of 1st rib (if neck stabilized)	cervical spinal nerves (ventral rami C3-C8)
Posterior scalene	TP of C5-C7 (posterior tubercles)	2nd and/or 3rd rib	lateral flexion of neck elevation of 2nd rib (if neck is fixed)	cervical spinal nerves (ventral rami C6-C8)
Scalenus minimus	TP C6-C7 (anterior tubercles)	1st rib and/or suprapleural membrane	flexion & lateral flexion of neck elevation of 2nd rib & superior pleura of lung (if neck is stabilized)	variable (cervical & brachial plexus)

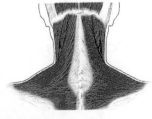
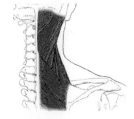
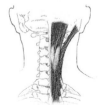

Muscle Tables

prohealthsys

Cover table with a piece of table and fill in the boxes - no peaking ☺
On-line Table quizzes available at: **prohealth**sys.com

Name:

%

Superficial Posterior Neck*

Muscle	Origin	Insertion	Action	Nerve
Trapezius	external occipital protuberance (EOP) medial side of superior nuchal line nuchal ligament SPs of C7-T12	lateral 1/3 of clavicle acromion spine of scapula	stabilization of scapula; elevation scapula; upward rotation of scapula (upper fibers) downward rotation of scapula (lower fibers) retraction (adduction) of scapula lateral flexion of head (unilateral) extension of head (bilateral)	spinal accessory (CN XI), ventral rami of C2-C4
Splenius capitis	nuchal ligament (lower portion) SPs of C3-T4	mastoid process (temporal bone) superior nuchal line (occipital bone)	bilateral contraction: extension of head & neck unilateral contraction: rotation & lateral flexion of head & neck to ipsilateral side	cervical spinal nerves (dorsal rami)
Splenius cervicis	SPs of T3-T6	TP of C1-C3 (posterior tubercles)	bilateral contraction: extension of head & neck unilateral contraction: rotation & lateral flexion of head & neck to ipsilateral side	cervical spinal nerve (dorsal rami)
Levator scapulae	TP of C1-C4	superior medial border of scapula	elevation of scapula extension & lateral flexion of neck	dorsal scapular nerve (C3, C4, C5)

Suboccipital Muscles

Muscle	Origin	Insertion	Action	Nerve
Obliquus capitis inferior	SP of axis (C2)	TP of atlas (C1)	rotation of head to ipsilateral side	suboccipital nerve (dorsal rami C1)
Obliquus capitis superior	TP of atlas (C1)	between superior & inferior nuchal line of occiput	bilateral: extension of head unilateral: lateral flexion of head to ipsilateral side	suboccipital nerve (dorsal rami C1)
Rectus capitis posterior major	SP of axis (C2)	lateral 1/2 inferior nuchal line (occipital bone)	bilateral: extension of head unilateral: lateral flexion & rotation of head to contracted side	suboccipital nerve (dorsal rami C1)
Rectus capitis posterior minor	posterior tubercle of atlas (C1)	medial 1/2 of inferior nuchal line (occipital bone)	bilaterally extends head	suboccipital nerve (dorsal rami C1)

*Longussimus capitis, semispinal capitis & spinalis captits are also considered superficail posterior neck muscles, they are discussed in the layers of the back

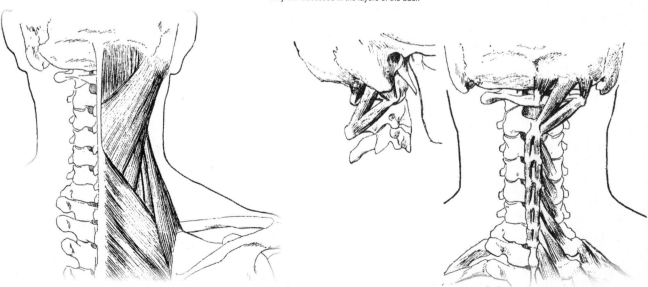

Muscle Tables

Cover table with a piece of table and fill in the boxes - no peaking ☺
On-line Table quizzes available at: **prohealthsys.com**

Name: _____ %

Muscle	Origin	Insertion	Action	Nerve
Trapezius	external occipital protuberance (EOP) medial 1/2 of superior nuchal line nuchal ligament SPs of C7-T12	lateral 1/3 of clavicle acromion spine of scapula	**elevation scapula** **retraction (adduction) of scapula** **lateral flexion of head (unilateral)** **extension of head (bilateral)** upward rotation of scapula (upper fibers) downward rotation of scapula (lower fibers) stabilization of scapula	spinal accessory (CN XI), ventral rami of C2-C4
Latissimus dorsi	SP T7-L5; thoracolumbar fascia iliac crest, posterior sacrum, ribs 9-12 inferior angle of scapula (occasionally)	medial lip of bicipital groove (humerus)	**adduction, medial rotation & extension of humerus** anterior pelvic tilt elevation of pelvis depression of scapula downward rotation of scapula	thoracodorsal nerve (C6, C7, C8)
Levator scapulae	TP of C1-C4	medial border of scapula (superior part)	**elevation of scapula** extension & lateral flexion of neck	dorsal scapular nerve (C3, C4, C5)
Rhomboid major	SPs of T2-T5 supraspinous ligament	medial border of scapula from scapular spine to inferior angle	**retraction (adduction) of scapula** elevation & downward rotation of scapula	dorsal scapular nerve (C4-C5)
Rhomboid minor	SPs of C7 & T1 ligamentum nuchae supraspinous ligament	medial border of scapula (medial angle/root of spine)	**retraction (adduction) of scapula** elevation & downward rotation of scapula	dorsal scapular nerve (C4-C5)
Serratus posterior inferior	SPs of T11-L2	ribs 9-12 (inferior external border)	**depression of ribs**	intercostal & sub costal nerves
Serratus posterior superior	SPs of C7-T3	ribs 2-5 (superior external border)	**elevation of ribs**	intercostal nerves

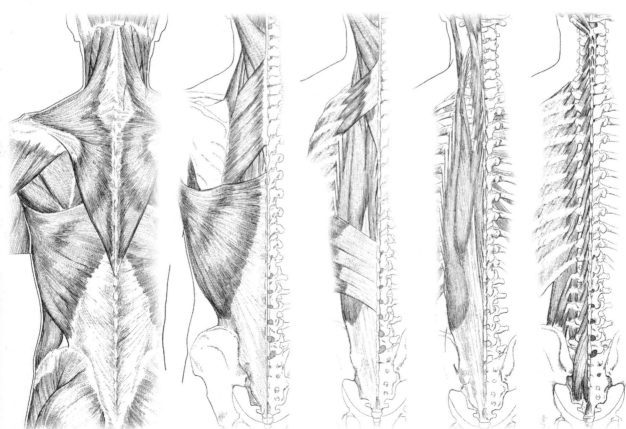

Name:

%

Erector Spinae Group

Muscle	Origin	Insertion	Action	Nerve
Iliocostalis	lumborum: medial iliac crest & sacrum thoracis: angle of ribs 7-12 cervicis: angle of ribs 3-6	lumborum: angle of ribs 7-12 thoracis: angle of ribs 1-6 cervicis: TPs of C3-C6	bilateral: extension of the spine (maintenance of erect posture); unilateral: lateral flexion & rotation to same side of the spine & head; opposite muscles contract eccentrically for stabilization	dorsal rami of spinal nerves
Longissimus	thoracis: iliac crest, posterior sacrum, TPs L1-L5 cervicis: TPs of T1-T5 capitis: TPs & articular processes of C5-C7 & TPs of T1-T4	thoracis: TPs of T1-12 & ribs 4-12 (medial to tubercle) cervicis: TPs & posterior tubercles of C2-C6 capitis: mastoid process (temporal bone)	bilateral: extension of the spine & head (maintenance of erect posture) unilateral: lateral flexion & rotation to same side of the spine & head; opposite muscles contract eccentrically for stabilization	dorsal rami of spinal nerves
Spinalis	thoracis: SPs T11-L2 cervicis: SP of C7 & inferior nuchal ligament capitis: TPs of C7-T6 & articular process of C4-C6 (medial part of semispinalis)	thoracis: SPs of T4-T8 cervicis: SP of C2 capitis: occipital bone (considered to be the medial part of semispinalis)	bilateral: extension of the spine & head (maintenance of erect posture) unilateral: lateral flexion & rotation to same side of the spine & head; opposite muscles contract eccentrically for stabilization	dorsal rami of spinal nerves

Transversospinalis Group

Muscle	Origin	Insertion	Action	Nerve
Semispinalis	thoracis: TPs of T6-T10 cervicis: TPs of T1-T5 capitis: TPs of C7-T6 & articular process of C4-C6	thoracis: SPs of C6-T4 cervicis: SPs of C2-C5 capitis: occipital bone (between superior & inferior nuchal lines)	bilateral: extension of head & neck controls lateral flexion to side opposite contraction (eccentric for stability) maintains head posture	dorsal rami of spinal nerves
Multifidus	lumbar: mamillary processes of L1-L5 (not TPs) thoracic: TP of T1-T12 cervical: articular processes of C4-C7 (not TPs)	SPs of all vertebrae extending from L5 - C2, 3-4 segments above the origin	bilateral: extension of vertebral column (trunk & neck) unilateral: rotate vertebral bodies (column) to opposite side control lateral flexion to side opposite contraction (eccentric for stability)	dorsal rami of spinal nerves
Rotatores	transverse processes of C3-L5 (most developed in thoracic spine)	spinous process (base) & lamina 1-2 segments above origin	rotation to opposite side, bilateral extension stabilize vertebra & are involved as organs of proprioception (position sense of the spine due to the large number of sensory nerve fibers in these tiny muscles)	dorsal rami of spinal nerves

Other deep group muscles

Muscle	Origin	Insertion	Action	Nerve
Quadratus lumborum	12th rib (inferior border) & TPs of L1-L4	posterior iliac crest & iliolumbar ligament	elevation of pelvis; lateral flexion of trunk depression of 12th rib	lumbar plexus (T12-L3)
Interspinalis	SP of vertebrae	SP of vertebrae above	extension of neck & trunk	dorsal rami of spinal nerves
Intertrans-versarii	TP of vertebrae	TP of vertebrae above	lateral flexion of neck & trunk	dorsal rami of spinal nerves
Levator costarum	TPs C7-T11 (posterior lateral tip)	ribs 1-12 (below the TP)	elevation of ribs (inspiration)	dorsal rami of spinal nerves

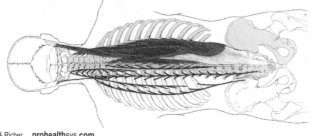

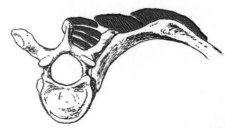

Muscle Tables

Cover table with a piece of table and fill in the boxes - no peaking ☺
On-line Table quizzes available at: **prohealthsys**.com

Name:

%

Muscle	Origin	Insertion	Action	Nerve
Deltoid	lateral 1/3 of clavicle, acromion & spine of scapula	deltoid tuberosity of humerus	abduction of arm flexion & medial rotation (anterior part) extension & lateral rotation (posterior part)	axillary nerve (C5, C6)
Rotator Cuff Muscles (SITS –supraspinatus, infraspinatus, teres minor & subcapularis)				
Supraspinatus	supraspinous fossa of scapula; muscle fascia	greater tubercle of humerus (superior facet)	abduction of arm stabilizes glenohumeral joint	suprascapular nerve (C5, C6)
Infraspinatus	infraspinous fossa; inferior portion of spine of scapula	greater tubercle of humerus (middle facet)	lateral rotation of arm stabilizes glenohumeral joint	suprascapular nerve (C5, 6)
Teres minor	superior lateral border of scapula	greater tubercle of humerus (inferior facet)	lateral rotation of arm stabilizes glenohumeral joint adduction of arm (weak)	axillary nerve (C5, C6)
Subscapularis	subscapular fossa of scapula	lesser tubercle of humerus	medial rotation of arm stabilizes glenohumeral joint	upper & lower subscapular nerves (C5, C6)
Other shoulder muscles				
Teres major	inferior, lateral border of scapula	medial lip of bicipital groove of humerus (just medial to insertion of latissimus dorsi)	medial rotation of shoulder adduction of shoulder extension of shoulder from a flexed position upward scapular rotation	lower subscapular nerve (C5, C6, C7)
Serratus anterior	ribs 1- 9 (outer surface)	costal surface of medial border of scapula	protract (abducts) scapula upward rotation of scapula stabilizes scapula	long thoracic nerve (C5, C6, C7)
Latissimus dorsi	SP T7-L5; thoracolumbar fascia; iliac crest posterior sacrum, ribs 9-12 inferior angle of scapula (occasionally)	medial lip of bicipital groove of humerus	adduction, medial rotation & extension of shoulder anterior pelvic tilt, elevation of pelvis; depression of scapula downward rotation of scapula	thoracodorsal nerve (C6, C7, C8)
Pectoralis major	medial 1/2 of clavicle, anterior manubrium & body of sternum, cartilaginous attachments of upper 6 ribs, external abdominal oblique aponeurosis	lateral lip of bicipital groove of humerus (crest of the greater tubercle)	adduction & medial rotation of shoulder flexion of shoulder (clavicular portion) horizontal adduction of shoulder	medial & lateral pectoral nerves (C5-T1)
Pectoralis minor	ribs 3-5 (anterior lateral portion)	coracoid process of scapula (medial aspect)	stabilizes scapula for arm movements depresses & downwardly rotates scapula assists in scapular protraction from a retracted position elevates ribs 3-5	medial pectoral nerve (C8, T1)
Subclavius	1st rib (junction of costocartilage)	middle 1/3 of clavicle (inferior surface)	assists in stabilization of clavicle depression of clavicle elevation of 1st rib	nerve to subclavius (C5, C6)

Online quizzes available at:
prohealthsys. com

▶ Video on website

Muscle Tables

prohealthsys

Cover table with a piece of table and fill in the boxes - no peaking ☺
On-line Table quizzes available at: **prohealthsys.com**

Name:

%

Muscle	Origin	Insertion	Action	Nerve
Anterior Arm				
Coracobrachialis	coracoid process of scapula	medial shaft of humerus (middle 1/3)	flexion & adduction of arm	musculocutaneous nerve (C5, C6, C7)
Biceps brachii	long head: supraglenoid tubercle & glenohumeral labrum short head: coracoid process of scapula	radial tuberosity bicipital aponeurosis	flexion & supination of forearm flexion of shoulder stabilization of anterior aspect of shoulder abduction of shoulder (long head), adduction of shoulder (short head)	musculocutaneous nerve (C5, C6)
Brachialis	anterior distal 1/2 of humerus	ulnar tuberosity coronoid process of ulna	elbow flexion (prime mover)	musculocutaneous nerve (C5, C6, C7)
Posterior Arm				
Triceps brachii	long head: infraglenoid tubercle & neck of scapula; lateral head: upper half of posterior surface of shaft of humerus (above radial groove) medial (deep) head: posterior shaft of humerus (distal to radial groove)	olecranon process of ulna	extension of elbow (prime mover) adduction & extension of shoulder (long head only)	radial nerve (C6, C7, C8) (axillary nerve may supply upper fibers of long head)
Articularis cubiti*	deep distal surface of medial head of triceps	posterior capsule of elbow joint	lifts capsule away from joint	radial nerve (C6, C7, C8)

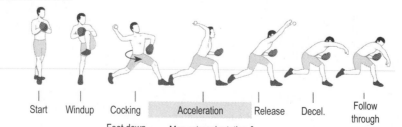

Throwing

Start | Windup | Cocking | Acceleration | Release | Decel. | Follow through

Foot down | Max external rotation & weight transfer forward

Muscle Tables

Anterior Forearm Muscles

Cover table with a piece of table and fill in the boxes - no peaking ☺
On-line Table quizzes available at: **prohealthsys.com**

Name: _____ %

Muscle	Origin	Insertion	Action	Nerve
Superficial layer				
Pronator teres	humeral head: medial epicondyle via common flexor tendon ulnar head: coronoid process of ulna	lateral radius at middle of shaft (pronator tuberosity)	pronation of forearm flexion of elbow (weak action)	median nerve (C6, C7)
Flexor carpi radialis	medial epicondyle via common flexor tendon	base of 2nd & 3rd metacarpals	flexion of hand at wrist radially deviation (abduction) of wrist flexion & pronate of forearm (weak)	median nerve (C6, C7)
Palmaris longus	medial epicondyle via common flexor tendon	flexor retinaculum & palmar aponeurosis	flexion of hand at wrist	median nerve (C7,C8)
Flexor carpi ulnaris	humeral head: medial epicondyle via common flexor tendon; ulnar head: medial aspect of olecranon & proximal 2/3 of posterior ulna	pisiform & hamate bones (via pisohamate ligament) base of 5th metacarpal (via pisometacarpal ligament)	flexion of hand at wrist ulnar deviation (adduction) of wrist elbow flexion (weak action) stabilizes wrist to permit powerful thumb motion	ulnar nerve (C7, C8)
Brachioradialis	lateral supracondylar ridge of humerus	styloid process of radius (lateral side)	flexion of elbow pronation of forearm when supinated supination of forearm when pronated	radial nerve (C5, C6)
Intermediate layer				
Flexor digitorum superficialis	humeral-ulnar head: medial epicondyle via common flexor tendon & coronoid process of ulna; medial (ulnar) collateral ligament radial head: oblique line of radius along its upper anterior boarder	base of middle phalanges of fingers #2-5 (tendon split at insertion)	flexion of fingers #2-5 (at PIP & MCP) flexion of wrist & hand flexion of elbow (weak action)	median nerve (C7, C8, T1)
Deep layer				
Flexor digitorum profundus	anterior & medial surface of ulna (proximal 1/2) & interosseous membrane	base of distal phalange of fingers #2-5	flexion of fingers (at DIP, PIP & MCP joints) flexion of wrist	median nerve (C8,T1) (radial 1/2 of muscle) ulnar nerve (C8, T1) (ulnar 1/2 of muscle)
Flexor pollicis longus	radius (middle anterior surface) & interosseous membrane may also originate from lateral boarder of coronoid process or medial epicondyle	base of distal phalanx of thumb (anterior aspect)	flexion of thumb (IP, CMC, MCP joints) flexion of wrist	median nerve (C7, C8)
Supinator	lateral epicondyle of humerus & supinator crest of ulna	proximal 1/3 of radius	supination of forearm (at proximal radioulnar joint)	radial nerve (C6, C7)
Pronator quadratus	anterior distal ulna (distal 1/4)	anterior distal radius (distal 1/4)	pronation of forearm	median nerve (C7, C8)

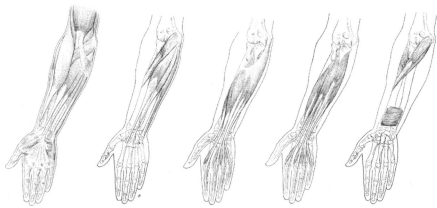

prohealthsys.com   Vizniak & Richer

Cover table with a piece of table and fill in the boxes - no peaking ☺
On-line Table quizzes available at: **prohealthsys.com**

Name:

%

Muscle	Origin	Insertion	Action	Nerve
Superficial layer				
Anconeus	lateral epicondyle of humerus	posterior ulna (lateral olecranon extending to lateral part of ulna)	extension of elbow supports elbow when in full extension	radial nerve (C6, C7, C8)
Extensor carpi radialis longus	lower lateral supracondylar ridge (below brachioradialis)	base of 2nd metacarpal	extension of wrist radially deviation (abduction) of wrist flexion & supination of forearm at elbow (weak action)	radial nerve (C5, C6)
Extensor carpi radialis brevis	lateral epicondyle via common extensor tendon	base of 3rd metacarpal	extension of wrist radial deviation (abduction) of wrist flexion of elbow joint (weak action)	radial nerve (C7, C8)
Extensor digitorum	lateral epicondyle of humerus (via common extensor tendon)	phalanges #2-5 (dorsal expansion hood)	extension of fingers #2-5 (at MCP, PIP & DIP joints) extension of wrist extension of elbow (weak)	radial nerve (C7, C8)
Extensor digiti minimi	lateral epicondyle of humerus (via common extensor tendon)	middle & distal phalanges of 5th digit (extensor expansion)	extension of little finger (5th digit) extension of wrist extension of elbow (weak action)	radial nerve (C6, C7, C8)
Extensor carpi ulnaris	humeral head: lateral epicondyle (via common extensor tendon) ulnar head: posterior shaft of ulna	base of 5th metacarpal (posterior side)	ulnar deviation of wrist extension of wrist extension of elbow (weak action)	radial nerve (C6, C7, C8)
Deep Layer (deep distal group of 4)				
Abductor pollicis longus	posterior surfaces of ulna, radius & interosseous membrane (middle 1/3 of forearm)	base of 1st metacarpal (lateral side)	abduction of thumb at metacarpophalangeal joint radial deviation (abduction) of wrist assists with extension & rotation of thumb assists with flexion & supination of wrist	radial nerve (C7, C8)
Extensor pollicis brevis	posterior distal 1/3 surfaces of radius & interosseous membrane	base of proximal phalanx of thumb	extension of proximal phalanx & 1st metacarpal of thumb radial deviation (abduction) of wrist	radial nerve (C7, C8)
Extensor pollicis longus	posterior middle 1/3 of ulna & interosseous membrane	distal phalanx of thumb	extension of thumb (at CMC, MCP, IP joints) assists in extension & radial deviation (abduction) of wrist	radial nerve (C7, C8)
Extensor indicis	posterior distal 1/3 of ulna & interosseous membrane	base of middle & distal phalanx of index finger (via extensor expansion & extensor digitorum muscle tendon)	extension of index finger (at MCP, PIP & DIP joints) extension of hand at wrist adduction of index finger (weak)	radial nerve (C7, C8)

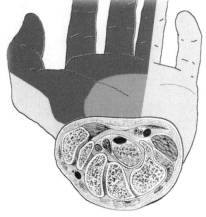

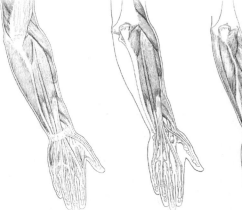

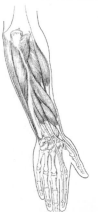

prohealthsys

Name:

%

Muscle	Origin	Insertion	Action	Nerve
Superficial Palmar Fascia				
Palmaris brevis	flexor retinaculum & palmar aponeurosis	skin of ulnar border of palm	tenses skin on ulnar side (used in a grip action)	ulnar nerve (C8, T1)
Thenar Eminence				
Abductor pollicis brevis	tubercles of scaphoid & trapezium flexor retinaculum	base of proximal phalanx of thumb (lateral side)	abduction of thumb (at CMC joint)	median nerve (C8, T1)
Flexor pollicis brevis	trapezium & flexor retinaculum	base of proximal phalanx of thumb (lateral side)	flexion of thumb (at MCP joint)	median & ulnar nerves (C8, T1)
Opponens pollicis	flexor retinaculum & trapezium	1st metacarpal (anterior lateral border)	opposition of thumb to fingers	median nerve (C8, T1)
Hypothenar Eminence				
Abductor digiti minimi	pisiform & tendon of flexor carpi ulnaris	base of proximal phalanx of little finger (ulnar side)	abduction of little finger (at CMC & MCP)	ulnar nerve (C8,T1)
Flexor digiti minimi	flexor retinaculum & hook of hamate	base of proximal phalanx of little finger (ulnar side)	flexion of little finger (at MCP joint)	ulnar nerve (C8, T1)
Opponens digiti minimi	flexor retinaculum & hook of hamate	5th metacarpal (anterior & medial surface)	opposition of little finger	ulnar nerve (C8, T1)
Central Compartment of Hand				
Adductor pollicis	oblique head: base of 2nd & 3rd metacarpals & capitate transverse head: 3rd metacarpal (distal anterior 2/3)	base of proximal phalanx of thumb (medial side)	adduction of thumb (CMC joint); flexion of thumb (MCP joint)	ulnar nerve (C8, T1)
Lumbricals	distal tendons of flexor digitorum profundus #1 & #2 have a single head of origin (from radial aspect of tendon) #3 & #4 have two heads of origin (each head from an adjacent tendon)	extensor expansion hood of digits 2-5	flexion fingers (MCP joints) extension of fingers (PIPs & DIP)	1 & 2 - median nerve (C8, T1) 3 & 4 - ulnar nerve (C8, T1)
Palmar interossei	metacarpals #2, #4 & #5	base of proximal phalanx of digit #2, #4, #5 & extensor hood of same digit(s)	adduction of fingers (hint: PAD) flexion of fingers (at MCP while IP joints are extended)	ulnar nerve (C8, T1)
Dorsal interossei	between each metacarpal	base of proximal phalanx of fingers #2, #3, #4 & extensor hood of same digit(s)	abduction of fingers (hint: DAB) flexion of fingers (MCP while IP joints are extended)	ulnar nerve (C8, T1)

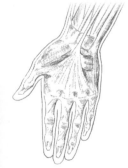
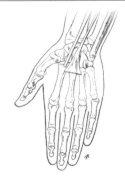
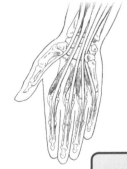
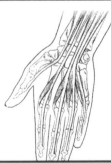

on-line quizzes available at:
prohealthsys.com

Muscle Tables

prohealthsys

Cover table with a piece of table and fill in the boxes - no peaking ☺
On-line Table quizzes available at: **prohealthsys.com**

Name:

%

Muscle	Origin	Insertion	Action	Nerve
Diaphragm	vertebral: crura from bodies of L1, 2 (left), L1-3 (right) costal part: medial & lateral arcuate ligaments, inner aspect of lower six ribs sternal: two slips from post aspect of xiphoid	central tendon of diaphragm (dome of diaphragm)	inspiration (increases thoracic cavity volume) assists in raising intra-abdominal pressure (valsalva maneuver)	phrenic nerve (C3, C4, C5)
External abdominal oblique	anterior 1/2 of iliac crest, inguinal ligament, public tubercle/crest, & abdominal aponeurosis (rectus sheath)	inferior border of ribs #5-12	flexion, lateral flexion & contralateral rotation of trunk (at spinal joints) posterior pelvic tilt (at spinal joints) compression/stabilization of abdomen	intercostal nerves (T7-T12)
Internal abdominal oblique	iliac crest, inguinal ligament, thoracolumbar fascia	ribs #10-12 & abdominal aponeurosis (rectus sheath)	flexion, lateral flexion & ipsilateral rotation of trunk (at spinal joints) posterior tilt of pelvis (at lumbosacral joints) compression/stabilization of abdomen	intercostal nerves (T7-L1)
Pyramidalis	pubic crest (anterior to origin of rectus abdominis)	lower linea alba	tension of linea alba (reinforces lower rectus sheath)	subcostal nerve (T12-L1)
Rectus abdominis	pubic crest & pubic symphysis	costal cartilage of ribs #5-7 & xyphoid process	flexion of trunk (at spinal joints); posterior pelvic tilt (at spinal joints) compression/stabilization of abdomen	intercostal nerves (T5-T12)
Transversus abdominus	iliac crest, inguinal ligament, thoracolumbar fascia & lower costal cartilage	abdominal aponeurosis (rectus sheath)	compression/stabilization of abdomen	intercostal nerves (T7-L1)
Posterior abdominal wall				
Quadratus lumborum	12th rib (inferior border) & TPs of L1-L4	posterior iliac crest & iliolumbar ligament	elevation of pelvis lateral flexion of trunk depression of 12th rib	Subcostal nerve; L1-L3
Psoas major	TPs of L1-L5, vertebral bodies of T12-L5 & intervening intervertebral discs	lesser trochanter of femur (via iliopsoas tendon)	flexion & lateral rotation of thigh (at hip) flexion & lateral flexion of trunk (at spinal joints) anterior pelvic tilt (at hip joint)	lumbar plexus ventral rami (L1, L2, L3)
Psoas minor	vertebral bodies of T12 & L1 & intervening intervertebral disc	pectineal line of pubis & iliopubic eminence	flexion of trunk (at spinal joints) posterior pelvic tilt (at spinal joints)	ventral rami of L1
Illiacus	inner surface of upper iliac fossa & sacral ala	lesser trochanter of femur (via iliopsoas tendon)	flexion & lateral rotation of thigh (at hip) anterior pelvic tilt	femoral nerve (L2, L3)

*Iliacus & psoas major together are known as the iliopsoas muscle

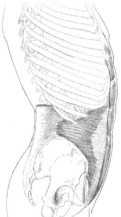
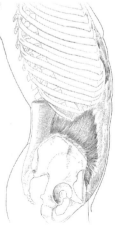
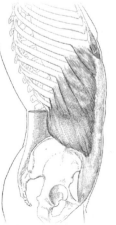
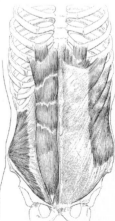

Muscle Tables

Cover table with a piece of table and fill in the boxes - no peaking ☺
On-line Table quizzes available at: **prohealthsys.com**

Name:

%

Muscle	Origin	Insertion	Action	Nerve
Gluteus maximus	posterior iliac crest, sacrum, coccyx & sacrotuberous ligament	iliotibial band (ITB) & gluteal tuberosity of femur	extension of hip lateral rotation of hip upper fibers assist abduction of hip, lower fiber assist in adduction posterior pelvic tilt (at hip joint) fibers of IT band stabilize a fully extended knee	inferior gluteal nerve (L5, S1, S2)
Gluteus medius	outer ilium (between anterior & posterior gluteal lines)	greater trochanter (superior & lateral surface)	abduction of hip flexion & medial rotation of hip (anterior fibers) lateral rotation & extension of thigh (posterior fibers) stabilizes pelvis & prevents free limb from sagging during gait	superior gluteal nerve (L4, L5, S1)
Gluteus minimus	outer ilium (between anterior & inferior gluteal lines)	greater trochanter (anterior surface)	abduction of hip medial rotation & flexion of hip (anterior fibers) lateral rotation & extension (posterior fibers) stabilizes pelvis & prevents free limb from dropping during gait	superior gluteal nerve (L4, L5, S1)
Piriformis	anterior sacrum (occasionally sacrotuberous ligament)	greater trochanter (superiomedial surface)	lateral rotation of hip joint abduction of flexed hip	nerve to piriformis (L5, S1, S2)
Superior gemellus	ischial spine	greater trochanter (medial surface)	lateral rotation of hip joint abduction of flexed hip	obturator nerve (L2, L3, L4)
Obturator internus	internal aspect of obturator foramen & obturator membrane	greater trochanter (medial aspect)	lateral rotation of hip joint abduction of flexed hip	nerve to obturator internus (L5, S1, S2)
Obturator externus	obturator foramen & obturator membrane (external surface)	trochanteric fossa of femur	lateral rotation of hip joint adduction of hip (weak)	nerve to piriformis (L5, S1, S2)
Inferior gemellus	ischial tuberosity (superior aspect)	greater trochanter (medial surface & intertrochanteric crest)	lateral rotation of hip joint abduction of flexed hip	nerve to quadratus femoris (L4, L5, S1)
Quadratus femoris	ischial tuberosity (lateral aspect)	intertrochanteric crest of femur	lateral rotation of hip joint adduction of thigh (weak)	nerve to obturator internus (L5, S1, S2)

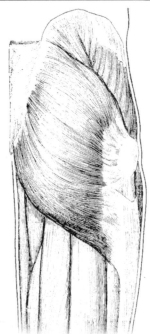
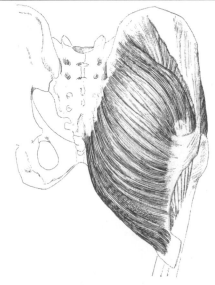
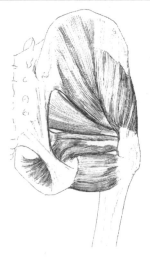

Cover table with a piece of table and fill in the boxes - no peaking ☺
On-line Table quizzes available at: **prohealthsys.com**

Name:

%

Muscle	Origin	Insertion	Action	Nerve
Posterior Thigh Muscles				
Biceps femoris	long head: ischial tuberosity short head: lateral lip of linea aspera	head of fibula (occasionally to lateral tibial condyle)	flexion of knee (both long & short head) extension of hip (long head) laterally rotation of leg when the knee is flexed	long head: sciatic nerve, tibial division (L5, S1, S2) short head: sciatic nerve, common per. (S1, S2)
Semimembranosus	ischial tuberosity	posterior medial aspect of medial tibial condyle	flexion of knee joint extension of hip medial rotation of tibia (with knee flexed)	sciatic nerve, tibial division (L5, S1, S2)
Semitendinosus	ischial tuberosity	proximal anteromedial tibia (pes anserine)	flexion of knee joint extension of hip medial rotation of tibia (with knee flexed)	sciatic nerve, tibial division (L5, S1, S2)
Anterior Thigh Muscles				
Sartorius	anterior superior iliac spine (ASIS)	proximal anteromedial tibia (pes anserine)	flexion, abduction & lateral rotation of hip flexion of knee; anterior pelvic tilt	femoral nerve (L2 ,L3, L4)
Tensor fascia latae	anterior superior iliac spine (ASIS) & anterior aspect of iliac crest	iliotibial band (below greater trochanter)	flexion, abduction & medial rotation of hip tenses iliotibial band to support femur on tibia during standing	superior gluteal nerve (L4, L5, S1)
Rectus femoris	anterior head: anterior inferior iliac spine (AIIS) posterior head: just superior to rim of acetabulum	tibial tuberosity (via common quadriceps tendon & patellar ligament)	extension of knee flexion of hip	femoral nerve (L3, L4)
Vastus intermedius	anterior lateral surface of femur	tibial tuberosity (via common quadriceps tendon & patellar ligament)	extension of knee	femoral nerve (L2 ,L3, L4)
Vastus lateralis	lateral lip of linea aspera (also intertrochanteric line & lateral intermuscular sep.)	tibial tuberosity (via common quadriceps tendon & patellar ligament)	extension of knee	femoral nerve (L2 ,L3, L4)
vastus medialis	medial lip of linea aspera (intertrochanteric line)	tibial tuberosity (via common quad. tendon & pat. lig.)	extension of knee	femoral nerve (L2 ,L3, L4)
Articularis genus	distal anterior femur (superior to knee)	knee joint capsule (synovial membrane)	pulls knee joint capsule superior with knee extension (prevents impingement of capsule between patella & femur)	femoral nerve (L3, L4)
Medial Thigh Muscles				
Pectineus	pectineal line of pubis (superior pubic ramus)	pectineal line of femur (just below lesser trochanter on posterior aspect of femur)	adduction & flexion of hip	obturator nerve (L2, L3, L4)
Adductor brevis	body & inferior ramus of pubis	medial lip of linea aspera (superior 1/3 of femur)	adduction & flexion of hip lateral rotation of hip	femoral nerve and/or obturator nerve
Adductor longus	anterior surface of pubis (just inferior to pubic tubercle)	medial lip of linea aspera (middle 1/3 of femur)	adduction & flexion of hip lateral rotation hip	obturator nerve (L2, L3, L4)
Adductor magnus	anterior head (adductor part): inferior pubic & ischial ramus posterior head (hamstring part): ischial tuberosity	anterior head: linea aspera posterior head: adductor tubercle of femur (above medial epicondyle)	adduction & extension of hip lateral rotation of hip (anterior head)	obturator nerve (L2, L3, L4)
Gracilis	body & inferior ramus of pubis	proximal anteromedial tibia (pes anserine)	adduction & flexion of hip flexion & medial rotation knee	anterior head: obturator nerve (L2, L3, L4) posterior head: sciatic nerve, tibial part (L4, L5)

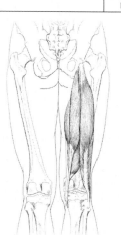
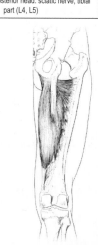

prohealthsys

Cover table with a piece of table and fill in the boxes - no peaking ☺
On-line Table quizzes available at: prohealthsys.com

Name: _____ %

Muscle	Origin	Insertion	Action	Nerve
Anterior Compartment:				
Tibialis anterior	anterior proximal tibia (lateral tibial condyle, proximal 2/3 of anterolateral surface of tibia & interosseous membrane)	medial cuneiform & base of 1st metatarsal (medial & plantar surfaces)	dorsiflexion of ankle inversion of ankle at tarsal joints	deep peroneal (fibular) nerve (L4, L5, S1)
Extensor digitorum longus	proximal 2/3 of fibula, interosseous membrane, lateral condyle of tibia (anterior surfaces)	dorsal surface of toes #2-5 (via dorsal expansion to middle & distal phalanges)	extension of toes #2-5 (at MTP & IP joints) dorsiflexion & eversion of foot	deep peroneal (fibular) nerve (L4, L5, S1)
Extensor hallucis longus	anterior middle 1/3 of fibula & interosseous membrane	dorsal surface big toe (base of distal phalanx)	extension of big toe at MTP dorsiflexion & inversion of foot	deep peroneal (fibular) nerve (L4, L5, S1)
Fibularis (peroneus) tertius	distal 1/3 of anterior fibula (distal & lateral aspect of extensor digitorum longus)	base of 5th metatarsal (dorsal surface)	dorsiflexion & eversion of foot	deep peroneal (fibular) nerve (L5, S1)
Lateral Compartment:				
Fibularis (peroneus) longus	head & proximal lateral shaft of fibula	medial cuneiform & base of 1st metatarsal (plantar surfaces)	eversion of foot plantar flexion of foot	superficial peroneal (fibular) nerve (L5, S1)
Fibularis (peroneus) brevis	distal lateral 1/2 of fibula	base of 5th metatarsal (lateral aspect)	eversion of foot plantar flexion of foot	superficial peroneal (fibular) nerve (L5, S1)

Muscle	Origin	Insertion	Action	Nerve
Superficial Posterior Compartment				
Gastrocnemius	medial head: above medial condyle of femur (posterior surface) lateral head: above lateral condyle of femur (posterior surface)	calcaneus (via calcaneal or Achilles tendon)	plantar flexion of foot knee flexion (when not weight bearing) inversion of foot (weak)	tibial nerve (S1, S2)
Soleus	soleal line of tibia & proximal 1/3 of fibula	calcaneus (via calcaneal or Achilles tendon)	plantar flexion of foot inversion of foot (weak)	tibial nerve (S1, S2)
Plantaris	distal posterolateral femur (above lateral head of gastrocnemius)	calcaneus (via calcaneal or Achilles tendon)	plantar flexion of foot knee flexion	tibial nerve (S1, S2)
Deep Posterior Compartment				
Popliteus	lateral femoral condyle	proximal posterior tibia (medial side above soleal line)	unlocks knee from extended position lateral rotation of femur on tibia or medial rotation tibia on femur flexion of knee (weak)	tibial nerve (L4, L5, S1)
Tibialis posterior	posterior proximal 2/3 of tibia, interosseous membrane & fibula	fans out over plantar surface of foot (navicular, all 3 cuneiforms, 2nd-4th metatarsals, cuboid & calcaneus)	plantar flexion & inversion of foot	tibial nerve (L4, L5, S1)
Flexor digitorum longus	posterior middle 1/3 of tibia	base of distal phalanges #2-#5 (plantar surface)	flexion of 2nd-5th toes plantar flexion & inversion of foot (weak)	tibial nerve (L5, S1, S2)
Flexor hallucis longus	posterior inferior 2/3 of fibula & interosseous membrane	distal phalanx of big toe (plantar surface)	flexion of big toe (hallux) plantar flexion & inversion of foot (weak)	tibial nerve (L5, S1, S2)

Muscle Tables

Cover table with a piece of table and fill in the boxes - no peaking ☺
On-line Table quizzes available at: **prohealthsys.com**

Name:

%

Muscle	Origin	Insertion	Action	Nerve
Dorsal Surface of Foot				
Extensor digitorum brevis	upper anterolateral calcaneus	middle & distal phalanges of toes #2-#4 (via EDL & extensor expansion)	extension of toes #2-#5	deep peroneal (fibular) nerve (L5, S1)
Extensor hallucis brevis	upper anterolateral calcaneus	proximal phalange of big toe (via EHL & extensor expansion)	extension of big toe at MTP dorsiflexion & inversion of foot	deep peroneal (fibular) nerve (L5, S1)
Plantar Surface of Foot				
Layer 1				
Abductor hallucis	calcaneal tuberosity, flexor retinaculum & plantar aponeurosis	base of proximal phalanx of big toe (medial plantar side)	abduction of big toe	medial plantar nerve (S1, S2)
Abductor digiti minimi	calcaneal tuberosity, flexor retinaculum & plantar aponeurosis	base of proximal phalanx of little toe (lateral plantar side)	abduction of little toe	lateral plantar nerve (S1, S2)
Abductor ossis metatarsi quinti*	fibers of the abductor digiti minimi muscle	5th metatarsal (tuberosity)	abducts 5th ray	lateral plantar nerve (S1, S2)
Flexor digitorum brevis	calcaneal tuberosity & plantar aponeurosis	base of middle phalanges of toes #2-#5 (tendon splits near insertion)	flexion of toes #2-#5	medial plantar nerve (S1, S2)
Layer 2				
Quadratus plantae	medial & lateral calcaneus	flexor digitorum longus tendon (lateral margin)	flexion of distal phalanxes (2nd-5th toes)	lateral plantar nerve (S1, S2)
Lumbricals	Flexor digitorum longus (1st: medial aspect of tendon to 2nd toe; 2nd-4th: two heads between tendons in which they lie)	tendon of extensor digitorum longus & extensor expansion (on the dorsal medial side)	extension of toes #2-5 (at PIP & DIP joints) flexion of toes #2-5 (at MTP joints)	1st lumbrical: medial plantar nerve (S1, S2, S3) 2nd-4th lumbricals: lateral plantar nerve (S1, S2, S3)
Layer 3				
Flexor digiti minimi	base of 5th metatarsal & distal of peroneus longus	base of proximal phalanx of little toe (5th toe)	flexion of little toe (at MTP joint)	lateral plantar nerve (S2, S3)
Flexor hallucis brevis	cuboid (medial side) & lateral cuneiform	base of proximal phalanx of big toe (medial & lateral sides)	flexion of big toe (at MTP joint)	medial plantar nerve (S1, S2)
Adductor hallucis	oblique head: base of 2nd-4th metatarsals & distal tendon of peroneus longus; transverse head: deep transverse metatarsal ligament & plantar ligaments at MTP joints	base of proximal phalanx of big toe (lateral aspect)	adduction of big toe (at MTP joint) flexion of hallux (at MTP joint)	lateral plantar nerve (S2, S3)
Layer 4				
Dorsal interossei	from both adjacent metatarsals	base of proximal phalanx closest to axis of foot (2nd ray)	abduction of toes 2-4 (at MTP) flexion toes 2-4 (at MTP)	lateral plantar nerve (S2, S3)
Plantar interossei	medial aspect of 3rd-5th metatarsals (each muscle has a single head)	medial aspect of base of proximal phalanx of same ray (of 3rd-5th rays)	adduction of toes 3-5 (at PIP & DIP joints) flexion of toes 3-5 (at MTP joints) extension of toes 3-5 (at PIP & DIP joints)	lateral plantar nerve (S2, S3)

*Abductor ossis metatarsi quinti is often absent

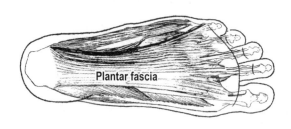

Plantar fascia

Muscle Tables

prohealthsys

Start with labeling the bones, then progress to drawing
□ muscles □ ligaments □ Os & Is □ nerves □ vessels

Name:

%

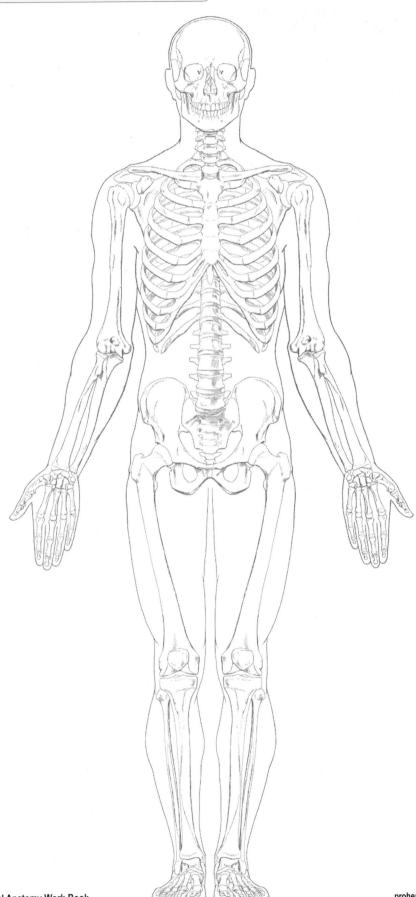

Muscle Tables

prohealthsys.com   Vizniak & Richer

prohealthsys

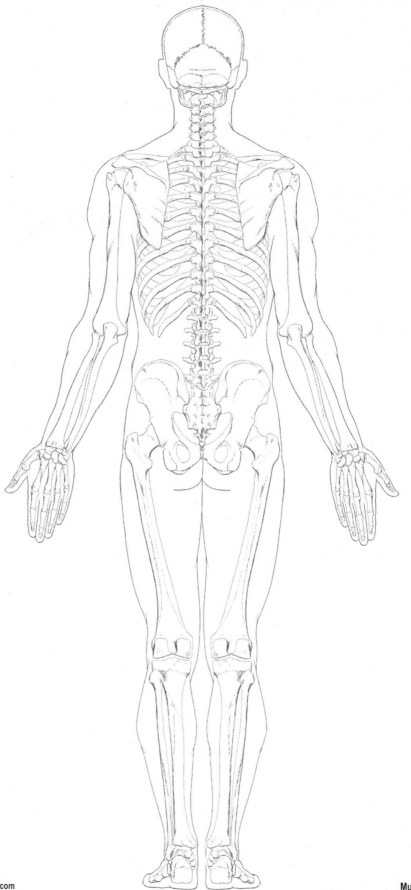

prohealthsys

Start with labeling the bones, then progress to drawing
□ muscles   □ ligaments   □ Os & Is   □ nerves   □ vessels

Name:
%

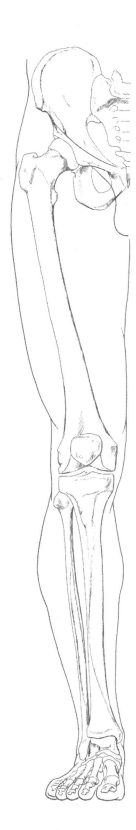
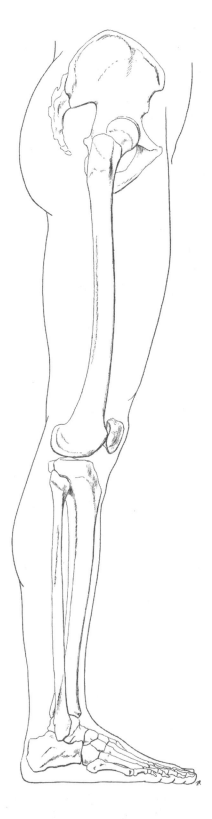
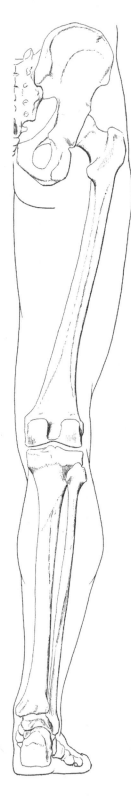

Start with labeling the bones, then progress to drawing
☐ muscles   ☐ ligaments   ☐ Os & Is   ☐ nerves   ☐ vessels

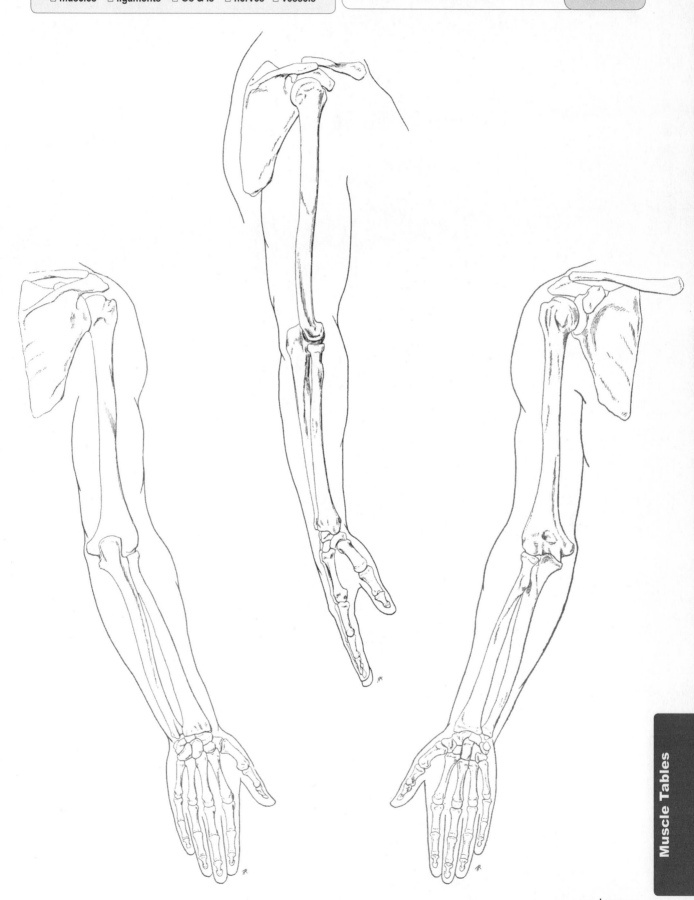

Muscle Tables

prohealthsys

Start with labeling the muscles, then progress to
□ origins   □ insertions   □ actions   □ nerves   □ exercises

Name:

%

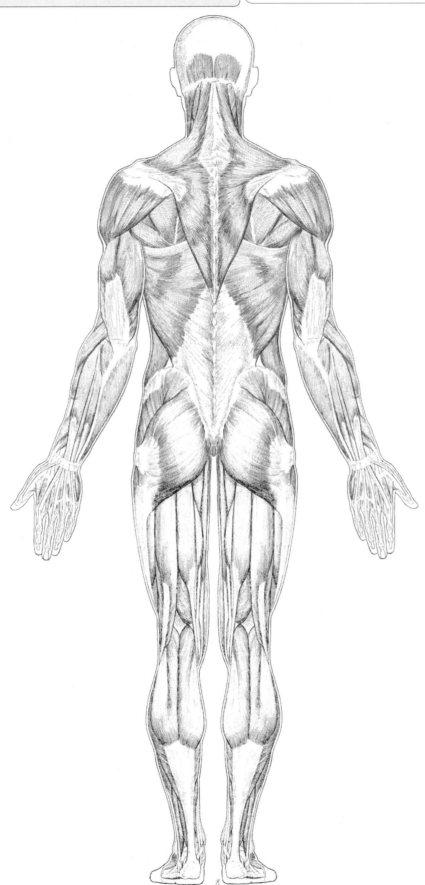

Muscle Tables

Start with labeling the muscles, then progress to

☐ origins   ☐ insertions   ☐ actions   ☐ nerves   ☐ exercises

Name:

%

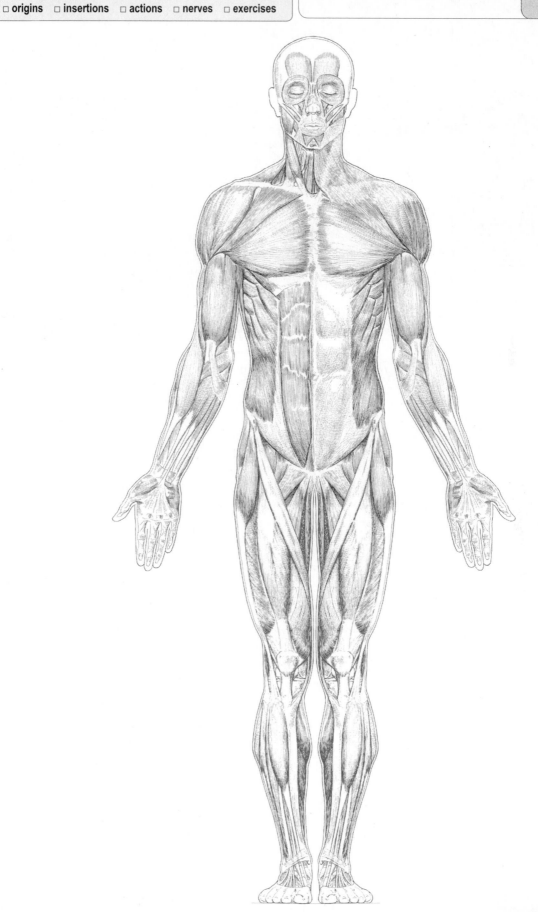

Name: _____ ____ %

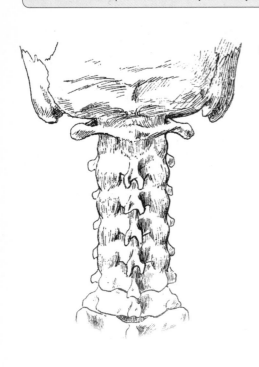

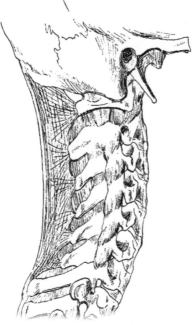

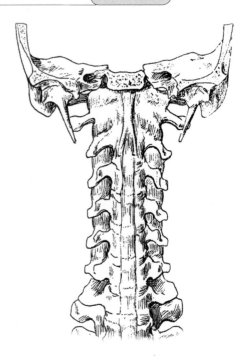

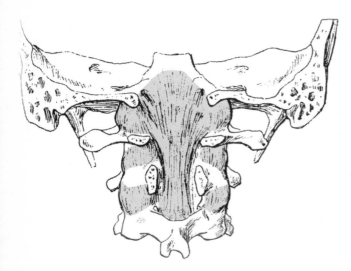

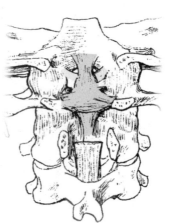

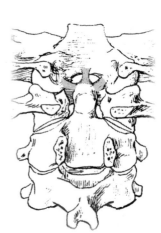

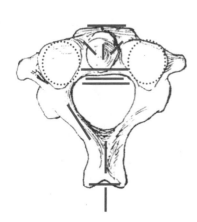

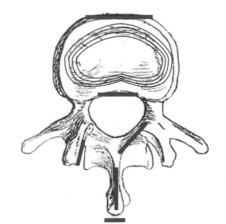

Muscle Tables

Name:

%

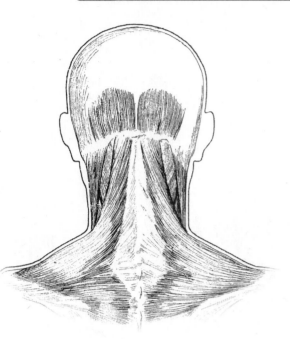
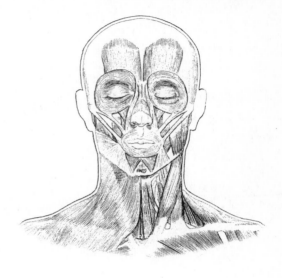
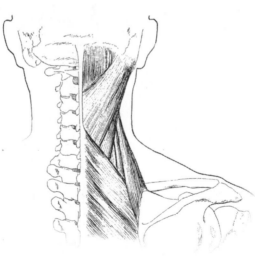
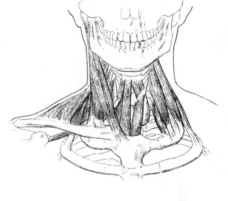
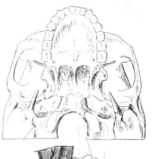
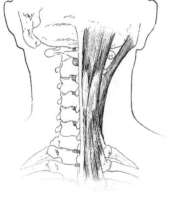
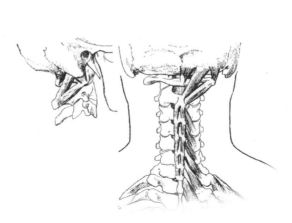
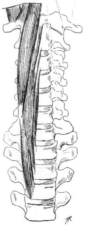

Muscle Tables

Start with labeling the muscles, then progress to

□ origins   □ insertions   □ actions   □ nerves   □ exercises

Name:

%

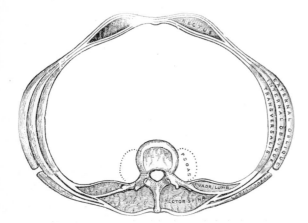

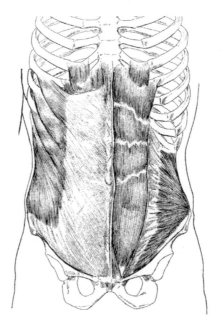

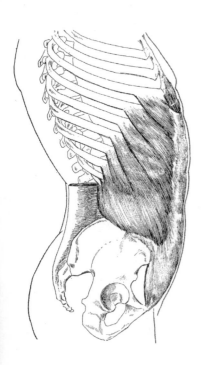

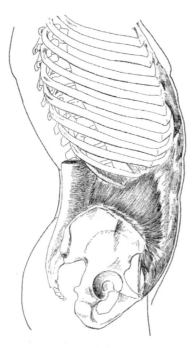

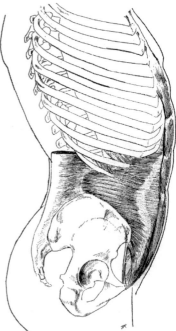

Muscle Tables

prohealthsys

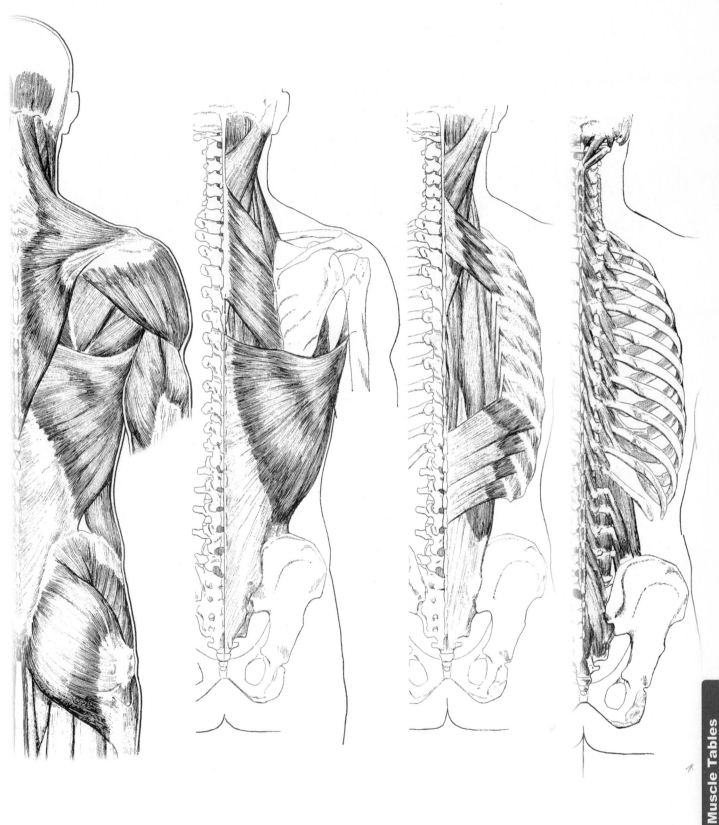

Start with labeling the muscles, then progress to

☐ origins ☐ insertions ☐ actions ☐ nerves ☐ exercises

Name:

%

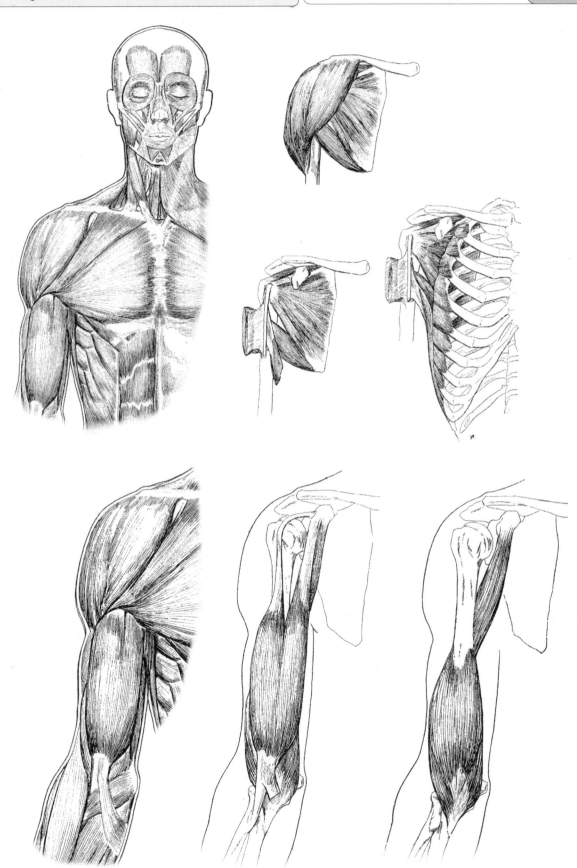

Muscle Tables

prohealthsys

Start with labeling the muscles, then progress to
□ origins   □ insertions   □ actions   □ nerves   □ exercises

Name:

%

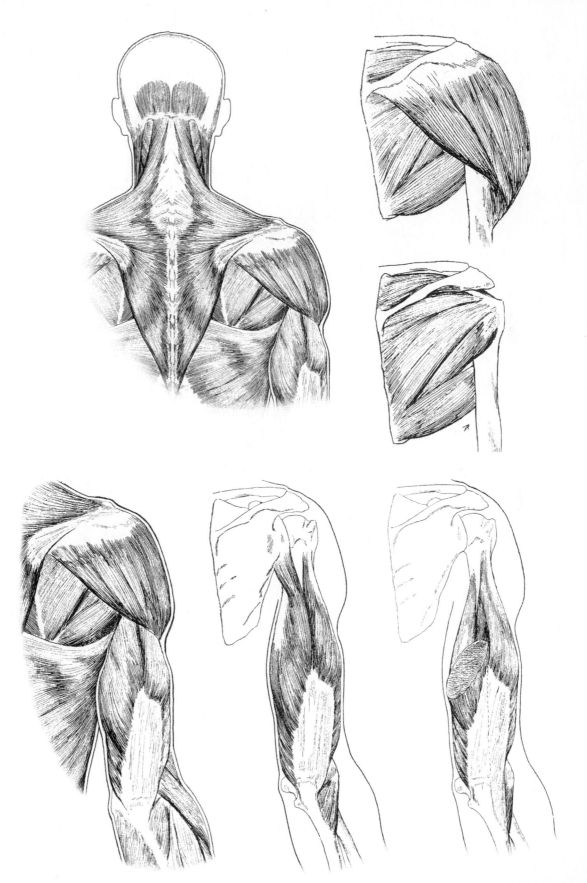

prohealthsys

Start with labeling the muscles, then progress to
□ origins □ insertions □ actions □ nerves □ exercises

Name:

%

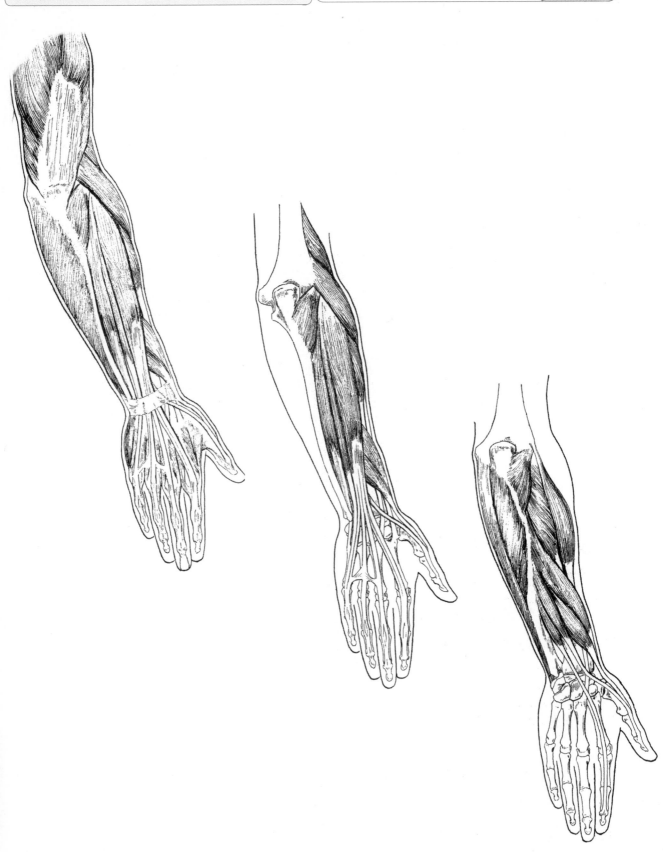

Start with labeling the muscles, then progress to
□ origins   □ insertions   □ actions   □ nerves   □ exercises

Name:

%

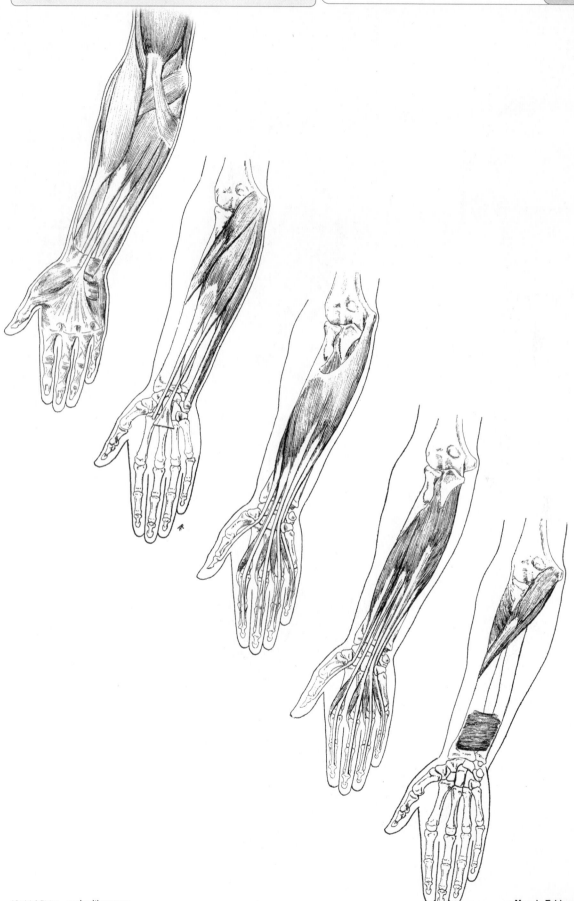

prohealthsys

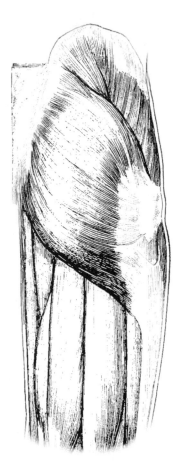
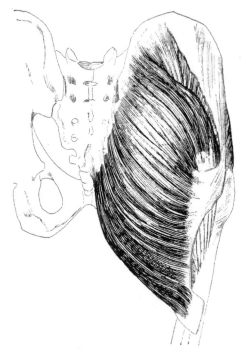
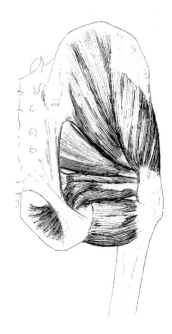

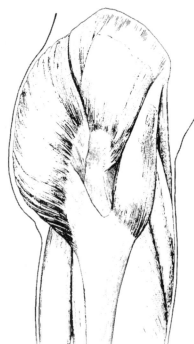
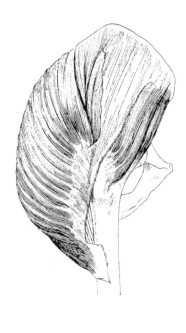

prohealthsys

Start with labeling the muscles, then progress to
☐ origins ☐ insertions ☐ actions ☐ nerves ☐ exercises

Name:

%

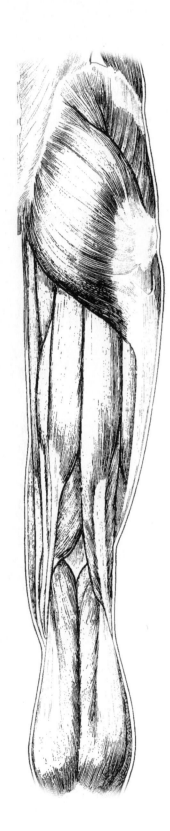
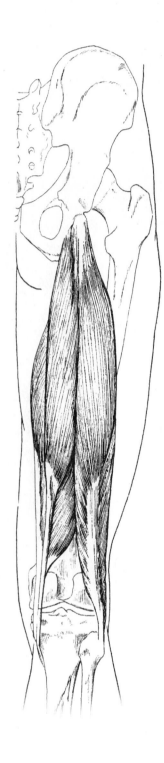
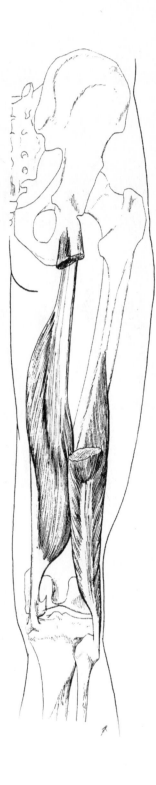

prohealthsys

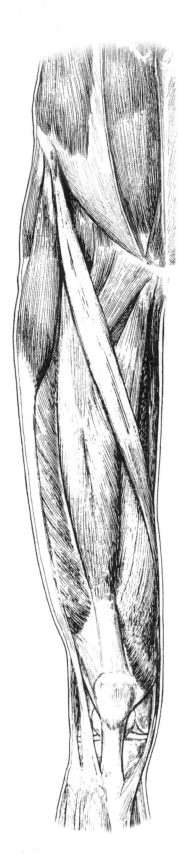
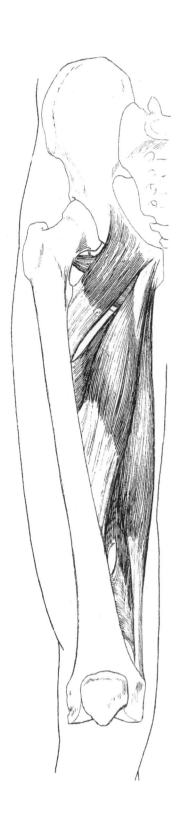
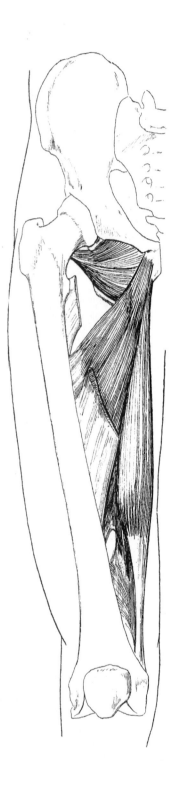

Muscle Tables

prohealthsys

Start with labeling the muscles, then progress to
□ origins □ insertions □ actions □ nerves □ exercises

Name:

%

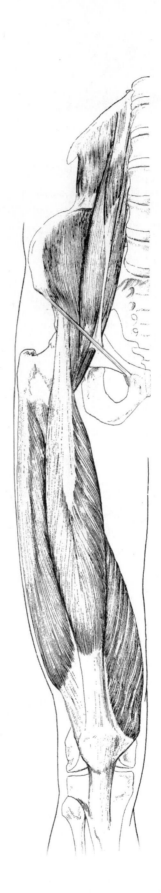
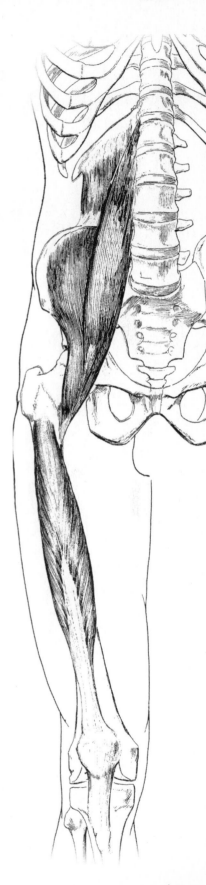

Muscle Tables

Start with labeling the muscles, then progress to
☐ origins   ☐ insertions   ☐ actions   ☐ nerves   ☐ exercises

Name:

%

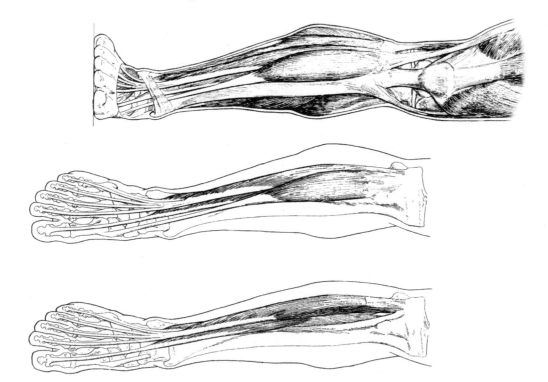

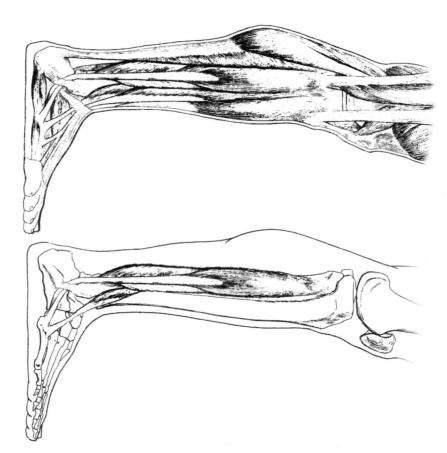

prohealthsys

Start with labeling the muscles, then progress to
□ origins □ insertions □ actions □ nerves □ exercises

Name:

%

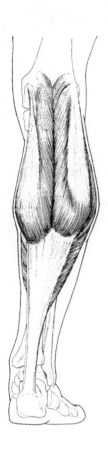
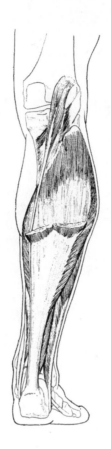

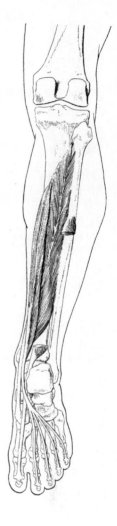

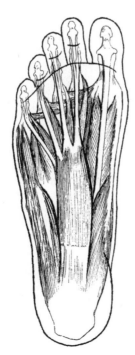
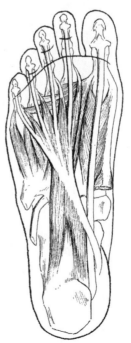
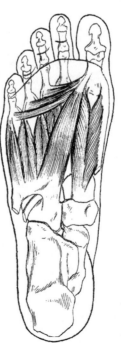

List the **Muscle Activated:** _____

List the **Tissue Stretched:** _____

Name: _____

%

Upper Body: Neck Rotation · Neck Decompress · Forearms · Biceps · Triceps · Chest Opener

Upper Body: Chest · Front Shoulder & Chest · Posterior Shoulder · Shoulder Back Rotation · Push Ups · Upper Back

Abs & Core: Plank · Abs Stabilizing · Scissors Balance · Abs Pushes · Balance Reach · Abs Raises

Abs & Core: Reverse Push Through · Knee Hold · Down Dog · Lunge + Rotations

Back: Back Stretch · Lats Side Roll · Lats Roll-out Stretch · Rhomboids · Upper Back Rotation · Middle & Upper Back

Back: Middle Back · Lower Back · Lower Back (Side) · Thoracic Spine · Thoracic Rotation "Bretzel" · Shoulder Lift off

Back: Thoracic Extension+ side to side · Alternating shoulder flexion · Shoulder Blade Reach · Foam Angel

Back / Lower Body: Erector Spinae · Arch Stretch · IT Band · Piriformis (Hips) · Hip Flexors

Lower Body: Groin Sit-backs · Hamstring Sit-backs · Roller Lunge · Rolling Mermaid Twist · Glutes · Glute Twist

Lower Body: Hamstrings to Glutes · Hamstrings · Outer Legs · Peroneals · Inner Thighs · Quads

Lower Body: Shins · Shins (Single Leg) · Calves · Calves (One Leg) · Outer Calves · Ankles · Feet

Muscle Tables

prohealthsys

List the **Muscle Activated:** _____

List the **Tissue Stretched:** _____

Name: _____   %

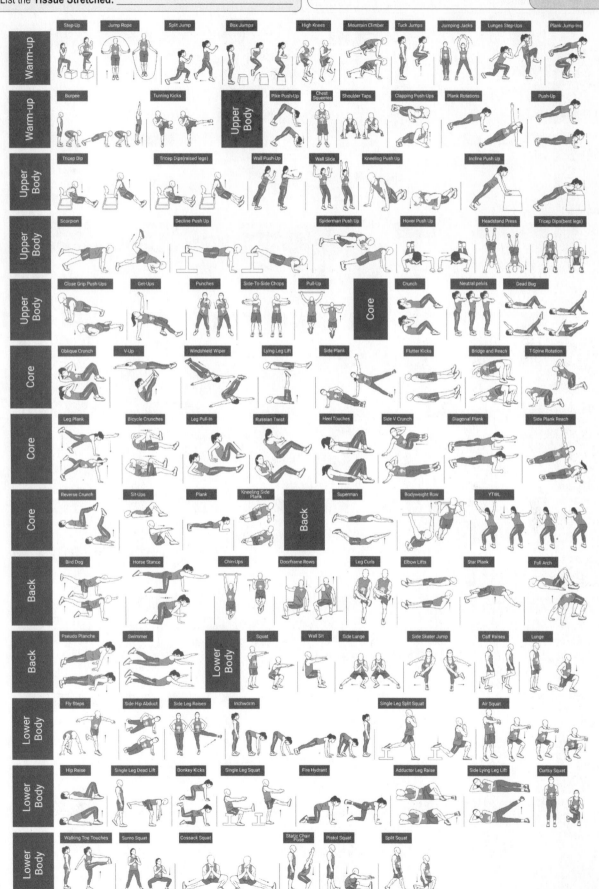

Warm-up
Step-Up · Jump Rope · Split Jump · Box Jumps · High Knees · Mountain Climber · Tuck Jumps · Jumping Jacks · Lunges Step-Ups · Plank Jump-Ins

Warm-up
Burpee · Turning Kicks · Upper Body · Pike Push-Up · Chest Squeezes · Shoulder Taps · Clapping Push-Ups · Plank Rotations · Push-Up

Upper Body
Tricep Dip · Tricep Dips(raised legs) · Wall Push-Up · Wall Slide · Kneeling Push Up · Incline Push Up

Upper Body
Scorpion · Decline Push Up · Spiderman Push Up · Hover Push Up · Headstand Press · Tricep Dips(bent legs)

Upper Body
Close Grip Push-Ups · Get-Ups · Punches · Side-To-Side Chops · Pull-Up · Core · Crunch · Neutral pelvis · Dead Bug

Core
Oblique Crunch · V-Up · Windshield Wiper · Lying Leg Lift · Side Plank · Flutter Kicks · Bridge and Reach · T-Spine Rotation

Core
Leg Plank · Bicycle Crunches · Leg Pull-In · Russian Twist · Heel Touches · Side V Crunch · Diagonal Plank · Side Plank Reach

Core
Reverse Crunch · Sit-Ups · Plank · Kneeling Side Plank · Back · Superman · Bodyweight Row · YTWL

Back
Bird Dog · Horse Stance · Chin-Ups · Doorframe Rows · Leg Curls · Elbow Lifts · Star Plank · Full Arch

Back
Pseudo Planche · Swimmer · Lower Body · Squat · Wall Sit · Side Lunge · Side Skater Jump · Calf Raises · Lunge

Lower Body
Fly Steps · Side Hip Abduct · Side Leg Raises · Inchworm · Single Leg Split Squat · Air Squat

Lower Body
Hip Raise · Single Leg Dead Lift · Donkey Kicks · Single Leg Squat · Fire Hydrant · Adductor Leg Raise · Side Lying Leg Lift · Curtsy Squat

Lower Body
Walking Toe Touches · Sumo Squat · Cossack Squat · Static Chair Pose · Pistol Squat · Split Squat

Muscle Tables

prohealthsys

List the **Muscle Activated:** _____

List the **Tissue Stretched:** _____

Name: _____

%

Entire Body

Ball Transfer

Alt. Arm & Leg Lift

Upper Body

Chest Press

Incline Chest Press

Shoulder Press

Upper Body

Decline Push-up

Incline Push-up

Tricep Dip

Tricep Extension

Chest Fly

Lat Pullover

Upper Body

External Shoulder Rotation

Knee Push-Ups

Core

Russian Twist

Pike Crunch

Twisting Knee Tuck

Core

Twist Crunch

Plank Shoulder Taps

Side Plank

Roll-in Roll-out

Ball Leg Lift

Knee Raises

Basic Rollout

Crunch Legs on Ball

Core

Ab Rollout

Table Tops

Jackknife

Oblique Crunch

Alternating Crossover

Raised Feet Sit-up

Crunch

Core

Plank

Back

Back Extension

Prone Cobra

Superman

Reverse Fly

Pelvic Tilts

Lateral Pelvic Tilts

Lower Body

Squeeze. Curl & Lift

Side Leg Raise

Hip Raise

Hip Extension

Single Leg Bridge

Lower Body

Squat

Knee Tuck

Butt Blaster

Single Leg Split Squat

Hamstring Curl

Kneeling Ball Squeeze

Side Leg Lift

Lower Body

Inner Thigh Ball Squeeze

Standing Side Leg Push

Hamstring Squeeze

Toe Pulls

Standing Calf

Mountain Climber

Muscle Tables

prohealthsys

List the **Muscle Activated:** _____

List the **Tissue Stretched:** _____

Name:

%

Standing Poses

| Upward Salute | Mountain | Goddess Squat | Prayer | Chair | Tree Pose | Eagle Pose | Extended Side Angle | Warrior I |

Standing Poses

| Warrior II | Warrior III | Reverse Warrior | Low Lunge | Low Lunge Variation | Runner's Lunge | Forward Bend | Ragdoll | Standing Forward Bend |

Forward Bend

| Wide-Legged Forward Bend | Revolved Wide Leg Bend | Downward Dog Leg Lift | Wide-Angle Seated Bend | Pyramid | Bound Angle | Bound Angle Bend | Seated Forward Bend | Head-to-knee |

Twisting Poses

| Extended Triangle | Revolved Triangle | Revolved Half Moon | Revolved Low Lunge | Thread the Needle | Seated Twist | Reclined Twist | Pigeon | Strap Pigeon |

Back Bend

| Camel | King Pigeon | Bow | Upward Bow | Bridge | Locust | Cobra | Upward-Facing Dog | Cow |

Arm Balances

| Cat | Crow | Low Plank | Plank | Side Plank | Upward Plank | Inverted Pose | Standing Yoga Seal | Dolphin |

Inverted Pose

| Downward-Facing Dog | Fish Pose | Plow | Shoulderstand | Headstand | Seated Pose | Lotus | Garland | Hero |

Seated Pose

| Comfortable Seat | Cow Face | Seated Staff Pose | Boat | Frog | Relaxation | Legs Up the Wall | Reclined Pigeon | Happy Baby |

Relaxation

| Extended Child's Pose | Child's Pose | Corpse | Supine Bound Angle | Partner Yoga | Folded Leaf | High Flying Whale | Double Plank |

Partner Yoga

| Throne | Straddle Navasana Twist | Candlestick | Star | Mini Back Pack | Easy Baddha Konasana with Backbend |

Muscle Tables

List the **Muscle Activated:** _____

List the **Tissue Stretched:** _____

Name: _____

%

Muscle Tables

Cover table with a piece of table and fill in the boxes - no peaking ☺
On-line Table quizzes available at: **prohealthsys.com**

Name: %

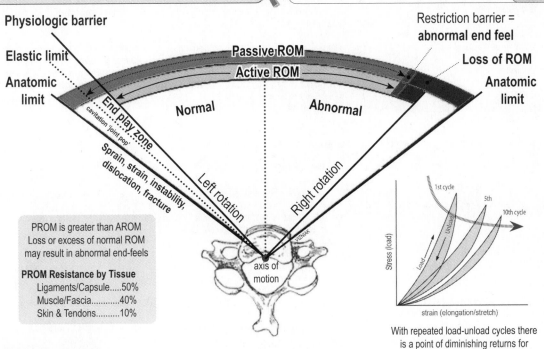

Physiologic barrier

Elastic limit

Anatomic limit

Passive ROM

Active ROM

Restriction barrier = **abnormal end feel**

Loss of ROM

Anatomic limit

End play zone
cavitation 'joint pop'

Normal   **Abnormal**

Sprain, strain, instability, dislocation, fracture

Left rotation   Right rotation

axis of motion

PROM is greater than AROM
Loss or excess of normal ROM
may result in abnormal end-feels

PROM Resistance by Tissue
Ligaments/Capsule.....50%
Muscle/Fascia............40%
Skin & Tendons..........10%

Stress (load)

1st cycle   5th   10th cycle

Load   Unload

strain (elongation/stretch)

With repeated load-unload cycles there is a point of diminishing returns for tissue elongation (trend line - arrow)

Lever Systems

1st Class Lever

Can produce mechanical advantage or disadvantage depending on location of force (effort) & resistance (load)

If force (muscle contraction) is further from fulcrum than load, then a strong load can be lifted

Average speed & mobility

2nd Class Lever

Mechanical advantage

Load is close to fulcrum

Sacrifice of speed for force

Slow & strong

proTip: use shorter levers to lower your effort as a clinician (stand closer to the patient)

3rd Class Lever

Mechanical disadvantage

Force is closer to fulcrum

Most common lever in body

Fast & weak

Speed and ROM over force - small amount of muscle contraction will move a body segment over a great distance = **energy efficient**

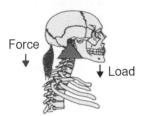

Force

↓ Load

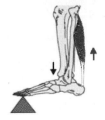

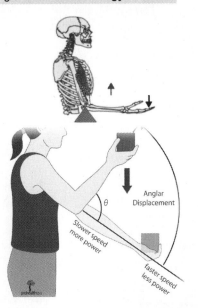

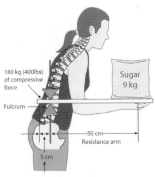

180 kg (400lbs) of compressive force

Fulcrum

Sugar 9 kg

50 cm Resistance arm

5 cm

As the load/resistance arm get longer it puts more stress on fulcrum (triangle). This is why it is easier to carry something close to your body (better **mechanical advantage**)

Angular Displacement

θ

Slower speed more power

faster speed less power

Muscle Tables

prohealthsys

1. What is the main action of the Gastrocnemius?
   a. Dorsiflexion of ankle
   b. Plantar flexion of ankle
   c. Flexion of knee
   d. Eversion of ankle

2. Which of the following muscles is/are innervated by the axillary nerve?
   a. Levator scapulae
   b. Deltoid
   c. Teres minor
   d. Both B & C

3. How many facets does a typical thoracic vertebra have?
   a. 8
   b. 10
   c. 12
   d. 14

4. "Winging" of the scapula can be caused by damage to which nerve? (youtube: vizniak scapular winging)
   a. Thoracodorsal nerve
   b. Long Thoracic nerve
   c. Axillary nerve
   d. Suprascapular nerve

5. Which of the following muscles does not have an insertion point along the medial border of the scapula?
   a. Levator scapulae
   b. Teres minor
   c. Rhomboid major
   d. Rhomboid minor

6. What muscle originates from the SPs of C7-T1?
   a. Levator scapulae
   b. Teres minor
   c. Rhomboid major
   d. Rhomboid minor

7. You have numbness & tingling over the lateral thigh, which nerve is most likely involved?
   a. Posterior femoral nerve
   b. Lateral femoral cutaneous nerve
   c. Femoral nerve
   d. Obturator nerve

8. A patient present with numbness & tingling unilaterally only in their lateral 3 fingers, where is the nerve pathology?
   a. Ulnar tunnel
   b. Pronator teres muscle
   c. Intervertebral foramen
   d. Carpal tunnel

9. What do you call excess curvature of the thoracic spine?
   a. Hyperlordosis
   b. Hypokyphosis
   c. Hyperkyphosis
   d. Hyperenarthrosis

10. How many joints are in the adult human body on average?
    a. 206
    b. 214
    c. 456
    d. 600

11. What muscle below does not cause flexion at the elbow joint?
    a. Biceps brachii
    b. Brachioradialis
    c. Brachialis
    d. Coracobrachialis

12. Which of the following muscles attaches to the lesser tubercle of the humerus?
    a. Supraspinatus
    b. Infraspinatus
    c. Subscapularis
    d. Teres minor

13. What muscle passes through the intertubercular groove of the humerus?
    a. Biceps brachii short head
    b. Biceps brachii long head
    c. Coracobrachialis
    d. Brachialis

14. Blood supply to the anterior compartment of the leg is provided by the _____?
    a. Popliteal artery
    b. Inferior lateral genicular artery
    c. Anterior tibial artery
    d. Posterior interosseous artery

15. Which of the muscles listed below does not have an attachment point to the coracoid process of the scapula?
    a. Pectoralis minor
    b. Coracobrachialis
    c. Pectoralis major
    d. Biceps brachii short head

16. Which group of the deep back muscles skips 1-2 vertebrae, running from transverse process to spinous process?
    a. Semispinalis
    b. Rotatories
    c. Multifidi
    d. Levator costarum

17. Which listed below shows the correct order for layers of the back from superficial to deep?
    a. Trapezius, rhomboids, erector spinae, semispinalis, rotatores
    b. Trapezius, rhomboids, semispinalis, rotators, erector spinae
    c. Rotatores, semispinalis, erector spinae, rhomboids, trapezius
    d. Trapezius, rhomboids, erector spinae, semispinalis, deltoid

18. Which of the muscles below does not have an attachment point on the femur?
    a. Adductor magnus
    b. Sartorius
    c. Pectineus
    d. Vastus lateralis

19. During a car accident you experienced a hyperextension injury to the neck, what muscle is most likely to be damaged?
    a. Levator scapulae
    b. Longus coli
    c. Rectus capitus posterior major
    d. Infraspinatus

20. The tubercle of a rib articulates with what facet of a thoracic vertebra?
    a. Costal facet
    b. Superior articular facet
    c. Transverse costal facet
    d. Inferior articular facet

21. What is the outer portion of an intervertebral disc called?
    a. Nucleus palposus
    b. Intervertebral cortex
    c. Annulus fibrosis
    d. Outer vertebral ligament

22. What nerve supplies the main innervation to muscles of the anterior forearm?
    a. Musculocutaneous nerve
    b. Median nerve
    c. Radial nerve
    d. Ulnar nerve

23. What muscle is innervated by both the ulnar and median nerves?
    a. Flexor digitorum profundus
    b. Flexor digitorum superficialis
    c. Flexor carpi ulnaris
    d. Extensor carpi ulnaris

24. What muscle does not exist in the upper extremity?
    a. Flexor digitorum longus
    b. Flexor digitorum brevis
    c. Extensor digitorum longus
    d. All of the above

25. In general, most of the forearm flexors originate from what point?
    a. Medial epicondyle
    b. Lateral epicondyle
    c. Lateral supracondylar ridge
    d. Flexor tuberosity

26. What is another name(s) specific for medial rotation of the forearm?
    a. Anterior inversion
    b. Supination
    c. Pronation
    d. Both A and B

27. What is the origin for most of the hamstring muscles?
    a. Sacrospinous ligament
    b. Ischial tuberosity
    c. Proximal linea aspera
    d. Sciatic nerve

28. What vertebrae have mamillary processes?
    a. Cervical
    b. Thoracic
    c. Lumbar
    d. Sacral

29. What muscle of mastication assists in the depression of the mandible?
    a. Masseter
    b. Lateral pterygoid
    c. Platysma
    d. Mylohyoid

30. How many tarsal bones do we have on one extremity?
    a. 5
    b. 6
    c. 7
    d. 8

31. What muscle inserts onto the base of the intermediate phalanx of phalanges 2-5?
    a. Flexor digitorum superficialis
    b. Flexor digitorum profundus
    c. Flexor Carpi Ulnaris
    d. Flexor Carpi Radialis

32. Which of the bones below does not have a styloid process?
    a. Ulna
    b. Radius
    c. Temporal bone
    d. Humerus

Muscle Tables